MASTER
of
VILLAINY

Sax Rohmer.

MASTER
of
VILLAINY

A Biography of Sax Rohmer

CAY VAN ASH
and
ELIZABETH SAX ROHMER

Edited, with Foreword, Notes, and Bibliography,
ROBERT E. BRINEY

Tom Stacey

First published in London in 1972
by Tom Stacey Ltd.,
28–29 Maiden Lane, London WC2E 7JP

Copyright © 1972 by
the Bowling Green University Popular Press,
Ray B. Browne, Editor

ISBN 0 85468 299 6

Printed in Great Britain by
C. Tinling & Co. Ltd.,
London and Prescot

CONTENTS

FOREWORD

SAX ROHMER'S LITERARY CAREER EXTENDED OVER A PERIOD OF FIFTY-five years, from 1904 to 1959. At the height of his fame, in the 1920s and 1930s, he was one of the most widely read and highly paid writers of popular fiction in the world. His books, led by the series featuring his famous creation Dr. Fu Manchu, have had combined sales in the millions. They have been translated into more than a dozen languages, and have served as a basis for adaptations in motion pictures, radio, television, and comic strips.

This book is the first extended account of Sax Rohmer's life and career. The book itself has a rather involved history. Its seeds can be traced back to 1936, in which year Rohmer wrote a series of articles in which he reminisced about places he had travelled and famous people he had known. These articles, under the running title of "Pipe Dreams," were published during the early months of 1938 in the Empire News, a Sunday newspaper originating in Manchester, England. Portions of these articles have been paraphrased or quoted at appropriate places in the present book, so that Rohmer himself may be said to have had a hand in its writing.

The book was conceived in the mid-1950s, when the Sax Rohmers were living in New York. It was to be a collaboration between Rohmer and his wife, but—for reasons which the reader will easily deduce from the last chapter of the book—was to be published under Mrs. Rohmer's name. Work on the book had progressed to such a stage that rumors of it began to circulate; one such report, in Hy Gardner's "Coast to Coast" column in the New York *Herald Tribune*, drew a reply from Rohmer (27 April 1956) in which he confirmed the book's existence. As it turned out, however, the manuscript had to be abandoned in favor of other tasks, and remained unfinished at the time of Rohmer's death. It was not until some years later that Mrs. Rohmer resumed work on the book. She was now joined in the project by Cay Van Ash, who had been a friend and protégé of her husband. What emerged from this collaboration was not so much a completion of the earlier manuscript as it was an entirely new book.

One feature of the original had, however, been preserved. The book had been planned not as a formal biography but rather as a collection of reminiscences and anecdotes. In consequence, the emphasis was on people and events; questions of location and date were sometimes overshadowed, and in places the chronology of the account was rather hazy.

At this point, the present writer entered the picture. At the request of Professor Ray Browne, Director of the Bowling Green University Popular Press, I undertook the task of annotating the manuscript, with the object of providing ancillary material on names, dates, places, and bibliographical matters, without altering the form or intention of the original text. During many years of reading and collecting Sax Rohmer's works, I had accumulated a substantial amount of bibliographical and biographical data. Not unexpectedly, much of the biographical material turned out to be erroneous. However, the bibliographical information provided a solid foundation on which to build—for, as the reader of this book will discover, Sax Rohmer's writing was very often tied closely to events and situations in his own life.

Most of the "annotations" have, with Mrs. Rohmer's permission, been incorporated directly into the text. A few others, numbered sequentially throughout the book, are gathered together in a separate section at the end.

Much of the additional information was provided by Mrs. Elizabeth Sax Rohmer, who has been a marvel of graciousness and patience throughout the process of preparing this manuscript for publication, and to whom I extend here my deep gratitude. Substantial votes of thanks are also due to Robert Galbreath, whose suggestion originally resulted in my involvement with this project, and whose continuing activities in the areas of editing, proof-reading, and general liaison have been invaluable; and to William O. G. Lofts, literary researcher *par excellence*, without whose diligent investigations at the General Register Office, the British Museum, the Hendon Newspaper Museum, and elsewhere, many of the details presented herein would not have come to light. I am also indebted to William J. Clark, Vernon Lay, Nigel Morland, and Douglas Rossman, for useful advice and information.

And finally, a debt of gratitude—perhaps the biggest of all—is owed to Sax Rohmer, for providing the subject matter of the lively and entertaining history which follows.

Robert E. Briney

Salem, Massachusetts
February 1972

INTRODUCTORY NOTE

I FIRST MET SAX ROHMER IN 1935, BY THE SIMPLE AND DIRECT PROCESS OF asking him for an interview. Only the fact that I was then seventeen years old gave me the confidence to suppose that he might consent; but he did. We met and talked for an hour. That alone was far more than I had expected—but our meeting began a friendship extending over many years. What skill I may have as a writer I owe entirely to him for the help and encouragement which he gave me from that time on.

During Sax's lifetime numerous interviews and biographical sketches appeared in magazines and newspapers. However, these were often inaccurate and slanted toward the sensational. In any case, they contained few personal details, since Sax disliked personal publicity. Such autobiographical notes as he has left us are chiefly descriptions of events in which he himself played the role of observer. The present account has, therefore, been compiled mainly from our own memories of what he told us, and of the experiences in which we shared. This, of course, has thrown by far the greater part of the work upon Elizabeth, who was closely associated with Sax in everything he did for more than fifty years. Thus, even though I have taken upon myself the responsibility for narrating this story, Elizabeth has been my co-pilot and navigator

1

throughout. It is more her story than mine, and fortunately, she has an exceptional memory.

This history was undertaken with the intention of paying tribute to the memory of a very wonderful man and a very wonderful friend. I have done my best with it, and I think it is at least readable. Nevertheless, looking back on it, I can but echo the words of the young disciple who, having composed a requiem in honor of his departed master, exclaimed: "But how much better it would have been if I had died and he had written it!"

Cay Van Ash

Department of Literature
Waseda University, Tokyo

LIMEHOUSE INCIDENT

FICTION LIVES LONGER THAN FACT. AT THE MERE MENTION OF THE NAME "Limehouse," what images spring inevitably to mind? A vista of dark streets, shadowy yellow-faced forms, the brief flash of a knife blade, a scream in the night, a bloated corpse fished up from the murky waters of the Thames. . . . London's Chinatown has long since vanished. But the legend of Limehouse lives on—due in no small part to the writings of one man: Sax Rohmer.

The legend was not always a legend. Before the First World War, it was a fact that the warren of narrow streets and alleyways in the neighborhood of West India Dock Road, Pennyfields, and Limehouse Causeway formed a no-man's-land which honest citizens hesitated to penetrate after dark. It was a fact that the Metropolitan Police honored the area with double patrols. The precise toll of lives lost in that sombre labyrinth cannot be estimated. The region housed an Asiatic community, firmly entrenched and largely criminal, which lived by laws foreign to and older than the laws of England. This was the secret empire controlled by the fabulous, but fictitious, Dr. Fu Manchu.

Or was he entirely fictitious?

Only Sax Rohmer, his creator, knew the answer. As I begin the story of that supreme master of fictional villainy, it is perhaps natural that my thoughts should go first to Limehouse.

I think of an evil night in the year 1911. Chilly fingers of mist were stealing up from the river. A vintage taxi with brass head-lamps crawled noisily and not too confidently through streets peopled only by furtive shadows. No fit background, certainly, for an attractive young woman, save in the opening pages of a Sax Rohmer story. Yet she was there. As the taxi drew level with a street lamp, the light gleamed momentarily on red-gold hair and revealed anxious eyes, searching—for this was a Sax Rohmer story in real life. The woman in the taxi was his wife. And Sax was missing—in Limehouse.

Then in his late twenties, Sax had so far shown no interest in things Chinese. As a writer of "Oriental" mystery stories, he was already establishing something of a reputation. But the stories he wrote were chiefly of Egypt and the Middle East, where his heart really lay, and where it always remained. His marriage to Elizabeth was happy and successful. By comparison with the early days when they had literally struggled against starvation, they were now comfortably settled.

And then, six months previous to the night in question, the shadow of Chinatown fell upon their lives, in the form of an un-expected commission from a magazine editor, requesting an article on Limehouse. The choice, from the editor's point of view, was logical enough. Sax's stories were "Oriental," and "Oriental" at that time meant anything east of Istanbul.[1]

More than half a century later, Elizabeth still shudders at the memory of what followed: the long lonely nights when Sax failed to appear at the dinner table, and often remained absent till the small hours of the morning. What the editor wanted was informa-tion about a certain "Mr. King." Nobody, apparently, had ever met Mr. King, but he was said to be a considerable property owner, a known drug trafficker and, according to rumor, the guiding hand in half the underworld activities of Limehouse.

Sax went boldly to work. He combed the squalid streets, night after night, in search of a man better avoided. That his success might well mean adding his own name to the list of Mr. King's alleged victims does not seem to have occurred to him, but it occurred vividly to Elizabeth. Not yet twenty-five and very

4

much in love, she spent sleepless hours at the bedroom window of their home in Herne Hill, watching anxiously for the returning lights of Sax's cab. To her secret relief, however, Sax's main objective remained unachieved when the deadline for the finished article arrived. It was written and printed. Sax had unearthed more than enough odd information to satisfy both editor and readers, and nobody complained except the author. He had not seen Mr. King.

For the next few months, life at Herne Hill was back to normal—or as normal as life with Sax was ever likely to be. Then, for the second time, the shadow fell. Suddenly, without a word of explanation, a new series of absences began. Again Sax failed to show up for dinner. Again the far watches of the night found him missing.

Elizabeth was piqued but not at first alarmed. Sax's movements were always erratic and often, by commonplace standards, totally inconsiderate. There were a dozen places he might have gone to. But so many late nights in a row were unusual even for Sax. She began to look for him and gradually, as it dawned upon her that he was missing from all his regular haunts, annoyance gave place to something like panic. The search became frantic. Theaters, the Eccentric Club, the Hambone Club. . . . No one had seen him!

Elizabeth returned home tired and bewildered. She could think of no other place where he might be. Least of all did she think of Limehouse; so far as she knew, the Limehouse business was over and done with. And then, shocking in its unexpectedness, came the telephone call from Helen Charles, an acquaintance from her stage days.

"My dear, I've just seen the most extraordinary thing! I'd been down to the docks to meet some friends off a boat, and there, on the way back, I saw Sax walking along the street with a Chinese girl who was carrying a baby in her arms!"

A quick word from the tall young man seated at Elizabeth's side, and the taxi jolted to a standstill by the lighted windows of a public house, evidently close to the river. The whistle of a tugboat hooted mournfully.

"Charley Brown's," Frank Wyatt said. "Hold on here while I take a look around." He climbed down into the street, vanished through a swing door and was out again in less than a minute, shaking his head.

"Not in there, anyway. But two of my deckhands are. I nipped out quick before they spotted me."

Frank Wyatt was the bachelor son of a nearby neighbor in Herne Hill. He was a ship's officer on a P. & O. boat sailing between London and Brisbane, and was soon to become the youngest liner captain in the Mercantile Marine. Knowing him to be on shore leave, Elizabeth had sought his aid in her search, and had been lucky enough to find him at home.

"What next?" she asked wearily.

Frank hesitated, frowning. "Let's have another look at those pictures."

Reaching into the cab, he took a crumpled magazine from the damp clutch of Elizabeth's fingers and spread out the creases in the light of the headlamps. Sax's "Limehouse" article was the only clue they had, and not a very good one, since he had very carefully avoided naming the places he visited. But to a man intimately familiar with the dock area, the photographs might mean something. Frank stared thoughtfully at a picture of what seemed to be a restaurant, and glanced at the caption beneath. "Where East is West." He grinned.

"Don't know what it's called, but I think I know where it is. In Limehouse Causeway. We could try."

Elizabeth said nothing. Weighed down by a cold sense of hopelessness, she felt half sorry for having started out on this crazy quest. Yet, back at the house, with Helen's maliciously triumphant voice still ringing in her ears (she was under no illusions about the quality of Helen's friendship) she had known she must do something or go mad.

"Brace up, old girl! Not on the rocks yet, you know!"

Elizabeth smiled faintly, though she felt more like crying. Frank was an incorrigible comedian, but she couldn't rise to his mood. Nevertheless, she was thankful for his presence, without which any attempt at a search would have been impossible.

Frank leaned forward in his seat, calling out directions. Fifty yards ahead, the street lamps glowed yellowly through a haze of mist. The taxi swung to the right into a road which appeared to lead straight into the river; they passed under a railway bridge

6

and halted before a dimly lit doorway.

"That's it," Frank said, "Will you wait, or—"

"Can I come in with you?"

"Yes, if you want to." He laughed and stepped out on the pavement, extending his hand. "Safe enough—anyway, till about midnight."

"And after that?"

"Well, it depends. Shipmate of mine once tried to break up the joint single-handed. We got him out, heavily holed, but not a total loss!"

They descended steps to a cellar furnished with cheap tables and chairs, a sizeable bar counter and an upright piano with a cracked front. At the moment there were few customers. Dotted about sparsely in twos and threes, they looked more sorrowful than sinister.

The man who came from behind the bar to take Frank's order for coffee (and a pint of beer for the driver) was the most unlikely cocktail of humanity that Elizabeth had ever seen. He had greying woolly hair, leering blue eyes, an acquiline nose, thick lips and a complexion like a dried lemon. The man stared at her for a moment, then shrugged and turned away. Elizabeth glanced around mechanically, without interest. She had seen immediately that it was the place shown in the photograph and that Sax was not there.

A Negro appeared from somewhere and sat down at the piano. Two couples stood up and began to dance. The bartender returned with thick china cups, hideously chipped and minus saucers, extorted a shilling, and vanished again behind the bar.

"Is he the proprietor?" Elizabeth asked.

Frank nodded.

"Then he'd probably remember about Sax being here with the photographer. Ask him."

"All right. Stay here and don't get into mischief."

He stood up and walked over to the bar. Elizabeth looked doubtfully at her cup and wondered if the coffee were doped. If so, it had been a pretty clumsy job, for the stuff certainly tasted nothing like coffee. Frank seemed to be taking a long time, and some of the customers were looking at her in a way she didn't like. She was relieved when he came back.

"He remembers all right, but he swears he's never seen him since." Frank was still laughing. "Well, I ask you! If old Sax really did have a fancy bit in these parts, which I doubt, do you think he'd bring her dancing down here?"

Elizabeth shook her head imperceptibly. Sax and a Chinese girl, and a baby. . . In her heart of hearts, she didn't believe it either. She knew that Helen would say anything to make trouble; she'd always had her eye on Sax. Yet a fantastic story like that . . . surely it couldn't have been made up. Elizabeth no longer knew what to think, but the mere suspicion of Sax being mixed up in some sordid affair in Limehouse was enough to make her feel ill.

"It was silly to come," she whispered. "I think we'd better go home."

"Rot!" Frank said breezily. "Still one more shot in the locker. Here, look at this."

He spread out the magazine on the table between them, pointing to a passage in the text.

Fong Wah, who deals in strange delicacies, is a powerfully built man, with a large mole above his left eyebrow; he is apparently prosperous and much respected by his neighbours, but in more ways than one something of a mystery. He is a person of considerable culture. On the matter which had really brought me to him, however, he proved no more helpful than the others. Any reference to the whereabouts of Mr. King was enough to make him change the subject. It is infuriating—because I am sure he knows. . . .

"That's the old bird to go after!" Frank grinned boyishly. "That's where Sax would go—if anywhere. Fong Wah's!"

"But we don't know where he lives!"

"Maybe I do. I've been thinking." Frank stood up, ramming the folded magazine down into his overcoat pocket. "Could be the place my purser buys China tea for his missus. It's a chance, anyway. Come on!"

The taximan, a taciturn stoic with a walrus moustache, drove on without comment. Now, turning back from the river, maritime Limehouse was left behind and the narrow streets were those of a foreign city. Lights from a profusion of tiny shops, most of them still open, shone on signboards lettered in vertical Chinese script. Strange, high-pitched voices and a flash of discordant music, patches of shadow out of which Oriental faces peered curiously at the intruders. . . .

Fong Wah's, though it proved not difficult to find, appeared at first sight to be closed. But lights within suggested life. The door swung inwards to a sound of distant tinkling, a smell of joss sticks, stale fish and cinnamon. The counter and the shelves were piled with tins, packages and jars. Aromatic and unidentifiable things dangled from the low ceiling.

"Chinese oysters, bamboo shoots, sharks' fins and water chestnuts. . . ." According to Sax, this mean little establishment was crammed with half the things dear to a Chinese palate. "Lily roots and edible seaweed; eggs buried for twenty years or more and preserved in a coating of earth; birds' nests. . . ."

But before Elizabeth could remember more, the bead curtain behind the counter parted to reveal a figure straight out of fantasy. Garbed in the high-collared sheath of a Chinese dress, she looked less a human being than a dainty work of art in porcelain.

"Is this Fong Wah's?" Frank demanded.

The girl nodded.

"Then we'd like a word with him, if you don't mind."

She nodded again and disappeared through the curtain. Frank turned towards Elizabeth with a grin on his face that made her want to slap him—because she knew he was thinking what she was thinking. For an instant she glared at him; then the swish of the beads switched her gaze back to the curtained opening. There, beside the Chinese girl, stood a slim young man in a lounge suit, a man with lean, ascetic features, dark eyebrows and strangely compelling eyes.

"My God! Sax!"

Elizabeth clutched vaguely at Frank's arm and held on hard till the room stopped spinning.

"Hallo, darling!" Sax said quietly. His face showed surprise, but neither embarrassment nor any consciousness that he had done anything unusual. "What's this, Frank? Have you taken on personally conducted tours of Chinatown?'

The girl, who appeared to be about sixteen, spoke suddenly in a soft, bell-like voice. "You are welcome to the house of Fong Wah. My husband begs you to take tea with him."

Still dizzy with bewilderment, Elizabeth found herself piloted

9

through the curtain and into a stuffy little room, curiously furnished, with a black lacquered shrine in one corner. Wisps of perfumed smoke wreathed up before the tranquil face of a brass Buddha. Near it, like a second image, a man in a loose silk robe and padded slippers sat upright in a high, square-shaped armchair of intricately inlaid wood, reminiscent of a throne. On the wall behind hung a peculiarly curved sword in a shagreen scabbard.

"My wife and my friend, Frank Wyatt," Sax said briefly. "They've come to look for me."

Fong Wah rose impressively from his throne and bowed twice. Tall for a Chinese, and curiously dignified, he looked nothing like a shopkeeper and old enough to be the girl's grandfather. His face was a mush of fine lines, like a map of Asia. With his own hands, he placed chairs for them, adding cushions. Elizabeth sat down gingerly, glancing nervously over her shoulder. In the dark interior of a narrow cupboard without a door, a long-bodied creature like an outsize weasel sat watching her with wicked, beady eyes. She stifled a scream.

"Mongoose!" Sax said, smiling. "Keeps the rats down. Won't hurt you, if you don't touch him."

Their host spoke rapidly to the Chinese girl in their own language. She said, "*Ho-a!*" and went out.

"Suzee will bring tea for us," Fong Wah explained. His eyes suddenly met Elizabeth's, and a smile touched the corners of his lips. "She is my fourth wife."

All at once, the atmosphere seemed to have become that of a Chinese fairy tale. Suzee reappeared, carrying a tray set out with tiny, eggshell-thin cups of pale, fragrant tea and a freshly sliced orange. When they were all served, she knelt on the floor beside her husband, looking up at him with what seemed to be genuine affection.

Fong Wah inclined his head gravely towards Elizabeth, at the same time indicating Sax with a courtly gesture of his left hand. "My honored friend has brought comfort into the life of an old man far from his own country. For he listens with respect to my tales of China—as China used to be. I was not always a merchant."

And, as he talked on, in his queerly poetic way, Elizabeth studied the shrewd, all-seeing eyes and felt her doubts fading away. No man would easily deceive Fong Wah, and no man but a

10

fool would try. Under the spell of his voice, hurt and anger slipped from her mind and time passed unnoticed till, suddenly, she was recalled to the present by the distant blare of a taxi horn. The frozen driver's stoicism had finally given way.

She stood up quickly. Then, while Sax lingered, taking formal leave of their host, she felt miniature fingers close upon her own—confidentially, like those of a child about to impart a secret—and looked round to find the Chinese girl beside her. "Before you go," Suzee whispered, "come and see the baby."

Elizabeth started. Baby? The girl looked little more than a baby herself. Still hopelessly bewildered, she allowed herself to be led into an adjoining room with an ornate sort of cot in one corner. Suzee went to it, beckoning her to follow. Looking down, Elizabeth saw a tiny face, like that of an ivory doll—all the rest hidden under the quilted mass of a scarlet eiderdown. He was sleeping.

"We are so proud of him," Suzee murmured. "Fong Wah has had three wives and seven daughters. But Huan is his only son." She stooped to arrange the eiderdown. "He is as beautiful as a flower. But now he is too pale, for he has not been very well."

She stood up. "I took him to the doctor's this afternoon," she said, casually. "And, on the way home, I met your husband coming to visit us. We walked back together."

So, simply enough, the mystery ceased to be a mystery. But, throughout the long drive homewards, Sax remained curiously silent. Hands clasped on knees, he sat forward in his seat, his regard seemingly fixed on some distant point in another dimension. From Fong Wah's to Royal Mint Street he had spoken scarcely a dozen words.

Elizabeth, accustomed to his silences, began to feel apprehensive. Now that her own anger had evaporated, she was wondering if he might be angry with her. Even the irrepressible Frank seemed subdued. Finally, the suspense became unbearable.

"Shouldn't I have followed you?" she burst out, impulsively. "Have I upset something?"

Sax turned his face slowly towards her, passing a hand over his forehead like a man rousing himself with difficulty from some unusually vivid dream.

"No, no—it's not that. Last night, now—well, last night might have been a different story, but . . ."

11

He broke off, evidently aware that he was not making very good sense and seeming for a moment to arrange his thoughts by a conscious effort of will.

"Tonight was just a social call," he said quietly. "But necessary. Not to have made it would have been the grossest of discourtesies." He hesitated, then spoke again, quickly. "I owe Fong Wah more than I may yet realize myself, more than any of us may realize."

Frank looked across at him, astonished. "Owe? To Fong Wah? What?"

"His confidence." Suddenly, the speaker's voice rose to a note of exultation. "After all these months, he made up his mind to trust me, to give me the chance I needed. And so, thanks to old Fong Wah, at last—I've seen him!"

"Seen whom?" Elizabeth asked, puzzled. Then, as memory returned and comprehension dawned, she gasped. "My God! You mean—Mr. King?"

For a long moment, Sax did not answer. Again he seemed to be staring fixedly into space. And then, when he spoke, his reply was unexpected.

"I have seen . . . Dr. Fu Manchu."

Elizabeth and Frank stared at each other blankly. Neither of them had ever heard that name before.

2

DARK GENESIS

SAX ROHMER IS FIRMLY IDENTIFIED IN THE PUBLIC MIND AS THE CREATOR of Dr. Fu Manchu. During his lifetime he wrote and published thirteen books which dealt with the deeds of that infamous Chinese villain, but he also wrote a further forty which did not, some of which were considerably better stories. Nevertheless, since the shadow looms larger than the substance, I have given the Devil Doctor his due by allowing Fu Manchu to introduce Sax Rohmer. Now, having done so, I shall go back three decades and begin again.

Both of Sax's parents were Irish. William Ward was the son of Timothy Ward, a stonemason and part-time schoolmaster from Wicklow. Margaret Mary Furey was the daughter of Martin Francis Furey, a merchant from Athlone. Both families had left Ireland and settled in Birmingham, in the English Midlands, where William and Margaret met and, in June of 1879, became man and wife. Although both families were Catholic, the couple were married in a civil ceremony at the Birmingham Register Office. William Ward was at that time an office clerk, and not highly paid. He and his bride established a modest household at 28 Rann Street in the Ladywood district, near the center of the city. It was here, on February 15, 1883, that Arthur Henry Ward—the future Sax

Rohmer—was born.

In later life, Sax claimed not to know the exact date or place of his birth. Once, when questioned by reporters, he replied simply, "I was born. Or rather, since I don't actually remember the event, I presume so." This indifference was only partly a pose. He literally did not know how old he was, and urgently desired that nobody should tell him. Among his unusual theories was a belief that ageing is largely psychological, and that a man is as old as he thinks he ought to be. This attitude kept Sax active and youthful almost to the end of a long life.

At any rate, the household into which Sax was born was not one in which birthdays and anniversaries counted for very much. He had no brothers or sisters. His father, much later to become a treasured companion, was at first a virtual stranger whom he saw only in the late evenings and on weekends. Childhood memories of his mother were confined, dreadfully, to a figure indistinguishable from his nightmares—a gaunt, hollow-eyed wraith that sometimes crept silently into his room and there, by fluttering candlelight, babbled out incoherent tales of goblins and ghouls. For, tragically, by the time of her son's birth, Margaret Ward was already a confirmed alcoholic, as her father had been before her. Passing her days between fantasy and unconsciousness, she seemed largely oblivious to her child's very existence.

William Ward, fully aware of what was going on, was a desperately worried man. Knowing that his son was far from receiving proper care at home, still there was nothing he could do about it. He was forced to spend long hours at the office, taxed to the limit of his resources by the expense of furnishing his wife with the slow poison which eventually would kill her, and lack of which would destroy her immediately.

Perhaps in an attempt to resolve this tragic problem he transferred his activities to an office in south London, and the family moved. Sax was then about two or three years old. The move did little to change the situation. Hard-working and rapidly advancing in the firm of civil engineers that employed him, Bill Ward seems to have been cursed with an inability to delegate assignments or, possibly, burdened simply with an incompetent staff. So long as he took personal responsibility for every part of the job in hand, his employers were well satisfied; otherwise, they were not. The

14

run of early mornings and late nights at the office went on unchecked.

So, consequently, did the strangely neglected childhood of Sax. Yet it left him with no particularly unhappy memories. He suffered no deliberate ill-treatment. He was simply allowed to "grow up wild," and perhaps in his childish heart, no small boy can think of a better way to live.

Sax received no formal schooling until he was about nine years old. Nursery schools and kindergartens did not exist; nursemaids and governesses were beyond the restricted budget of the Ward household. In the few free hours at his disposal, Sax's father did what he could, and fortunately he was able to help more than most fathers. Home-educated himself, he had a mind like an encyclopaedia. But time was limited.

A biographer who did not know the man might be tempted to write that Sax suffered from a neglected childhood. On the contrary, he seems to have profited by it. Rather than becoming a neurotic or an ignoramus, he became a man of strong will, better read and better able to express himself than many popular writers of his day.

I know of only one respect in which Sax may have suffered psychologically from the disturbed nights and strange fancies of his childhood: during his later youth and for some years thereafter, he was badly afflicted with somnambulism.

Bill Ward never forgot the night when, investigating a noise in the kitchen of their home, he found that Sax, in his sleep, had clambered up on a table next to the window and was on the point of hurling himself out through the glass.

Another disconcerting episode occurred during Sax's bachelor days, throughout which he shared a bedroom with his father, keeping his own room for a study. One night, Bill Ward was most unpleasantly awakened by a man pouncing upon him and clutching at his throat. He rolled out of bed and crashed to the floor with the attacker on top of him. For a few seconds they rolled over and over, the older man fighting, as he thought, for his life— till the ray of a streetlamp, striking through the bedroom window, fell upon the face of his assailant and he recognized his own son. Even then, arousing him to his senses proved difficult. Had Bill Ward not been an amateur boxer in his youth, he said later, he would almost certainly have been strangled.

Elizabeth did not know of Sax's sleep-walking when she married him. The first intimation came when, one night, she opened her eyes suddenly to find her husband's hands outstretched, clawlike, towards her. Her scream woke him.

"Thank God!" he said, dazedly. "I dreamt you were being run over, and I was trying to drag you out of the way!"

Later experiences were more alarming. On a second occasion, she was shaken out of her sleep, to be told that a huge spider had gone under her pillow. A hurried exit from bed and a frantic search followed until it dawned upon her that Sax was fast asleep. A third time found them both creeping about the house, armed with poker and fire tongs, hunting for an imaginary burglar.

Sax's tendency toward sleep-walking was probably inherited from his father's side of the family. But his own strange studies and his preoccupation with murderous schemes for his stories no doubt combined to give it a pronounced sinister character. Whatever its cause or nature, however, Elizabeth soon cured him of it. Her method was simple and direct. Whenever she found Sax in a somnambulistic state, she simply swatted him on the head with a pillow.

It seems fairly certain that Sax first went to school when he was about nine years old. Dates are hazy, and the name or location of the school is not known.[2] Sax spoke very little about his school days. Elizabeth remembers nothing beyond an occasional reference to his having gone "up to London" as a day boy, and having sometimes stopped at a pastry shop on the way home. I never heard him refer to his schooling, beyond saying that he and some other pupils once produced a minor panic by introducing grass snakes into a classroom.

On the whole, I doubt that he was as happy at school as he had been at home. Among boys of his own age, he would not easily have made friends. In formal studies, he was far behind them; in imagination and in knowledge of bizarre subjects, far ahead.

His scholastic record was anything but brilliant. Yet throughout his life, Sax was remarkable for his powers of observation and memory. He missed nothing and forgot nothing. But he could not and would not take an interest in anything that failed to attract him, and there was little enough to attract him in the range of subjects covered in a normal secondary school curriculum.

By the age of nine, he had already done a good deal of reading, though when exactly he had learned to read is not clear. Afterwards, it seemed to him that he had always been able to do so, as far back as he could remember. But his reading had been confined chiefly to currently popular novels, mostly fantastic, brought into the house by his mother. So long as she could focus her eyes on print, poor Margaret Ward was a voracious reader.

Now, with all the world of books at his disposal, Sax set about serious reading—serious but unconventional. What he had to do now was to reconcile fantasy with fact. Hitherto, he had lived in a world in which they were not distinguished, the former often more real to him than the latter, and infinitely more attractive. How much was true, and how much false?

Already, in this last decade of the nineteenth century, all the rigid beliefs and values of the mid-Victorian period were coming into question, to the point where Richard le Gallienne could write, "We changed from a stolid into a volatile nation." Ideas were changing, unexplored territories were being mapped, developments in the exact sciences were rapid to a degree. Sax was no opponent of progress, either social or scientific. But he felt that in the general haste to advance, too much might be cast aside unexamined, too much ignored. Paradoxically, one was required to reject the existence of all that could not be physically demonstrated, and at the same time, on no better evidence, to have blind faith in the existence of God.

Soon enough, in his search for truth, Sax was bound to run head-on into religious difficulties. As he examined the major religions of the world, he came to the conclusion that there was much nonsense in all of them, concealing a possible glimmer of spiritual truth. To the astonishment of his father, he suddenly declined any longer to attend Mass, saying that he had not ceased to have faith in one religion but had found faith in all. Bill Ward, feeling out of his depth, called in the help of a priest—a family friend and a frequent visitor to the house—and begged religious instruction for his son. Sax remained unconvinced. From that time onwards, he never subscribed to orthodox religion in any

17

form. But his conversations with the priest left him with a considerable knowledge of and respect for the Roman Catholic Church.

It is natural to wonder if Sax, who later made so much of the Unknown in his writings, had any personal reasons for believing in it. In truth, he did. Long before making any deliberate attempt at exploration, he had experienced that rare and still inexplicable phenomenon, the recurrent dream. It came to him first when he was twelve or thirteen years old and continued at intervals, so frequently that he was not afterwards able to remember how often it occurred. It was a dream which never varied; it began and ended always at the same points.

In this dream he saw himself, a boy as he then was, accompanied by his father, the pair of them walking along a narrow path high up on a rocky coast. Both wore clothes which he later judged to have belonged roughly to the period of George III. The path, climbing ever higher, finally gave access to a low cave of considerable extent. This they entered, lighting their way with candles, and traversed to the end, where it opened into a chamber. Thence a very narrow passage inclined steeply downwards, and through this they crawled into a second roughly hewn chamber having a stout wooden door at one end. Here the father gave an urgent signal for silence and, listening intently, they heard a faint sound from above, suggesting that they stood in the foundations of a building.

And at this intriguing point, Sax invariably woke up. Where the scene might have been set, or what it portended, he could never guess. But that the dream represented some kind of hereditary memory, he felt convinced.

Sax's boyhood search for truth was, admittedly, not disinterested. He was seeking a factual basis for believing in what he wanted to believe. He found it soon enough, or at least found where to look for it: in the ancient world of the Middle East.

Earlier in the nineteenth century the key to ancient Egyptian writing had been found. Now Sir Flinders Petrie was digging in Egypt, and new discoveries were being made. Papyri and inscriptions were being deciphered, revealing the former existence of a civilization sophisticated to a degree hitherto unsuspected. Sax became intensely interested in Egyptology. The claims of Herodotus, hinting at a forgotten wisdom older than the Pyramids, had yet to be disproved. Many thought that they might soon be proven.

At the same time, Sax found an equal fascination in the civilization of Islam. The warmth and color of Arab literature appealed to him tremendously. Lane's *Modern Egyptians* and Burton's monumental translation of *One Thousand Nights and a Night* figured prominently on his reading list, though where he got hold of the latter is a mystery, since it was then virtually a forbidden book.

Sir Richard Francis Burton, who had explored hostile Africa and, disguised as a Moslem Indian, made the pilgrimage to Mecca, was a hero to command youthful respect anywhere. What was more important, from Sax's point of view, he told his tales of wonder with great depth of feeling and an individual style alternating curiously between archaic classicism and rough outspokenness. (Sax later attempted to emulate this style in some of his short stories, most notably "Pomegranate Flower" in *Tales of Secret Egypt.*)

For lighter reading, Sax's favorites seem to have been Bret Harte and, more particularly, Mark Twain. The thrill of his boyish life came when he chanced to meet the latter author on the top deck of a London bus. (This was probably about 1895, when Twain was making a lecture tour in England.)

It was during Sax's last year of school that his mother died. In recent years her alcoholism had been conjoined with tuberculosis, and in March of 1901 the combination finally proved fatal.

It was about this same time that Sax adopted a new middle name. In her delirious imaginings, Margaret Ward had claimed descent from Patrick Sarsfield, an Irish general of the 17th century who had distinguished himself in the service of James II. The name "Sarsfield" appealed to Sax, as did the career of its bearer, and by the time he passed his eighteenth birthday he had discarded "Henry" as a middle name and had christened himself Arthur Sarsfield Ward. (The "Henry" was not entirely forgotten. As late as 1931 the editors of *Liberty Weekly* would inform their readers that Sax Rohmer's real name was Arthur Henry Sarsfield Ward.)[3]

Sax's attitude to learning was on the one hand unworldly and on the other, eminently practical. He was avid for knowledge, but *new* knowledge. He saw no point in memorizing established

19

facts that could be looked up in commonplace reference books; he had little interest in carrying out laboratory experiments to re-prove what was already known; he found no incentive to learn languages that thousands of others could learn.

His father found himself at a loss. He could see no obvious career open to a lad with such ideas in his head. Yet, when Sax left school, he must somehow contrive to earn his own living.

Urged by his father, Sax began to read for the Civil Service—no doubt dreaming, as he did so, of a Colonial appointment that would take him to the mysterious lands which he wished so ardently to visit. Certainly, at that time, he could see no other way of getting there, and his efforts to make the grade were undoubtedly sincere. But a grounding in ancient Egyptian hieroglyphs, Arabic, the history of occult practices and the elements of hypnotism, was no sound preparation for a Civil Service examination. The result was a foregone conclusion: he failed.

Several weeks later, schooldays ended; retribution came upon him. He had become neither archaeologist nor Orientalist nor yet Messiah of some new and bizarre religion. He was a bank clerk in Threadneedle Street.

3

THE YOUNG BOHEMIAN

SAX'S STAY IN THE CITY WAS BRIEF BUT ILLUMINATING. HE HAD NOT BEEN there more than a few weeks before his startled employers arrived at two definite conclusions: (a) that they had never had such a clerk before, and (b) that, God willing, they never would again. Taxed with the complaint that his daily figures failed to show any relationship either to reality or reason, he agreed sadly that it was so, but added, "Nevertheless, I have devised a foolproof scheme for burgling the vaults!"

What the manager replied is not recorded.

Younger colleagues, astonished but admiring, pressed for particulars. Sax gave them. Simple in its essentials, the crime would first necessitate hypnotizing a member of the staff. They were skeptical. At this time, hypnotism still lay in the realm of black magic. Sax insisted that he could do it, and so a test was proposed and accepted. That afternoon, when the bank closed to the public, a group of black-coated young men met in the vaults. Before the doubting but eager eyes of his small audience, Sax took a heavy office ruler and placed it in the hands of the selected victim, a bank messenger named Gedge. Then, stepping back a pace, he fixed the man with a steady gaze and commenced to intone softly, "You must not drop it . . . you must not drop

21

it . . . you *can't* drop it. . . ."

"Gedge," Sax explained later, "was a foxy-looking character with a swivel eye—the left—which seemed to swing right around to one side and come out on the other. I was curious to discover if I could hypnotize such a person."

He could, and he did. Gedge tried suddenly to unclasp his fingers from the ruler; they remained fixed. As he realized this fact, an awful expression came over his face. All at once, he became hysterical. He began to run madly about the room, screaming, "I can't drop it! I can't drop it!"

Sax, to his consternation, found his subject out of control. Gedge would not look at him. The ruler had to be pried loose, finger by finger and, when at last his hands were freed, the messenger bolted upstairs, chattering with terror. An embarrassed silence supervened.

Something of the affair evidently reached the ears of authority, for shortly afterwards it was quietly suggested to Sax that he might transfer his services to another branch. Sax took the hint and transferred—by the simple process of never going back.

"Well, you see, the customers were nearly all stockbrokers," Sax said. He sighed. "How much happier the world would be if there were no Stock Exchange!"

With his escape from Threadneedle Street, Sax had achieved freedom—of a sort. But, from here on, the real struggle would begin. He was not, in the full sense of the word, destitute. He had at least a roof over his head, and breakfast was included in the terms of the lodging which he shared with his father in Stockwell Road. For the rest, he must now fend for himself.

Sax did not tell his father that he had left the bank, reasoning that it would be both unkind and purposeless to do so. His father could logically have done nothing about it but urge him towards some alternative employment likely to prove equally unsuitable. It was a deception easily kept up—for a time, anyway. Bill Ward still left home long before the hour when Sax was supposedly due to start out for the City. He took his meals in cafés near his office, and assumed that his son's work was providing him with sufficient money to do the same.

But, in the meantime, Sax nearly starved while he sought desperately for some means of capitalizing his only assets—a fertile

22

imagination and a fund of knowledge in outlandish subjects. His thoughts turned naturally to fiction writing. Thanks to his father's preoccupation with office work, there was at least a typewriter and a good supply of paper in the house. A barrage of short stories went out to all the popular magazines—and came back as rapidly. He had yet to serve the hard apprenticeship of a writer and learn its bitter lesson: that which the author feels most urgently disposed to write is that which the great general public feels least disposed to read. Disappointed but undaunted as the little colored rejection slips continued to flow in, he pasted them up in his room till they covered a whole wall. "In order to complete the color scheme, I sent one MS to the same magazine three times. But the third time, they lost it."

Just when and why he abandoned his first attempt at authorship is obscure. Sheer hunger may have driven him to it, or his father—a shrewd man, from whom nothing could long be concealed—may have found out what was going on and insisted. My guess is the latter, for I think Sax would literally have starved himself to death rather than turn back on his course.

At all events, he did turn back and, for a few days, we find him most uncongenially employed as a clerk in a gas company. But the outcome of this *mésalliance* must have been obvious from the outset. The bald banality of business correspondence insulted Sax to his depths. Almost without conscious direction, his rebellious pen garnished his letters to consumers with unexpected novelties:

. . . Accept our assurances, dear lady, that our engineer will attend to your defective gas cooker on Monday next, assuming that the same has not, in the meantime, exploded. . . .

One wonders if anybody has kept one of these letters. If so, it should be a museum-piece today. Needless to say, Sax did not write very many of them before his resignation was requested.

Again he was out looking for a job. He may in fact have found several, but no details are available. Eventually, however, he managed to obtain what looked like being a position better suited to him, on the reporting staff of a weekly newspaper called *Commercial Intelligence*. Here, to his surprise, he found himself under the direction of Swinborne Sheldrake, who had been educated at the same school.[4]

Overly conscious, perhaps, of his limitations as a "cub reporter," Sax was afterwards wont to speak of himself as "grossly incompetent." But he had nothing but praise for Sheldrake who, he maintained, gave him his only basic training in writing for the press. In later life, they were firm friends.

Swinborne Sheldrake, afterwards to become editor of one of the financial columns in the London *Times,* was a man with a dry, drawling voice, a poker face and a wry sense of humor which sometimes involved his subordinates in quite unlooked-for situations. One such situation, in which he had been the victim, Sax never forgot.

On this occasion, he had been sent across to Victoria Street with instructions to obtain an interview, if possible, with the High Commissioner for Canada. Sax arrived there to find a waiting room packed with senior reporters from all the great daily newspapers. All had been waiting to see Lord Strathcona for upwards of three hours. Clearly enough, a junior from a weekly journal had no chance at all, and Sax returned disconsolately to his office to admit as much.

"Don't waste my time!" Sheldrake said irritably, hunched over his desk. "Haven't you got any initiative? The thing to do is this: go back there at exactly three o'clock, get hold of some other clerk, and tell him you have an appointment with Lord Strathcona. Then, when he takes your card, just follow him through into the office, and there you are!"

Fearful but admiring, Sax retired from his chief's presence unquestioning, and did precisely what he had been told. It worked like a dream. Lord Strathcona—a kindly-faced man with silver hair and a grey beard—received him affably and without any apparent suspicion.

"I shall never know," Sax said, "whether he really thought he had appointed a meeting or whether, detecting my tensed-up inexperience, he just decided to be kind. He was a wonderful old gentleman."

Having answered all Sax's queries (which had to do with an extension of the Canadian Pacific Railway), Lord Strathcona instructed a secretary to furnish a sketch map, and shook hands with

24

Sax. The young reporter returned triumphant to Sheldrake's office, and presented his notebook.

"Good God!" Sheldrake said, jumping up. "You thought I meant it? I wouldn't have done a thing like that for six months' salary!"

He snatched the notebook from Sax's hand, glaring at it. The weekly newspaper was on the verge of going to press. In bland ignorance of what he was doing, Sax had "scooped" all the dailies in the country.

Sad to say, such lucky accidents—or near-accidents—come but seldom. Sax's newspaper work was not of the kind calculated to inspire confidence in editors. As had happened before, his love of fantasy betrayed him. With the best intentions in the world, he could not resist the temptation to embroider the drab fabric of fact with details of his own imagining, and the result was inevitable. Once again he was out of work.

"I cannot pretend that I had set Fleet Street on fire," Sax said wryly. "But I had created a moderately high temperature in the office!"

Following the collapse of his earnest but ill-timed endeavors in journalism, Sax made no further attempts to seek employment. He had failed as a humble clerk, failed as a reporter, and failed dismally at breaking into the fiction market. His next decision was to try his luck as an illustrator. He had always been interested in art and could handle his materials proficiently. He began to attend art schools, at the same time submitting black-and-white drawings to illustrated publications. All of them came back.[5]

(Personally, I must confess that I do not know why. Sax's work in black-and-white, and in color, has always seemed to me excellent. This skill remained with him all his life.)

Seeing no likelihood of an escape in that direction, Sax decided to turn back to his first love, writing. Where he had failed previously, the experience he had gained in Fleet Street might now enable him to succeed. From Sheldrake he had learned how to tell a story; the unbridled imagination which had ruined him then and elsewhere might now guide him to a choice of the story to be told.

In the noisy, squalid environment of his suburban lodgings, Sax sat down and let his unruly thoughts reach out to ancient

25

Rome and the arid lands of the Pharaohs. Nightmare and the news story . . . what happened when they became one? What if the phantoms of legend appeared against the background of familiar, everyday things? He began to write, unconscious of the fact that, as he did so, something new in popular literature was born. Here was fantasy, reported with the neat precision of Fleet Street, enhanced by the stylistics of the masters and the dry humor of Mark Twain.

Two short stories resulted. But for the time being the effort had drained him. He had hardly the energy to seal them up and put them into the post.

Sax's father, aware of how matters stood, watched his son with anxiety but without disapproval. Why Sax could not settle down to the plain, undemanding routine of a legitimate career he frankly did not understand. But Bill Ward was not the man to criticize another for being unlike himself. Recognizing that, in his own peculiar way, his son was engaged in an honest struggle for survival, he looked on with sympathy and now, fearing that the boy was driving himself to a nervous collapse, packed him off for a holiday in Guernsey.

For several days, Sax tramped the rugged coasts and highlands, while the strong sea air swept the dust of London from his lungs and cleared the fog of depression from his mind. Then, caught one evening in a thunderstorm and hastening back to his modest hotel, drenched to the skin, he saw two letters in the rack. One was marked *Pearson's Magazine,* the other *Chambers's Journal.* Sax's hand trembled as he lifted them out. He had aimed high, intending to work down the scale when "The Mysterious Mummy" and "The Leopard-Couch" returned from their first submission. But they had not returned; both stories had been accepted.[6] The year was 1903, and Sax was twenty years old.

4

THE EGYPTIAN DANCER

SAX RETURNED TO LONDON, ELATED AND FULL OF CONFIDENCE. WITH two short stories to his credit, his ambition soared. Now, he decided, he would go to work on a novel—a romance of Ancient Egypt which should place him at one bound beside Rider Haggard, or perhaps Flaubert. The enthusiasm of youth is unlimited, but rarely rewarded. The great work *Zalithea* led to no such result—it died, uncompleted. But it led to Sax's second experience of the clairvoyant dream, an experience even more startling than the first.

Backed by a knowledge of Egypt based entirely upon reading, Sax set to work and wrote his first six chapters. This carried him to the point where a daughter of Seti I was to disguise herself as a dancing girl, in order to penetrate a banquet attended by her lover. And there Sax stuck, realizing that his Egyptology had failed him.

He had no idea of the setting in which such a banquet would take place—what people would wear—what they might eat and drink. Above all, he had no idea of what his central character, the dancing girl, should look like. Abandoning Chapter Seven of *Zalithea* at a late hour, he went to bed.

Sax closed his eyes, slept and woke—or rather, dreamed that he woke—to discover himself a guest at just such an entertainment as he had tried vainly to describe. Hovering curiously between waking and sleeping, he was aware of his own identity—aware that the body he occupied was not his own. Through the eyes and ears of this other self, he saw and heard clearly but without understanding. His companions spoke to him in a strange tongue, and he heard his own voice answering in the same—yet not knowing what the words meant.

Oddly, he was conscious of no fear. He knew that he was an observer, and knew why he had to observe. He concentrated his attention eagerly upon the scene—astounded to find it utterly unlike anything he had imagined. Everything was new to him. The complexions of his neighbours—exclusively masculine—were much lighter than he had supposed; a spirit of childish gaiety dominated the place.

It was a sort of courtyard, partly covered by a brightly striped canopy of what appeared to be silk, or more probably some vegetable fibre. Brilliant moonlight flooded the garden upon which one side of the courtyard opened, and a number of lamps were set in niches in the walls.

From the direction of a curtained opening, a chord of music sounded. The curtain twitched and, anticipating what was about to happen an instant before it did happen, he felt a quick thrill of excitement. The curtain parted and a dancer came out.

She wore a violet colored robe of transparent gauze, and many bangles. An apparently endless chain of tiny pink flowers was wound around her hair, around her shoulders and waist, terminating in a sort of floral girdle.

The dance—a series of postures, elusive in significance—brought her near. He could see the heavy make-up on her eyes—lashes blackened and eyelids darkened. Her hair was dyed a dull, lustreless red. Her finger nails and toenails were stained and varnished. The rope of flowers swung immediately before him. He drew back slightly . . . and found himself sitting bolt upright in his own bed.

Moonlight was streaming in at the window. Half right there was an armchair, untidily draped with discarded clothes. Just beyond, clearly visible in the bright moonlight, was a familiar chest of drawers . . . but between the bed and the armchair stood the dancing girl!

"Rarely, if ever, have I been more terrified," Sax said gravely. Many years had passed but, from the expression on his face, it was clear that the episode remained fixed in his mind as if it had happened only the night before. "I was wide awake. The background of the dream had gone, the scene, the company, the music—but the girl was there, in my room! I could hear the faint sound made by her bare feet as she twisted slowly on the carpet—the chink of bangles . . . I thought I had lost my reason. How long I watched, trying to convince myself that I still dreamed, I can't say. But, slowly, the dancer from Ancient Egypt dissolved, as an opaque cloud slowly becomes transparent, passing from firmly material to shimmering vapor, gradually to invisibility."

That, then, is the story—and if you had heard Sax tell it, as I did, you would know that he believed every word of it.

The present day reader may not be unduly impressed. We know today that this kind of "waking dream" may be explained by a number of theories, excluding the fantastic. But, though the latter part of Sax's unnerving experience was certainly the most dramatic, it was not the most strange.

Years afterward, when he came to know Egypt better and Egyptologists had unearthed later evidence, Sax found that all the details which he had so carefully observed in that dream were, in fact, authentic!

It was probably about the same time as the Egyptian Dancer affair that Sax became a member of certain occult societies. One of these was The Hermetic Order of the Golden Dawn. Existing accounts of the origin and history of this Order are contradictory, and much remains to be elucidated. The date most often given for its founding is 1887. During the following three decades, many famous names appeared on the Order's membership rolls, and those of various splinter groups: William Bulter Yeats, Arthur Machen, Arthur Edward Waite, and "Dion Fortune" (Violet M. Firth), among others. Another member, ultimately disowned, was the notorious Aleister Crowley, whom Sax knew and disliked.

Sax may also have become a member of a Rosicrucian Society, and by this I mean a branch rather less well known and rather more significant than the brotherhood which currently operates under this name in the United States. Rudyard Kipling is said to have been admitted to the Society at the same time. The Society, which came into existence at least as early as the sixteenth century, is international, with lodges or orders in all civilized countries. What goes on within these lodges is not much known outside. It is known only that the Society is founded on a belief in the existence of a fund of secret wisdom handed down through the ages and transmitted only to the initiated.

Sax's introduction to these societies came through Dr. R. Watson Councell, who was the Ward family doctor and had treated Margaret Ward during her final illness. Dr. Councell was an enthusiast of the occult, and became Sax's mentor in this area over a period of years. When, some years later, Dr. Councell's book *Apologia Alchymiae* was published (London: John M. Watkins, 1925), it contained a Preface by Sax Rohmer, the only known instance when Sax wrote introductory matter for another person's work.

Some of the things that Sax learned in these occult societies probably found their way into his stories, and here, obviously, is the source from which he obtained the idea of a secret brotherhood holding arcane knowledge, which he has used in such books as *The Bat Flies Low*. What specific things he may have learned is impossible to say. It is certain that he did a great deal of research and some practical experiment in this shadowy field, and never wholly ceased from doing so, but he found it impossible to keep up the strictly ascetic life said to be necessary to an "adept." Ultimately, he left the societies, but he kept their secrets faithfully. He never spoke of his memberships even to Elizabeth, and it was not until after his death that his connections with these societies became known.

Sax's life during the years 1904-1907 presents no very clear picture. He was writing, and occasionally selling, stories: *Pearson's Magazine* published "The Green Spider" (October 1904), "The Mystery of the Marsh Hole" (April 1905), and "The McVillin" (December 1906), all with the byline A. Sarsfield Ward. Sax was also active in freelance journalism, and tried his hand at quite a few other things as well. Without going back to the drudgery of paid employment, he was now supporting himself—at least in his daily needs; he was still living with his father—but they were lean times. His lunch generally consisted of bread and cheese, a Breton onion, an apple, and a pint of beer.

We know that he contributed a good many "Turnovers" to the *Globe*. These were feature-interest articles, deriving their name from the fact that they consisted invariably of one column on the front page plus a short segment on the reverse side of the page. All were published anonymously. The *Globe*, though now extinct, was at that time a long-established and reputable journal, and a record of the anonymous writers of these columns-and-a-bit would read like an honors list. The contributors had included Dickens, Kipling, Conan Doyle, G. K. Chesterton, and P. G. Wodehouse.[7]

In the same period, Sax found a new market for his writing in the backstage world of the theater. At that date, the live theater and particularly the music hall were thriving concerns. Comedians and singers required nearly as much material for their acts as their television counterparts do today. With his immense vocabulary and ready wit, Sax proved himself an excellent writer of lyrics and comedy sketches. His clients did not pay very much, but it was enough to make a useful addition to his erratic earnings. This work also brought him into contact with unusual people. For the most part, they were amusing, and a few of them were later to become valuable allies.

During his school days Sax had made no particularly close friends, but it was not likely that an energetic young man in his early twenties would remain long without finding kindred spirits to share his adventures. Perhaps in one sense he had found them already among his fellow students of occult lore, but most of the latter were probably a good deal older than himself and over-inclined to seriousness.

Sax's interest in the Unknown, though certainly not frivolous, was not morbid. He saw it as a new frontier, offering exciting possibilities of exploration, alternately dangerous and rewarding. A purely monkish approach which aimed at the cultivation of some esoteric philosophy was not in the least attractive.

The new era of King Edward VII was a lively one and produced its loosely banded groups of "Bohemians," just as any period of change will do. Sax was a part of those days and one of those outcasts.

Although his home base was still in Stockwell, Sax now found himself spending much of his free time at a flat in Oakmead Road, Balham. The flat was a kind of headquarters for three other young rebels against society, named Cumper, Bailey and Dodgson. It was the latter who actually lived there. Dodgson, who looked like a pugilist, was a nephew of Lewis Carroll and a student at medical school who had thus far failed to obtain his degree three years running.

All four had one thing in common. In no possible circumstances would they consent to sell the greater part of their lives into slavery for the price of a few annual weeks of freedom. Some means of living by doing what they were best pleased to do had to be found. Sax, for his part, had made some progress in writing, but as yet he was by no means convinced that the life of a writer was what he really wanted. He was still ready to try alternatives. Between them, in more or less felonious partnership, they tried a good many.

Sax, with one foot in the theatre, and inspired by the rising fame of C. B. Cochran, suddenly decided upon Management. Partnered by Marcus Cumper, who professed to know something about show business, he engineered the printing of some impressive notepaper headed "Macready & Rollander Productions" (based on what flight of fancy nobody will ever know) and sallied forth to find talent.

Haunting the restaurants where staff dinners, reunions and Masonic banquets took place, and at which entertainers were usually employed, they soon found their man. He was an incredibly funny comedian, giving his own interpretation of numbers popularized by the big stars.

They grabbed him, put him under contract and went to work on him. Sax wrote a complete act for "Hal Sherry, the Different Comedian." They trained him, put him on a diet, exercised him and rehearsed the act till they were all sick of it. Then, satisfied at last, they tried him out on a Stock Exchange dinner.

Success seemed imminent. Hal Sherry was a riot. Convinced that they had found a new star, but still moving cautiously, the two "managers" secured a trial engagement at an obscure variety theatre with a twice-nightly bill.

Everything went smoothly. In the dressing room, waiting to be called, Hal Sherry showed not a trace of nervousness. The call came. The orchestra struck up the opening music and the curtain went up.

The Different Comedian, resplendent in evening dress, walked briskly on, halted—and stood rigid, dumb as a wax figure till the audience howled for blood and the harassed stage manager dropped the curtain on him.

The house manager appeared, furiously angry.

Sax, for once in his life, could think of no plausible excuse. It was Marcus who hastily explained, tactfully but untruthfully, that Mr. Sherry had had bad news that afternoon, but would most certainly be himself before the next house. The manager replied that if he wasn't, he would have worse news.

The two promoters gave their assurances earnestly, and rushed to the dressing room, fully expecting to find their protégé with his throat cut. They found him seated, perfectly self-possessed, but unable to give the slightest explanation of what had occurred.

Taking him out to a local bar, they bought him several drinks and quietly ran through the act. He was letter perfect. Back they went to the theatre. As they stood in the wings, waiting for the curtain to rise on the second house, Sax and Marcus looked anxiously at each other. It couldn't possibly happen again. But what, exactly, had happened the first time? An old hand in the theatre might have known. "First night nerves" and "stage fright" are not the same thing. The one is just plain nervousness, the other a psychological block that may, without warning, be triggered by almost anything. "Macready & Rollander" were not old hands. They did not know.

Again the orchestra struck up—again the curtain rose—and again Hal Sherry walked blandly onto the stage, to freeze and stand mute as a lemon. For one breathless instant, Sax and Marcus stared at him, then, by common consent, turned tail and bolted for the stage door with the yells of the enraged audience ringing in their ears.

"I hope they tear him to pieces!" Sax panted, as they ran hell-for-leather down the street.

5

WHAT'S IN A NAME?

SAX AND HIS VAGABOND ASSOCIATES CONTINUED TO CAST ABOUT THEM for some not too demanding means of gaining fame and fortune. Disappointed by their first attempts in theatrical management, Sax decided they would next try their hands at chemistry. He had always been interested in the subject, or at least in that side of it about which nobody knew anything. Now, putting his mind to commercial possibilities, he came up with the idea for a Wonderful Moth Ball.

He wrote some suitably attractive advertising. Guaranteed lethal to any moth at a range of ten yards or so, the moth ball was stated to do its stuff "whilst imparting to your furs, your clothing, not an unpleasant odour, but the aromatic fragrance of spring."

The headquarters of the Oakmead Road gang became, temporarily, a laboratory. Materials and skilled labor were conveniently to hand. Dodgson's uncle and guardian (not Lewis Carroll, but another uncle), beginning to lose all hope of his nephew ever becoming a doctor, had sharply cut down his allowance and Dodgson, in reduced circumstances, had been forced into taking a temporary job as assistant dispenser in a busy chemist's shop. The latter (unknowingly) was going to contribute the necessary ingredients.

I suspect that Sax invented the advertising before he invented the formula. No one knows from what storehouse of ancient and secret wisdom it was finally derived, but Sax appears to have confused it with some medieval alchemist's prescription for chemical warfare.

Preparation commenced. At what stage the transmutation took place and the product acquired the "aromatic fragrance of spring" nobody ever found out. Halfway through the manufacturing process, the chemists shut down the burners, threw open the windows and, putting on their coats, hurried out to find a cheap hotel. The Wonderful Moth Ball had stunk the place out and rendered half a street of flats uninhabitable for the rest of the night.

Sax's interest in organic chemistry was genuine, even if not strictly scientific. Fans of Fu Manchu will remember that Sax suggested the possibility of anaesthetic properties latent in certain heavily scented flowers, notably mimosa and hawthorne. Yet another of his ideas was that the spikenard of the New Testament (still not satisfactorily identified) might have been obtained from flowers of the common spinach plant.

The Papyrus Ebers gives directions for the preparation of *kyphi,* a type of sacred incense used in ancient Egypt, and reputed to have more or less magical effects. This intrigued Sax immensely, and I believe he actually attempted the experiment. The ingredients, as Sax later listed them in *The Romance of Sorcery,* included resin, wine, galangal root, juniper berries, root of aromatic rush, asphaltum, mastic, myrrh, Burgundy grapes, and honey. We know where Sax got the more obscure of these substances: from Dodgson. And we may suspect where *he* got them. Whether any results came of this experiment is not known.

After the moth ball disaster, no further attempts at chemistry were undertaken in Oakmead Road. Neighbors had threatened reprisals. Likewise, the Hal Sherry disaster should have discouraged any further attempts in management, and probably would have done, had not Sax come across prospects of an entirely different nature: I refer to the affair of Helène, the Perfect Woman.

The physical culture craze had hit England. Books and magazines urged young men to exercise, and gymnasia were springing up everywhere (mostly to be turned into warehouses when the craze died down again). The commendable ideal was that men should be Strong and women Shapely.

In support of this, advertisements all over London featured terrifying pictures of Eugene Sandow, the Strongest Man in the World, less terrifyingly accompanied by Helene, the Perfect Woman.

Sax became interested. He loathed exercise, but in the scantily clad figure of La Belle Helène he saw distinct possibilities. He insisted, by the way, that he meant theatrical possibilities. The Macready & Rollander notepaper was dusted off.

Just how he got into contact with the lady, and how he persuaded her to join in their madcap schemes is one of the unsolved mysteries. Elizabeth has noted, however, that when women met Sax they were either instantly frightened or instantly attracted. She could not quite understand how this operated, but suspected that it was an effect which he was able to turn on and off at will. She observed that the pretty ones were seldom frightened.

Helène was not frightened. Sax invented a posing act in which she would appear—nude, of course—as the central figure in famous paintings. (To give him his just due, we should note that in doing this he anticipated by a good few years a familiar act later to be staged in almost every variety house in the world.) To all of this, Helène agreed with equanimity and apparent enthusiasm. We have no details from Sax (who was unusually reticent on the subject) but may assume that rehearsals were conducted at least as meticulously as they had been in the case of Hal Sherry.

A well-known agent was successfully approached and, once again, the future looked bright. Then came the snag. It came, tangibly, in the form of a very angry old lady with a very formidable umbrella. Helène's mother had other plans for the future of her daughter, who was engaged to a ship's captain. Not only was he a ship's captain, but he also had shares in the line.

It was about midday. Marcus had gone to Sax's lodgings, and was waiting patiently in the living room for his partner to get out of bed when the apparition manifested itself on the doorstep. Breathless with rage, she demanded to see Mr. Macready.

Marcus said, hastily, that Mr. Macready wasn't up yet.

This information was enough. She burst straight into the bedroom and wakened Sax, who was fast asleep, by prodding him in the ribs with her umbrella. He got up, rather quickly, from the other side of the bed. Helène's mother followed him round, screaming abuse and lunging with the umbrella. They did three quick laps round the bed, and then Sax broke for the doorway. Here, with laudable presence of mind, he allowed his pursuer to catch up with him, shoved her headlong into the living room, banged the door shut and locked himself in the bedroom.

"Get her out, Marcus!" he bawled through the panels.

Marcus did, by the simple but involuntary expedient of being chased ignominiously down the stairs, out into the street, and along to the next corner, where he outdistanced her.

Sax sat down wearily at his desk, turned over his stack of neatly headed notepaper and began to write manuscript on the plain side.

For a time at least, Sax concentrated his attention more or less wholeheartedly on authorship. There seemed to be no easier money to be had from any other source. Writing was, after all, what he liked to do best. But he did not like writing to order. Nevertheless, he did it. He produced a short historical story in the Dumas style, called "The McVillin," and it went better than anything he had done previously. The editor of *Pearson's Magazine* called him for an interview, and proposed a contract for a series.

Sax went home, jubilant; at last, he was really getting somewhere. But his jubilation lasted only until he sat down to write the next story—and found that, try as he would, he could think of nothing to write! All at once, his imagination had dried up on him. His confidence deserted him, and he panicked. It was the biggest thing of his career, and he couldn't do it. . . . The desire to escape, to go anywhere, became stronger than he could resist. A mere trip out of town would not satisfy it. He decided that he must leave the country.

How? He could not afford the passage money even across the Channel, if he was to have anything left when he reached the other side. Casting around for an answer, he thought of Dirk Fisher, a lad he had known for some time. The latter's father had an interest in the Dutch eel-boats which, under the ancient charter of Queen Elizabeth I, brought live eels to the Port of London.

So it came about that Sax made his first journey overseas in a Dutch eel-boat. Later, and throughout his life, he had such a great love of ships that he would never go anywhere by air. But he could hardly have acquired it from that voyage which, as he afterwards described it, must have been one of the roughest he ever made. One wonders that it did not cure him of the sea for good. The eel-boat was a pot-bellied craft with a tendency to go round and round in a head wind, and the weather was fresh off the Nore. The crew's accommodation was entirely subject to the comfort of the eels. With the exception of the deck and a tiny cabin, the whole ship was allotted to the latter.

The shipper's assurance that his eccentric vessel was unsinkable failed to convey much comfort. Sax made the greater part of that voyage with his legs wedged firmly under a little table and one hand clutching a bunk rail, while he marvelled at the acrobats on deck. He, himself, could not even have reached deck. The movements of the ship were unpredictable. She had an alarming trick of jumping straight up in the air, or so it seemed, and dropping back with a shattering crash.

Sax discovered that he was a "good sailor"; he was amazed to find that his stomach survived the ordeal, and amazed to find himself hungry. But the wind freshened, so that the galley fire had to be doused. For luncheon, they had cold boiled bacon, bread and cheese, and beer. The weather continued to get worse rather than better.

"I expected at any moment to be knocked out," Sax said. "Either I would bang my head on an iron post behind me, or pitching forward, bang my head on the table. I don't know if I fell asleep in the end, or merely got knocked out."

When he returned to consciousness, dinner was ready. It consisted of bread and cheese, cold boiled bacon, and beer.

So far as I can find out, Sax never told anybody what he did in Holland, or how long he stayed there. Rather curiously, too, he has written nothing about it—curiously, because he generally got some kind of a story out of every place he visited. He may have been there a few days, or even a few weeks. Or, having once reached the Continent, he may simply have taken a train to Paris or elsewhere.

But when he came back to England, he had recovered his

nerve and gained a new identity: Arthur Sarsfield Ward had gone out; Sax Rohmer returned.

Of course, the matter was not really that clear-cut or dramatic. For several years after his return, Sax used both names. The new name was used occasionally in his private life, but more often in his contacts with the entertainment world, and as a byline on the songs and comedy sketches he was writing. It was not until 1912, after he had settled down seriously to a career of writing fiction, that he succumbed to Elizabeth's urging and began to use the Sax Rohmer byline on his stories.

From that point on, the name crept more and more into his private life. Both Sax and Elizabeth became so accustomed to it that they often forgot it was not their legal name. (Once, on an ocean voyage, Elizabeth was thrown into a mild panic when the purser on the ship appeared to have lost her passport. It was found in time, filed quite properly under "Ward.") Eventually, even Sax's will was signed with the name "Rohmer" rather than "Ward."

There has been a great deal of speculation about Sax's choice of his peculiarly striking pen name. His own explanation was recorded in an interview in *The New Yorker* in 1947: "In ancient Saxon, 'sax' means 'blade'; 'rohmer' equals 'roamer'. I substituted an 'h' for the 'a' as a gesture in the direction of phonetics—pretty obscure gesture, I guess." Obscure or not, in retrospect there is no doubt that the pen name—exotic sounding, yet easily remembered—was a definite asset to Sax Rohmer's literary career.[8]

6

ELIZABETH

ROSE ELIZABETH KNOX CAME FROM A SIZEABLE FAMILY VERY ACTIVELY concerned with the theatre. She had a sister and six brothers. One of the latter died young; all the rest were, at one time or another, in show business. When Elizabeth was in her teens, her eldest brother was already managing a repertory company in the north of England. Her youngest brother, then at school, was eventually to become Teddy Knox of the Crazy Gang. Their father, George Thomas Knox, had been a well-known comedian in his youth, and was now a lessee of theatres and promoter of shows. Their mother, Julia Phillips Knox, had been a dancer, and her father a contortionist.

In the summer of 1905 Elizabeth, still in her teens, was sharing a south London flat with her sister Julia, and rehearsing a juggling act with her brother Bill. One particular evening, however, found her strolling across Clapham Common, in the company of an escort whose intentions now struck her as somewhat less honorable than they had at first appeared. In every leafy patch of shadow, his arm snaked about her waist. Elizabeth countered neatly with her elbow. She was not in the least frightened, but she was becoming a little annoyed.

She walked on warily, watching out for shadowed areas, and thinking sadly of her regular boy-friend, recently departed to seek his fortune in Guatemala. An earnest soul, he had shown himself remarkable chiefly for his peculiar habit of stuffing his pockets with cheese, which he used the way some others used chewing gum.

As another tree shrouded the path Elizabeth, disengaging herself automatically from her companion's grasp, glanced over her shoulder to see three young men walking behind them. She studied them idly for an instant, then with more interest. They were a strange-looking group—one was strikingly handsome, a second looked like a prize-fighter, the third, in a belted tweed topcoat, with a tight tweed cap pulled down over his face, resembled Sherlock Holmes after an overdose of cocaine.

Something about that briefly glimpsed, ill-assorted trio left her tingling with anticipation. She was preoccupied to the extent that she no longer noticed the agile arm slyly encircling her. Listening, she heard the footsteps approaching rapidly, closing the distance, until suddenly they slowed to a lazy, indolent gait matching her own. She risked a second glance back and saw the three young men now only a few yards behind, keeping pace with her companion and herself.

In the same moment, taking advantage of her relaxed vigilance or mistaking it for acquiescence, her escort slewed her artfully off the path into the obscurity of a convenient bush. Exploring fingers moved down over her hip; her escort's right hand swung across, turning her towards him. Elizabeth stiffened, jerked back her head, and brought her heel down smartly on his instep. The importunate fellow emitted an inelegant "Yow!" and stepped back quickly into the waiting arms of the handsome one and the prize-fighter.

Elizabeth could never quite sort out what happened next. It was carried off with the neat precision of a tumbling act. She felt lean fingers close firmly on her arm, and in the next instant she was walking along the path, side by side with the man in the tweed coat, while a confused altercation went on dimly in the background.

"It was clear to us that his attentions were unwelcome," he murmured. "My friends will remonstrate with him. Meanwhile, allow me to accompany you safely to your door."

41

Elizabeth stared up at him. She was petite and, by comparison, her rescuer or her kidnapper (as yet, she wasn't quite sure which) seemed very tall. She looked up into eyes of a strange intensity, veiled by the longest and thickest lashes she had ever seen. Then and there she decided that they were the eyes of a murderer; but she felt excited rather than scared.

A daughter of the theatre, she had no illusions about men, and no lack of confidence in her ability to protect herself. Far across the world, at the same era, the young ladies of Japan ornamented their hair with stiletto-like *kanzashi,* useful for self-destruction when loss of virtue threatened. Elizabeth's white hat was secured likewise to her tight mass of auburn curls with an 8-inch hatpin. But it was not intended for self-destruction.

The murderer walked on placidly, keeping a steady grip on her arm, treating the matter rather as if a duty had been wished upon him and making no attempt at conversation. At the end of some minutes, this became slightly unnerving.

"What are you thinking about?" she demanded impulsively.

"Death!" he said.

Elizabeth started, suppressing a squeal. She was sure, now, that he was not only a murderer but mad. "Why—why should you think about that?"

"Why not?" For a moment, the deeply set eyes that seemed to look through rather than at her scanned her startled face, and she saw that he was laughing at her. "You are so young and full of life . . ." he paused and added, as an afterthought, "also pretty. One is led, naturally, to think of the antithesis. Doubtless this is the reason why the Ancient Egyptians arranged for a coffin to be dragged around the room in which they feasted." He seemed suddenly to become contemplative, speaking as if to himself. "But with them life and death were so inextricably mixed up. Isis, the Goddess of Life, herself conceived Horus by means of necrophilia."

"Did she?" Elizabeth said. As she had heard neither of Horus nor of necrophilia, there seemed not much else to say.

They walked on in silence for a few minutes. Then, unexpectedly, the icy reserve of her companion's manner dropped away from him, and he began to talk naturally—making the light, meaningless conversation that a man might make with any chance acquaintance. What he said was amusing. Yet it left her feeling

42

shy and, oddly, a little sad. It was as if he was carrying out a commission—as if he didn't really wànt to be bothered with her.

Why this should matter to her she couldn't understand—but it did matter. Her own feelings puzzled her as much as the extraordinary behavior of this thoroughly incredible young man who, aided and abetted by his gang of thugs, carried her off like some desert sheikh—only to treat her, thereafter, as he might have treated a maiden aunt. His seeming indifference exasperated her, for she was sure that a fire smouldered behind that mask of cold politeness.

Nothing happened, however, until finally they arrived at her own doorstep. For a moment they looked at each other.

"Well—" Elizabeth said, "thank you for seeing me home."

She held out her hand formally. The cold young man ignored it, swept her into his arms in one decisively quick movement and kissed her. Locked in his embrace, she had just the time to tell herself that she had had no possible chance to resist—it had all happened before she knew it—and then to realize with horror that she was not trying to resist. She pulled back violently and stood gasping.

"I'll see you again," the man said quietly. He reached out and touched her hair lightly with his fingertips. "Good night, Curly!"

"But . . . but you haven't even told me your name!"

"Haven't I?" He seemed to consider this. "Oh, well—if it really matters—my name is Sax Rohmer. Good night!"

Overcome with confusion, Elizabeth burst blindly into the sitting room and collided with her sister, who was on her way out to the kitchen.

"What's the matter with you?" her sister demanded.

"Nothing. Nothing at all. . . ." Elizabeth threw her hat down on the settee and began to search along the bookshelf. "I say—isn't there a dictionary here somewhere? What does 'necrophilia' mean?"

"God knows!"

"Yes—" Elizabeth said absently, "a god called Hocus or something." She found the book, riffled through the pages and read, then shut it with a bang. "Oh! How disgusting! How dare he!"

43

"Who?"

"Sax Rohmer! The man I'm going to marry!"

The words were out before she knew she had spoken them. Yet, in the same instant, came a strange but absolute conviction that they were true. It was less the expression even of her own subconscious will than an intuitive glimpse of the future—something that *had* to happen.

"Marry?" Elizabeth's sister stared at her blankly; then, as she didn't answer, shook her head. "Really, you're completely crazy! You always used to say you were going to marry an author. Forgotten that?"

Elizabeth walked slowly into her bedroom. Yes, she had forgotten. All at once, it didn't seem important any more. Right from her schooldays, she had idealized authors—those godlike beings with the mysterious power to create what others could only read and admire. To be married to one must surely be the highest honor and the greatest happiness that any woman could hope to attain.

Who was Sax Rohmer? She didn't know and she didn't care. With a name like that, he might be a foreigner. On the other hand, he could equally well be a coal miner from the Rhondda. Whichever he was, she was going to marry him.

But, as the days passed, lengthening into weeks, and still no word came from that mysterious young man, Elizabeth's hopes began to fade. She watched the post eagerly, but without avail. Letters came—but not the letter she was waiting for. The others she left unanswered. Every ring at the doorbell set her heart jumping.

It was a sad blow to her self-confidence. Hers were not just the silly imaginings of a plain girl infatuated by a man's unexpected attention. Elizabeth was more than commonly attractive, and not used to neglect. Had he, after all, thought of her only as a casual pick-up?

She felt sure that he had not. He had said, "I'll see you again" and something about him convinced her beyond any common sense reasoning that here was a man whose word was absolute. Disappointment was, consequently, the more difficult to bear. A woman may survive loss of faith in her power to attract; she can less easily survive loss of faith in her intuition.

44

Making a deliberate effort, she began to go about again with men friends who made no secret of enjoying her company. But, in these days, they found her a sorry companion. The usual run of parties and dances bored her, bringing no relief.

Elizabeth decided on the classic solution. Work must be the antidote. But the juggling act with Bill was too trivial and too closely bound up with the light, inconsequential world of the music hall to offer any satisfaction. She made up her mind to go north and browbeat her eldest brother into giving her a part in his stock company. The tried and tear-stained favorites of *Lady Audley's Secret* and *East Lynne* were better suited to her mood. Besides, by removing herself from London, she would no longer feel the temptation to turn her head at every approaching footfall, and stare into the faces of every group of passing strangers.

Her plans, such as they were, were quickly made and as quickly carried out. Grimly resolved to her bleak future, she prevailed upon her brother to take her into his company. But she had been there only a matter of days when her father arrived, bristling with indignation, to conduct her back personally to London and the light-hearted theatre to which she was best suited. His daughter's private life was her own, but in show business he made the decisions. There was going to be no breaking up of acts in *his* family.

So Elizabeth went back to her spangled tights, the spinning plates and the birdcages balanced on broomsticks. Subconsciously, she may have been happy—for, while she remained in London, hope could never be quite dead. But, consciously, she was miserable. Viewed in the light of reason, hope was now so dim as to be negligible.

And then, with the same swift unexpectedness as before, it happened.

Again she was walking homeward across the same common— but this time alone. As she passed the spot where it had all begun, her mood of depression deepened and she walked on, neigher seeing nor hearing, till all at once firm hands grasped her shoulders from behind, spinning her around—and again she was in his arms with his lips pressed tightly upon hers.

In the instant that she looked up into his face and recognized him she ceased to struggle. She clung to him shamelessly.

"Oh, Sax!" she sobbed, half laughing and half crying. "You beast! Why didn't you write?"

"Never thought to ask you your name!" he muttered. "Couldn't even find my way back to the darned road!"

7

THE PHANTOM DOG

THE LIFETIME PARTNERSHIP OF ELIZABETH AND SAX HAD BEGUN, BUT IT is doubtful whether the opening stages of any romance were ever conducted on lines more haphazard. One looks in vain for the familiar pattern of friendship deepening into understanding. Nothing of the sort happened. From the very beginning, these two were held together by the tacit recognition of a mutual necessity, mysterious but real, from which neither could escape.

They made no regular dates. Sax appeared out of the blue and disappeared into it as frequently. Elizabeth asked no questions. She knew that he would come back. During his absences, she waited patiently and bedevilled her sister to keep the blue and white checked dress, which she had worn at their first meeting, neatly laundered and pressed in readiness for their next meeting. It was a romantic fancy with her that she wanted him always to see her as he had first seen her. Not that it very often worked out that way: Sax usually turned up without warning, when and where least expected. When he did make dates, he had a habit of keeping them plus or minus an hour, or else forgetting them altogether.

It was on these uncertain terms that Elizabeth received her first invitation to take tea with him at the Oakmead Road rendezvous.

47

Arriving there to find no one at home, she spent a furious half hour walking up and down the street. Eventually Sax appeared, carrying a bottle of milk and what turned out to be a cake in a paper bag. He explained artlessly that he had been diplomatically employed in seeing off a previous visitor—a girl who had come to see Dodgson. But Dodgson had forgotten his date too.

Sax produced a key and conducted his guest into a room furnished principally with beer crates. The walls were decorated with unframed photographs of girls, over-dressed, under-dressed and not dressed, and a numerous collection of charcoal nudes. These, Sax said hastily, he had done at the life class in art school. Elizabeth thought it wiser to make no comment. Judging from the poses, it had been a singularly advanced art school.

They had a cosy tea party, throughout which Sax behaved with a correctness beyond reproach. True, he invited her to stay the night (which he seemed to think part of his duty as a host) but he appeared neither surprised nor greatly disappointed when Elizabeth politely declined.

When they parted that evening at her sister's door, she had still found out very little about him but had formed a fairly accurate impression of his character. He had no respect for conventions, and very little for the law. For marriage he had no use at all. He considered all men to be born polygamous and bound to observe God's will in accordance with this state. The Church marriage service he described as "blasphemous perjury."

Elizabeth decided that she was going to change his mind about that. But she had plenty of time. It would be the better part of three years yet before she could marry him without the consent of her parents, and she certainly wouldn't get that. She now knew that, far from being rich, Sax was in a financial state even more precarious than her own. But this was a relief. He was not inaccessible, after all. They could begin on a level at rock bottom and work upward together.

For two people destined to share so closely in one another's lives, the conduct of Sax and Elizabeth over the next few months was ironical in the extreme. Each was aware of the image in the mind of the other and desperate to maintain it. Consequently, Sax had no idea that she worked in a variety theatre, and Elizabeth had no idea that he was the writer of the comic songs sung in the

48

same theatre.

Some absurd situations resulted. As junior half of the juggl-ing act with Bill, one of the lowly duties which fell to Elizabeth was to carry the necessary "props" to and from the theatre. On one occasion, these chanced to consist of a bucket and a mop, and burdened with these unlikely objects, she was struggling aboard a bus when, to her horror, she ran full tilt into Sax.

"Hallo, Curly!" he murmured, staring at her load. "Just off to do a spot of charring?"

I should mention, in passing, that "Curly" was the first of a long string of pet names by which Sax called Elizabeth—occa-sioned, of course, by her hair. Elizabeth's tight mass of red-gold curls fascinated him to a degree which may easily be judged by anyone familiar with his stories. To the end of his life, the great majority of his heroines always had auburn hair.

At this period, Sax was still living a hazardous existence, supporting himself as best he could by freelance journalism, the occasional story and a good deal of song writing. On a short-term basis, the latter paid off best, but he was ashamed of it. Furnishing the repertoire of red-nosed concert artists who sang in beer halls and workmen's clubs was poor satisfaction to a young man whose thoughts ran persistently on other-worldly mysticism. Neverthe-less, he had to do it and when Elizabeth ultimately found out about it—as, of course, she was bound to do, sooner or later—she was able to help him more than a little.

Sax needed all the help he could get, and in more ways than one. Knowing nothing of the circumstances in which he lived, Elizabeth was startled, on her first visit to his lodgings, to find him, at midday, attired in an ancient dressing gown and attempt-ing to warm up the chilled remains of breakfast on an incandescent gaslamp. In the matter of home comforts, there was no one to look after him, and he was palpably incapable of looking after himself.

Elizabeth asked nothing better of life than the chance and the right to fulfill that need. But she had to tread warily. It was not only the Celtic streak of romance which Sax had inherited, but also the stubborn independence of an Irishman. Subconsciously, he knew that he needed her in every possible way that a man can need a woman, but he was not yet ready to admit it consciously to himself. It was many years before he was ready to admit it to her.

As so often occurs in human relationships, the extent to which he had come to rely upon her presence did not dawn on him till the occasion when Elizabeth's partnership with her brother sent her away from London on a tour of the provinces. The old adage that "absence makes the heart grow fonder" is only a qualified truth. The belated realization of necessity is brought about less by separation than by the threat of separation. In the past, when it so suited him, he had not seen her for weeks at a time—selfishly, but justifiably convinced that when he chose to go to her she would be there. This time *she* was the one who was going away.

This time, Sax was at the station to see her off on her journey. Their first real vows were exchanged on a crowded platform amid the hustle and confusion of a theater company on the move. He promised to write, and, this time, he did.

Over the next few weeks, Sax continued to follow his erratic way of life, outwardly unchanged but haunted by a lovely but persistent ghost. Since it was a ghost to which he could at least send letters, the sense of loss was, fortunately, not complete. But it was strong enough to make itself felt. Studying the itinerary of the touring company, and deciding where to address the next letter, he suddenly noted a familiar name which touched off a brilliant string of ideas.

Elizabeth and her brother were booked to appear at the Derby Castle, in Douglas, Isle of Man. (The Derby Castle was not actually a theatre, but a dance hall with cabaret acts.) And Dodgson's uncle lived on the Isle of Man.

Sax made a quick decision. It was high time that Dodgson went to visit the old boy. And it was high time that he, Sax, looked into that fascinating business concerning the Phantom Dog of Holm Peel.

The legend of the Mauthe Dhug, the phantom dog of Peel Castle, is one of the strangest ghost stories in fact or fiction.

Holm Peel, as it stands today, is little more than a playground for the holidaymakers who flock to the Isle of Man during each summer. But at night, when the last visitor has gone and the great gate is locked, the ruins of this grim old fortress become again a place of mystery with a history fading out in a misty past to be finally lost in Norse legend.

The legend of the Phantom Dog is less ancient, though ancient enough. It dates back to the reign of Charles II. According to eye-witnesses (against whose characters nothing can be said excepting that they are dead) the Mauthe Dhug is described as a large black spaniel, or possibly a retriever, shaggy coated and often seen in various parts of the castle. Its favorite haunt, however, seems to have been the guardroom, from which a subterranean passage led to the quarters of the captain of the guard.

Soon after dark, the dog appeared from time to time out of this passage and lay down before the guardroom fire. Newcomers amongst the troops were terrified, but after a while all grew accustomed to the periodic visits of the creature and, whilst allowing it plenty of elbow room, ceased to regard it with horror. Some time in the early morning, it would go out as it had come in.

It seems to have been a singularly sociable and well-behaved phantom; but no man would remain alone with it, or go alone through that passage. When, at some hour after sunset, the time came to lock the great gate and deliver the keys to the captain of the guard, they were delivered by two men, until the night that one man, a hardy guardsman and possibly not sober, insisted upon going alone.

Dissuasion failed. He went alone. The keys were delivered safely to the officer. But on the way back, something occurred. A loud outcry was heard in the guardroom, proceeding from the haunted passage—and the man returned, dumb with fright.

He never spoke again to the hour of his death—which took place a few days later. Following this, the passage was blocked up. The keys were taken to the captain of the guard by another route.

True to form, Sax duly arrived unheralded in Douglas. Here, smitten by a curiosity to see Elizabeth on the stage (which he had not previously taken the trouble to do) he turned up casually in the dance hall, with the foreseeable result that she spotted him in the audience, when she supposed him to be still in London, and narrowly avoided a disaster involving seven colored balls and three dinner plates.

Elizabeth, who had begun her day by hiking the full length of the sea front with her arms full of "props" (because Bill was careful about paying bus fares) was in no mood to feel very pleased about it.

"It's not so much that I mind having you kill the act," she explained, kissing him first and slapping him afterwards, "but the plates are expensive."

"Do you eat off them between turns?" Sax inquired interestedly.

But to two young people in love, the summer holiday spirit of the Isle of Man is infectious. The following afternoon, peace restored, they joined the crowd of trippers on their way across the island to the celebrated ruins of Peel Castle. Here Sax hoped to test certain theories concerning the origin of the Mauthe Dhug.

Separated from the town proper by an inlet, the castle occupies a position of great natural strength, being built upon the top of a giant rock descending at some points sheerly to the sea. Below, on the westward side, is a cavern into which the waves thunder and roar ceaselessly, through a vast opening like the nave of a church.

As the ferry boat brought them in under the shadow of that sombre pile of rock, Elizabeth felt a chill less of the flesh than of the spirit. Lacking her companion's active imagination, there were nevertheless times when she was more sensitive to impressions than he was.

They toiled up a flight of fifty or sixty steps to a huge wooden gate set in a formidable outer wall. After the gate came more steps, leading up to an inner wall and a wide open space surrounded by ruined buildings.

One of the better preserved—that of a chapel—held a particular interest for Sax. Beneath the crypt (according to early historians) lay a series of dungeons cut out of the solid rock and situated directly above the roof of the cavern. Perpetually damp and in pitch darkness, the whole labyrinth shuddering to the sullen booming of the sea below, it had been aptly described as a place dreadful beyond imagination.

But, to the secret relief of Elizabeth, access to the infamous dungeons proved to be no longer possible. The steep, narrow staircase said to exist under the ruins of the chapel had either collapsed or been deliberately closed. Sax was dissatisfied. He believed that the underground passage from the guardroom had communicated not only with the quarters of the captain of the guard but also with the dungeons.

Unable to enter the latter, he turned his attention to the guardroom, which remained although reduced to a state of desperate ruin. He knew that the passage had been blocked up, but he hoped to locate the spot at which it had opened out. In this, at least, he was successful, and what he found lent support to his theory. It seemed a reasonable conjecture that the officers' apartments had been in the main building; and, starting from the site of the blocked passage, it was obvious that this must have passed under the chapel.

"Even phantoms behave with some logic," Sax said thoughtfully. "A ghostly dog which materializes, for no good reason, in the middle of a passage makes no sense. Such a creature originating in that hellish catacomb and penetrating to the world above *through* a passage is conceivable. I wish I could get into those dungeons!"

Elizabeth shrugged and sat down to unwrap sandwiches. "I might have known," she said dolefully, "that you wouldn't have come all the way down from London to see me. It had to be a damned dog!"

Once set upon a quest, Sax was not the man to give up easily. Further investigations could not be carried out unless he could reach the catacombs which reputedly lay between the floor of the ruined chapel and the roof of the great cave. On the face of it, this seemed impossible. The way down from above was blocked.

But, Sax remembered, his peculiar researches into little-known records had hinted at the existence of another way up from the cave. This might not be blocked. Very well. Given a suitable calm evening, he would try to get a boat into the cave!

He did not mention this to Elizabeth, realizing that it could be risky. As a Londoner, with, as yet, little experience of the sea, what he evidently did not realize was that it would be suicidal.

The faithful Dodgson was sought out and invited to come along as second. Poor Dodgson, who had already been prevailed upon, by some obscure means, to beg hospitality for both of them under the roof of an uncle whom he feared worse than the Mauthe

Dhug, accepted with alacrity. Anything that would gain him an evening's freedom from the company of that awful old man would be cheap at the price.

The evening seemed placid enough and well suited to their purpose. The sea was almost oily in its smoothness, visibility wonderful. Armed with lights, measuring tapes, sketch plans and all other essential equipment, the intrepid ghost-hunters began pulling around from the harbor. Confident of a perfect night, they ignored gathering clouds in the west. They came off the entrance to the cave.

Viewed from a small boat, that entrance which, viewed from the land, had resembled the nave of a church, now resembled the nave of a cathedral. Big oily rollers bored their way in, roaring as they crashed into the jagged opening, booming from bend to bend till the forbidding sound died away, an eerie whisper, in some low, distant aisle of the rocks.

All at once, Sax remembered the small opening, barely visible at high tide, on the other side of the crag. The strong current sweeping in suggested that the sea went right through. At the same moment, he became aware of the half-submerged bayonet points of rock guarding that fearsome portal. With the rise and fall of the swell, they emerged from the hallows of the waves like giant sharks' teeth.

The alarming size of the waves at last drew the attention of the explorers to the west. Black, angry clouds were massing. Unnoticed by either, the storm was coming up fast—and the current was dragging the dinghy nearer and nearer to the guarding bayonets. Their former eagerness to get into the cave gave place to an urgent desire to get out.

There was no foothold anywhere on those sheer rocks: the nearest point at which a swimmer could have hoped to get ashore was somewhere on the other side of the castle. Two lengths away, the bayonets were waiting, and a sea was developing which already tossed the boat about contemptuously.

They took to their oars and pulled like galley slaves. How much time actually elapsed before they fought their way out of the clutch of that hungry current neither of them could afterwards guess. Some considerable time, certainly. When at last they got round the headland and found shelter in the little harbor, the storm was right upon them.

Sax walked back from the jetty silent and shaken, hands in pockets and collar turned up to the rain. The point on which he could not honestly make up his mind, then or later, was this: way back in the dark recesses of that awesome cavern, amid the distorted echoes roused by the lashing breakers, had he or had he not heard something else—a high, keen sound like the howling of a dog?[9]

8

DEED OF PARTNERSHIP

I HAD THOUGHT OF USING "WEDDING BELLS" FOR THE HEADING OF THIS chapter, but decided against it. The only bell which rang at the wedding of Elizabeth and Sax was that of the door. In fact, it was a wedding which only by the narrowest of margins ever took place at all.

The first two years of their courtship—if any such romantic and misleading term can be applied to the behavior of that un-conventional couple—were several times interrupted by the theatri-cal tours which Elizabeth had to make with her brother. It was not she but her father who, failing to see eye-to-eye with Bill on plans for the future, finally decided to break up the act. Elizabeth took this opportunity to quit the stage altogether, and moved in again with her sister and the latter's husband, determined to devote every possible minute of her time to Sax.

Sax and his father had recently moved from Stockwell Road to a new location about half a mile to the north, and were now quartered at 24 Wyke Gardens, Liberty Street, in north Brixton. As regularly as Sax's erratic habits would allow, Elizabeth visited his lodgings and tried to look after him. But since neither of them had any money, any sort of genuine housekeeping was impossible. Sax's father, leaving his son to work out his own salvation—no other course seemed possible—subsidized the effort with a weekly fifteen shillings, and with that Elizabeth did what she could.

She helped also with the song writing. Sax's clients sometimes demanded not only the words but the music as well. Sax had an ear for music and a good sense of melody, but could play no musical instrument. There was, however, a small piano at the new lodgings, and Elizabeth could play it. So, when the occasion required, she sat down at the keyboard and did her best to pick out notes to his direction. ("It wasn't too difficult," she remarks. "It was always the same tune!") In addition to writing songs for individual clients, Sax also sold some of his work to the music publishing firm of Francis, Day & Hunter, in Charing Cross Road.

In addition to this lowly work, which he did not much like, Sax continued to exercise his imagination on stories and articles. Elizabeth herself learned how to use the typewriter, which they both detested. She has reason to remember that at this period Sax was still contributing occasional "Turnovers" to the *Globe*: one in particular was called "The Beneficent Bamboo," and she had to type it out four times before she could get it right.

They never discussed the question of marriage. Rather it was simply understood and accepted between them without any need for discussion that their partnership would naturally and inevitably go on. To Sax's way of thinking, the mere act of marriage was superfluous—unnecessary in the case of two people who wished to live together, and futile in the case of two who did not.

Elizabeth, in consequence, never possessed an engagement ring. But she once thought she possessed an engagement locket.

They were sitting, one day, in a small café which they occasionally frequented (if they had earned anything) when, to her surprise and delight, Sax suddenly produced a tiny, old-fashioned locket from his pocket and handed it to her across the table.

"I thought you might like this," he said. "It belonged to my mother."

Elizabeth was overjoyed. This, she told herself, was his way of proclaiming an engagement. Nothing so sordid and conventional as a ring would enter the thoughts of a man like Sax. She carried it home proudly in her purse, her head swimming with fantasies. She would save up, somehow, for a thin gold chain and wear it with his photo inside, and hers opposite, and never take it off day or night.

In the seclusion of her bedroom, she sat down and opened it. The locket contained, on the one side, the picture of an unknown female and, on the other, a small piece of paper bearing the words, "Poppy, I am ever thine." The absent-minded Sax had forgotten to remove them after the last disillusioned holder of the locket had thrown it in his face.

Elizabeth did not throw it in his face. She kept it and waited till she had a wedding ring to throw at him. In fact, in the course of a long and lively married life, she threw four of them. But fifty years later, when he died, she was still there by his side.

By the time she was twenty-one, Elizabeth had rather come to share Sax's views on marriage. She could no longer be so naive as to suppose that a wedding ceremony would make any difference to the way he felt about her or, for that matter, the way she felt about him. But she was also wise enough to realize that they were not yet in a position to snap their fingers at prejudice. If they simply began living together there would be criticism and hostility from all quarters, certainly including her own family. Therefore she wanted a wedding.

Sax consented without much enthusiasm, rather in the spirit of one who concedes something to the obviously sincere but inexplicable wishes of a friend. He was fond enough of Elizabeth to give her anything that lay in his power to give, even the tiresome worthless formality of a wedding. But he insisted that, for the time being, their marriage must be kept secret. Knowing that he was scarcely able to support himself, let alone a wife, he was sure that his father would never agree to it.

So, on these rather nebulous and distinctly unromantic terms, a marriage was arranged.

Secret weddings conjure up visions of a coach and horses racing towards Gretna Green with an irate parent in hot pursuit. Such colorful features were regrettably absent from the secret wedding of Elizabeth and Sax. Several times postponed for lack of funds, the venture was finally attempted on a total capital of £6.

Everybody was in the secret, excepting (they hoped) Sax's father. Bill Ward's household at Wyke Gardens now included a "daily help"—a lanky platinum blonde of eighteen or thereabouts, answering to the name of Ada. She was in the secret too, vastly excited by the whole thing, and eager to assist.

For weeks in advance, Elizabeth and Ada practiced with mixtures for a wedding cake. Ada experimented with a marzipan top and icing, and crowned the effort with two sugar angels left over from a Christmas cake. The effect was no doubt suitably impressive, if a little extemporaneous. In fact, the only thing wrong with it was that Ada's cookery seems to have had a good deal in common with Sax's chemistry; when the cake came to be cut, no knife in the house would go through it. This, however, was a detail not discovered until the end of proceedings, by which time so much else had happened that no one felt very disturbed.

The great day dawned, with the wedding fixed for 12:30 at the Brixton registry office. At 11:30 Elizabeth arrived at Wyke Gardens, discreetly attired in a new brown suit and a flimsy brown hat, trimmed by her own hands with artificial pink rosebuds. She also carried a small bouquet of real ones.

The table in the small living room was loaded with highly colored jellies, cold ham, a decanter of dangerous-looking scarlet wine, and the impenetrable wedding cake. But there was no sign of the bridegroom.

"Not up yet," Ada said nonchalantly.

"But we're expecting the guests at twelve!"

Elizabeth seized her by the arm and dragged her towards the bedroom door. They banged on it, together and by turns, till a sleepy voice answered. Twenty minutes later, Sax wandered in absently from the bathroom, wearing his old grey flannel trousers and a tweed coat.

The two girls grabbed him, rushed him back into the bedroom, and ransacked the place for a clean shirt and one of his father's suits. They found one, threatened him with death if he went to bed again, and shut the door on him. Anxious minutes passed till he reappeared, correctly habited, but still bewildered and yawning.

"Have you got the ring?" Elizabeth asked.

"What ring?" Sax said sleepily.

"It is usual," Elizabeth said, with dangerous placidity, "to have a ring at a wedding ceremony. In fact, it's essential."

"Good Lord!" he muttered. "I forgot!"

The girls exchanged glances, took two sovereigns out of the

six stored in a vase on the mantelshelf, stuffed them into Sax's pocket and bundled him out into the street, telling him to go to the jeweller's shop around the corner and not to lose the ring before he got back. Sax went, saying something under his breath about "confounded mumbo-jumbo" and fumbling for his pipe and tobacco.

He had not been gone five minutes when the doorbell rang. Elizabeth jumped up and went to answer it, expecting to find wedding guests. It was not wedding guests. It was not even an irate parent. It was an irate dressmaker.

The irate dressmaker demanded £4 for the nice new brown suit that Elizabeth was wearing, and declared her intentions of staying there till she got it. Elizabeth was stricken. The four remaining sovereigns in the vase represented all the money they had in the world. If she paid the dressmaker, she couldn't get married. Not that morning, anyway.

She tried eloquent persuasion. She tried abject entreaty. She tried awful warnings of the divine punishment waiting for dressmakers who stopped weddings. Ada burst helpfully into tears. But nothing would move that dressmaker.

Finally, trembling with rage and frustration, Elizabeth snatched up the precious vase and, only just conquering the impulse to throw it at her persecutor's head (because the vase wasn't hers), shook out the last four sovereigns. She thrust them into the woman's hand, banged the door behind her, and collapsed onto the couch. Ada collapsed into an armchair.

"No wedding!" Elizabeth gasped. "Again!"

Ada looked thoughtfully at the laden table.

"The cake will be all right, miss," she said hopefully, "if we put it in a tin. But I don't know about the jellies."

The doorbell rang again. This time it was wedding guests—Elizabeth's sister and her husband. They were supposed to be the witnesses. Now the awful news had to be broken to them; there was not going to be anything to witness.

They were shocked and sympathetic, but helpless. Both were young and struggling, and £4 in those days was more than a week's wages for a skilled man. Elizabeth's brother-in-law offered to dash off to his father and try to borrow it. But Elizabeth shook her head. She was beginning to think that Fate was against her. Their marriage was just not meant to be.

The point was still being debated when Sax sauntered in with the ring hung on his little finger. The changed situation surprised but failed to disconcert him. In fact, if anything, he looked a trifle relieved.

"Oh well!" he observed. "What's the difference? Everyone's used to seeing us around together, and we can get married any old time. So let's just shove the ring on your finger and say we *are* married!"

He was reaching out for Elizabeth's left hand when they all swooped on him and restrained him by main force. The doorbell rang for the third time, in the midst of the ensuing confusion. The third and last guest had arrived.

This was Helen Charles, a popular entertainer at the piano, and an old acquaintance of Elizabeth's stage days. She stalked into the room, a model of the well-dressed woman, and before anyone could say a word, went up to Elizabeth.

"Darling, I didn't have time to buy you a wedding present. You won't mind, will you?"

With an apologetic smile, she held out a £5 note.

If Helen, whose jealousy was in later days to cause more than a little trouble, had ever found out her role of *dea ex machina* at that moment, she would no doubt have poisoned herself. But, fortunately, she never did find out.

"So kind of you!" Elizabeth said sweetly. She stood up, slipped the £5 note casually into her empty purse, and linked arms with Sax. "Ready, dear?"

They were married at 12:30 in the afternoon of January 14, 1909, in the Lambeth Register Office.

For almost two years, Sax and Elizabeth kept their marriage a secret from all but their own chosen circle of associates. Sax still lived a seemingly bachelor existence at Wyke Gardens, sharing a bedroom with his father. Elizabeth went on living with her sister for a time, later moving into rooms from which she could more conveniently make her daily visits.

In the meantime, life proceeded very much as before. Despite the fact that Sax had sold and was selling his work to the press, there was as yet no indication that he was ever likely to achieve even a modest living as an author. At that time, it even seemed more likely that he would succeed better as a song writer. Gradually, the nature of his clientèle was improving. The general run of variety performers, who commissioned their material at a few shillings a time, were served by needy writers who, for the most part, had little more talent than money. Sax had no money, but he did have talent, plus the advantages of a considerable, if unconventional, education. His sense of dry comedy, aptly revealed in cleverly contrived turns of expression which often passed over the heads of less sophisticated audiences, began to attract the attention of bigger names in show business.

Sax wrote some numbers for George Robey and, to his surprise, found "the Prime Minister of Mirth" a cultured man interested in Egyptology, and an enthusiastic collector of Oriental porcelain. They became good friends. Long after, when his few shelves of books had expanded to a considerable library, Sax remained proud of an unusually fine edition of the ancient Egyptian *Book of the Dead,* a gift from George Robey.

Bad luck continued to alternate with good. Afterwards Sax was never to forget an apparently trivial conversation which he had, about this time, on one of those rare occasions when sheer necessity compelled him to spend sixpence on a haircut. The barber, loquacious in accordance with the affable manner of his trade, told him that his family had long possessed an old painting in a heavy gold frame, and he was anxious to get rid of it. He thought that Sax, knowing something about art, might care to inspect it—not that he imagined the picture to have any value, but the frame should easily be worth the £5 that they hoped to get for it.

The offer left Sax unmoved. He did not greatly fancy himself as a dealer in antique picture frames, in addition to which he did not have £5.

Three months later, when his hair next reached the level of his collar, he found the barber no longer there. In the interim, he had taken the picture to Christie's. It was a painting of Lady Hamilton, by Romney, and it sold for £60,000.

Confronted by this news, Sax fought down his chagrin with his usual acid humor. He wrote a song called "Bang went the chance of a lifetime" and sold it to George Robey. It became one of the latter's best numbers, and did very well.

62

But it did not make £60,000.

On the more intellectual plane, Sax continued to take a keen interest in occult research. His experiences in that direction had quite definitely inclined him to believe in the existence of unseen forces either unsuspected or denied by the majority. But, unlike most researchers in that much disputed field, he was content to admit that he did not know what those forces might be or how they operated. When he came across some purported means of invoking those nameless powers, his attitude was not to theorize wildly on the possibilities but simply to try it and see what, if anything, might happen.

He had reason to believe that Elizabeth might possess latent psychic powers in advance of his own, but she could rarely be persuaded to join in these games with the unseen. Not that she was skeptical. On the contrary, she believed in such things more readily than he did, but they terrified her. It is unnerving to sit at a table with a ouija board skating around under one's fingertips, spelling out words from a lettered chart, in response to no conscious direction—unnerving whether you believe the movements of the board to be occasioned by your own subconscious thoughts or by the guidance of your deceased Uncle Harry.

Sax, however, felt no great curiosity as to what made the board move. What interested him was the fact that it *did* move. And, on one of the rare nights when he had managed to cajole Elizabeth into the experiment, the ouija board moved in a most singular fashion.

Having established a contact with whatever it might be that answered "yes" or "no" to a few preliminary questions, Sax went to the heart of the matter with a straight question of a nature which might have shocked more ethereally minded inquirers.

"How," he demanded, "can I best make a living?"

Sax's ideas on the ethics of occultism were refreshingly sane. If the unseen forces could not be turned to everyday human account, then it was all one whether they existed or not.

To the astonishment of both Elizabeth and himself, the pointer moved rapidly over the chart and, not once, but repeatedly, spelt out: C-H-I-N-A-M-A-N . . .

Elizabeth and Sax looked at each other and shook their heads. They had not the faintest idea what it meant.

Hard times for the Sax Rohmers were by no means over. Life from day to day was still a matter of turning the hands to anything that might show an immediate profit. In one notably bad patch, they even looked back to chemistry. Elizabeth suggested the manufacture of a cheap face cream.

This time the situation was a trifle different from the previous experiments. She really knew how to do it. During her stage days, Elizabeth had made her own face cream, and what she had done then on a small scale could obviously be done on a much larger scale.

Sax was interested and was easily prevailed upon to do what he could do best: write the advertising. They laid in a good stock of the inexpensive ingredients, and inserted their advertisements in the kind of journals favored by the girls most likely to need cheap cosmetics. Orders came pouring in, and Elizabeth rolled up her sleeves to commence production.

Then a dreadful thought came to her.

"What," she asked, "are we going to put the stuff in?"

They exchanged blank looks. Neither of them had considered that. They had the orders, and the means to make the product, but no money to buy the containers! So another Good Idea came to grief.

Progress was erratic rather than steady. In those dark days, had Sax ever ventured to suggest that the time would come when they might be the owners of a 14-acre property with two cars in the garage, Elizabeth would have accused him of experimenting with *hashish*. Yet progress was being made.

The year 1910 marked an historic event in Sax's career, though at the time it passed almost unnoticed. George Robey, whose personal tastes were vastly different from the slightly vulgar brand of comedy for which he was famous, had an idea for a series of imaginative essays. Lacking the time and the professional skill to write them up, he suggested that Sax should do it. Sax did, and the collection entitled *Pause!* thus became the first writing of his ever to appear in book form. It was published by Arthur Greening & Co., bound in shiny paper covers decorated with the design of a man's hand (a visual pun presumably instigated by Robey). The book contains some good writing, but rather strangely neither of its creators felt inclined to put his name on it, and the work was published anonymously. Later biographical notes attributed *Pause!* to George Robey, but it certainly belongs at least equally to Sax, who did the actual writing.[10]

By the end of the year, Elizabeth decided that she had really had enough of "secret" marriage, and urged Sax to confide in his father. With considerable misgivings, he eventually agreed. The decision taken, they presented themselves nervously before that kind but sternly upright man, and Sax, more apprehensive than at any meeting with an editor, shyly introduced Elizabeth as his wife.

"Known about it for ages!" Bill Ward said calmly. "Thank God my crazy son's found somebody to take care of him!"

9

HERNE HILL

BILL WARD'S SATISFACTION WAS NOT AFFECTED. THE "SECRET" MARRIAGE
had long since ceased to be a secret to him, but any interference
in the lives of others, even when applied to his own son, was so
completely foreign to his nature that he had chosen to say nothing
until they came to him of their own free will. Now that they had
at last done so, he was unfeignedly glad, for now he had the chance
to put forward a proposition which had been in his mind for quite
some time.

Throughout the greater part of the last twenty-five years, he
had been denied all the simple comforts of a normal home life.
Ever since the death of his wife, he had lived in lodgings and,
during the ten years before that, had lived in the totally neglected
household of a mental invalid. But now, with the help of his son
and his son's wife, he would rebuild his home. He outlined the
plan to them.

Out of his savings, he would put down the deposit for a small
house to accommodate the three of them. Elizabeth should take
charge of the housekeeping, and they would go halves on the
mortgage repayments.

Elizabeth and Sax agreed without hesitation, and house-hunt-
ing began immediately.

But even this commonplace business, delightful to the hearts
of every newly married couple, did not pass off without an intru-

66

sion of the bizarre. The extraordinary nature of Sax's writings made it natural enough for him to spend a good proportion of his time searching in extraordinary places for extraordinary incidents. Yet, the number of times he came into contact with them quite by chance stretched coincidence to the limit where he soon ceased to believe in it. The reader may think what he likes, but when Sax wrote of a metaphysical principle which makes a man the natural focus of the phenomena his behavior invites, he wrote from personal experience.

Armed with the keys of a small "desirable residence," the three happy house-hunters went off to inspect the property. They opened the door and entered the lobby to find the distempered walls covered with indescribably hideous pencil drawings—not the mere scribblings of a child, but distorted human shapes and horrifying faces, like the illustrations to some ancient work of necromancy.

Only the professional curiosity of Sax persuaded them to explore further. In every room, the same loathsome drawings leered from the walls. And, as if that were not enough, as they made their way through that empty house of horrors, doors left open closed behind them. An atmosphere of nameless tragedy hung like a mist, and the windows of the upper floor were secured with iron bars.

Bill Ward, a practical business man, with his feet planted firmly on the ground, led the retreat out of that house faster than he had gone in. They did not find it a "desirable residence."

The house which they finally chose stood upon Herne Hill. It consisted of a living room, a dining room, a small study for Sax, a bedroom for Elizabeth and himself, and another for his father, plus a drawing room and two extra bedrooms for which they had no furniture. Altogether, it was a trifle larger than they really needed. (Bill Ward looked forward hopefully to grandchildren, but in this he was to be disappointed.)

Elizabeth settled down seriously to the business of housekeeping, though having had no slightest previous experience it was a little difficult to know just where to begin. Such furniture as they had consisted of the things from Wyke Gardens. The settee and the armchairs were Victorian antiquities of the horsehair variety. With bitter memories of their scratchy surfaces, she made

67

covers for all of them. She padded the tops of her old theatrical skips (wicker hampers used to transport costumes and other impedimenta) and turned them into ottomans. She sewed curtains for the windows—thick ones, because they couldn't afford window-blinds as well.

Above all, she thought, Sax must have a proper writing desk, She bought him one for thirty shillings, paid in weekly installments of one shilling each. It was a good choice, a beautiful piece of furniture which today would fetch a high price. (For this and also for sentimental reasons, it survived all their various moves, and Elizabeth is still using it to this day.) All the other new furnishings had likewise to be bought on the installment plan, and keeping up the payments was frequently a headache. There was more than one crisis. (The local pawn shop sent them Christmas cards for some years!)

A period of hectic activity followed. Sax was now often kept busy writing magazine cover stories. It was at that time a popular practice with editors to commission an artist to execute some highly dramatic cover picture for the magazine, and then to find an author to write a suitable story around it. Sax's vivid imagination was easily stimulated by this kind of assignment and, no matter how outlandish a scene was represented, he could always be counted on to find some equally outlandish explanation for it. Some of the stories which he wrote in this way were later included in the collections titled *The Haunting of Low Fennel* (1920) and *Tales of East and West* (U. S. edition, 1933).

Although his writing still failed to provide anything like a steady income, Sax's name was gradually becoming known in the publishing world. It was at this juncture, in the spring of 1911, that he received the fateful commission which sent him off to Limehouse in search of the mysterious "Mr. King." At the time, it was a job which represented no more than a period of annoyance and anxiety for Elizabeth. Neither dreamed that it might have repercussions which would change the entire course of their lives.

Sax was now finding himself driven towards making a choice between writing stories and writing songs. The stories took longer and, proportionately to the songs, paid less. But he preferred doing them and Elizabeth encouraged him, firmly convinced that he would never find real happiness in anything other than the exercise of his literary talent. Even the magazine stories were, she felt, unworthy of him. Nevertheless, song writing still made so large a contribution to their meager funds that he dared not discontinue it.

One man cannot serve two masters, but two might master it. In an endeavor to cope with the song writing business and yet leave himself sufficiently free to deal with the fiction side, Sax went into partnership with a young man who lived nearby and who had some musical experience. The scheme worked well enough for a time, but failed to produce the expected return in cash. Sax found out why when he came across one of the numbers for which he had provided both lyrics and music sold and printed under his partner's name. It is easier to steal a man's talent than to steal his money, and throughout his life Sax was to find himself the natural prey of quick-witted rogues who robbed him wholesale.

For once, Sax reacted violently. Despite the fact that murder and outrage were the stock-in-trade of his stories, he abhorred physical violence and, so far as I know, never resorted to it on any other occasion. But this time, just indignation got the better of him, and the partnership was broken up at the same time that a chair was broken over the head of his defaulting partner.

Elizabeth, meanwhile, was struggling to keep home for two men on a shoestring budget. During those first few months at Herne Hill, the silverware was more often in the pawn shop than on the table. Sometimes they were even short of food to the point where Sax's father came home to the evening meal unaware that his son and daughter-in-law had eaten nothing since breakfast. Knowing and appreciating that he was already doing all he could to help, they never told him.

Under such conditions, unnecessary waste was intolerable. Elizabeth decided that she could best economize by learning to cook efficiently—starting from scratch, since she knew nothing whatever about it. Over the years, it got to be such a habit with her that, in the end, when they had a house full of servants, she still had to do most of the cooking, for guests preferred hers to anything that the most highly paid cook could provide.

Mention has already been made of the odd way in which Sax's professional interest in the uncommon seemingly attracted

69

the uncommon. The abominable, and usually outsize, insects which crawl through the pages of a Fu Manchu story have done much to bring fame to their creator. Happily, they are rare in real life. The average person may quite likely go all through the tropics and meet nothing more alarming than a mosquito. But the Sax Rohmers needed to go no farther than Herne Hill.

Late one evening, while Sax and his father sat talking in the living room, Elizabeth was relaxing in a hot bath. Thus pleasantly occupied, she presently became aware of a tickling sensation in the region of her left shoulder blade. Supposing this to be due to a trickle of water, she reached up languidly with the sponge to find an enormous spider making its way up over her shoulder.

She came out of that bath in a bound that flooded the bathroom floor, and bolted down the passage, with the spider hanging on for dear life. Her scream brought the two men starting up from their chairs. But they had no more than got to their feet when the living room door crashed open and Elizabeth burst in, stark naked and dripping, and too frightened to speak.

For a moment they thought she had gone mad—and, for that moment, so she had. Speech had deserted her along with modesty. She stood in the middle of the room, gesturing wildly till Bill Ward saw the spider. He knocked it smartly off her shoulder, and it hit the carpet with an audible *plop*. But as he lifted his foot to step on it, Sax intervened.

"No!" he said anxiously. "Don't kill it!"

The great master of villainy was incapable of killing anything, or of watching it killed. He scooped up the wet and terrified spider onto a newspaper and put it carefully out of the window, leaving his father to take off his coat and put it gallantly around the wet and terrified Elizabeth.

The easy comradeship of Sax and Elizabeth so little resembled the traditional picture of man and wife that the elderly lady who lived opposite sent her eligible son, Frank, to invite Elizabeth to tea, under the impression that she was Sax's sister. Frank found this a tremendous joke, as, indeed, he found almost everything, and the error led to a warm friendship with both, lasting a lifetime. It was this same Frank Wyatt who, shortly afterwards, accompanied Elizabeth on her wild journey through Limehouse.

Sax and his father had, over the past ten years, fallen so much into the ways of an exclusively male household that Elizabeth sometimes felt like a housekeeper looking after two old bachelors. She got her own back by treating them both like children, and solemnly dosed them with brimstone and treacle every spring. This, she supposed, must come under the heading of good housekeeping, since her mother had made her take it—and, therefore, it must be equally good for her men.

Such was the general pattern of life at Herne Hill during the first six months or so, leading up to the second series of nightly disappearances by Sax—more alarming than the first, since, this time, Elizabeth did not know why he disappeared—in his renewed pursuit of "Mr. King."

And that, if you remember, is where we came in.

10

THE BIRTH OF FU MANCHU

"I MADE MY NAME ON FU MANCHU BECAUSE I KNOW NOTHING ABOUT the Chinese!" Watching the astonishment spread over my face, Sax grinned and added: "I know something about Chinatown. But that is a different matter."

Both of us pipe smokers, we were pacing up and down the length of Sax's exotically furnished writing room, like two sentries ordered to combine patrol duty with setting up a smoke screen. Sax, as usual, wore ancient flannels and an old dressing gown. No one ever saw him in a new dressing gown—which in itself is a minor mystery, since all dressing gowns must presumably at some time or other be new.

The windows looked out upon a vista of green lawns, sloping down gently to a distant lotus pool, from the far border of which a half-moon bridge arched over to a small island. A family of grey squirrels scampered about the bole of a big tulip tree halfway down the slope.

Much had happened since the days of Herne Hill. Our conversation was taking place some thirty years after the events we were talking about. But since I believe that what Sax told me then is the most complete and authoritative statement ever made concerning the origin of Fu Manchu, it will be best if I give it here, as nearly as I can recall, in his own words.

"Nowadays," Sax went on, "I like to think that a Chinese and a Chinaman are not the same thing. When I began writing, 'Chinaman' was no more than the accepted term for a native of China. The fact that it has since taken on a derogatory meaning is due mostly to the behavior of those Chinamen who lived in such places as Limehouse.

"Of course, not the whole Chinese population of Limehouse was criminal. But it contained a large number of persons who had left their own country for the most urgent of reasons. These people knew no way of making a living other than by the criminal activities which had made China too hot for them. They brought their crimes with them. Naturally, it took our police some time to get their measure. They were dealing with enemies who did nothing in the expected way, who thought differently, who communicated with one another in a language that few Englishmen could speak and fewer still could read.

"That was the situation when I was first sent out to get what I could on 'Mr. King'—vaguely referred to as 'a Chinese master criminal' backed by 'a syndicate'. It was assumed that the activities of this syndicate were concerned solely with opium and cocaine. But, in fact, gambling was its principal source of revenue. That Mr. King also controlled the opium traffic is by the way. His genius lay in the fact that he was never charged.

"My researches were successful to the extent of providing me with a little information and a lot of local color. To round off the article, however, I wanted particularly to get a look at this mystery man. But this, seemingly, was impossible. Inspector Yeo of K Division gave me the tip to cultivate Fong Wah.11

"I gathered that Fong Wah had run a restaurant for some time in San Francisco. He turned up next in Nanking Road, Shanghai, as a storekeeper. His third manifestation was in Canal Street, New York, where he managed a restaurant again. His appearances and disappearances were most intriguing. I learned, from Inspector Yeo, that he was believed to be an official of the Hip Sing *tong,* and this no doubt had something to do with his erratic movements.

"Fong Wah received me most hospitably and seemed quite willing to talk for hours about everything but the one thing I really wanted. To my annoyance, I had to write the article without having once set eyes on Mr. King. There, I thought, the matter ended. It had been an interesting experience, but I did not actually contemplate writing a story around Limehouse.

"The idea took shape gradually, as I realized that what was happening in Limehouse was happening likewise in the Chinese communities of foreign cities throughout the world. To the Asiatic mind, our conception of humanity in terms of individuals is an absurdity. We were fighting against crime organized not even into gangs but into guilds—guilds which were international! Mr. King ran *pakapu* in Limehouse on a financial backing in Canton.

"The Chinese *tongs,* with a combined membership running well up into six figures, were not just secret societies in the usual sense of groups banded together for some more or less fanatical purpose. Many of them were not secret at all, and not all of them were criminal. They were organizations holding monopolies on every kind of profitable activity—political, religious, commercial and criminal.

"Members of these organizations who, for one reason or another, had found it convenient to take up residence abroad, simply re-grouped themselves to set up local units of the same kind. And—this is the significant point—these local units overseas were not independent, but continued to maintain links with the parent society!

"Do you realize what this means? Here you would not come across the spectacle, familiar enough in fiction, of a man pursued around the world by remorseless avengers from the Black Hand or the Ku Klux Klan. No such pursuit would be necessary. Falling foul of these people, a man could be murdered in London on a directive issued in New York!—and his murder would be the more difficult to solve, since nobody in the vicinity would have had any ostensible motive for killing him.

"That much was established fact. Here, in Limehouse, it was actually happening. And, from that, I fell to dreaming. Supposing, I asked myself, a number of those sinister organizations—perhaps, even, all of them—were in turn responsible to the direction of some super-society? Such a society would hold the power to upset Governments, perhaps change the very course of civilization . . .

"I began to wonder what the president of my imaginary

super-society would be like, what manner of man could dominate that world-wide shadowy empire. He would have Caesaresque qualities. He must be a man of great scientific culture, a genius.

"But, to my disappointment, I could get no further. When it came to visualizing the personal appearance of such a being, my imagination refused to function. This was maddening, for now I had become convinced that I was on the right track. Conditions for launching a Chinese villain on the market were ideal. I wondered why it had never before occurred to me. The Boxer Rebellion had started off rumors of a Yellow Peril which had not yet died down. Recent events in Limehouse had again drawn public attention eastwards.

"Yet, for the moment, I found myself defeated. No writer with the slightest claim to integrity can write of something that he himself believes impossible. Belief in a fantastic organization such as I had imagined rested on belief in the possible existence of a superman to control it. I had to convince myself not that he did exist but that he *could* exist. This, I felt, was beyond me unless I could see with my own eyes some actual person who might possess the required attributes.

"More than ever, I regretted my failure to catch sight of Mr. King. He, for a known fact, headed an organization formidable enough—for all I knew to the contrary, an organization comparable with my dreams. But what did he look like? No one could say.

"I determined to make another attempt, and began to haunt Chinatown again. This time, I concentrated all my attention on Fong Wah. I was sure that he alone held the key. He knew what I was after. I was perfectly frank about it. All I asked of him was to trust in my discretion. But if Mr. King were only half the man I suspected him to be, it was a lot to ask.

"Night after night, we fenced with each other, while he weighed me up and made his decision. I still seemed to be getting nowhere, but I had the impression that he was gradually developing a real fondness for my company. My patience was rewarded. At long last, just as I was leaving one evening, he said:

" 'If it would really please you to obtain a glimpse of a very strange man who sometimes visits Limehouse, it is possible you might do so tonight. Do you know Three Colt Street?'

"I knew it quite well—a dingy little street running down to

75

the riverside, near the canal called the Limehouse Cut, with rows of small houses opening right onto the pavement.

" 'This man has an office in one of those houses,' Fong Wah told me. 'Two things you must observe. First, avoid arousing suspicion. This would be dangerous. Second, give me your word that you will never mention this house, or anyone you may see go in or come out of it, to Inspector Yeo.'

"Needless to say, I gave my word. I was already planning how to go about the thing. Fong said, 'You possess the virtue of patience. Exercize it, and you will not be disappointed.'

"He told me just where the house was situated, and as I had explored the neighborhood on several occasions, I thought I knew a point from which I could keep it under observation without attracting attention.

"The night was rather foggy and, down by the riverside, an unwholesome night to hang about. I took up my position in a narrow alley, from the mouth of which I had an unobstructed view. I waited.

"Not one of the mean little houses showed any sign of life, and there wasn't a soul in sight. After waiting for perhaps three quarters of an hour, I was seriously thinking of pushing along to Charley Brown's for a tot of rum and calling it a day, when something happened—something so completely unlikely to happen in Three Colt Street as to qualify as a phenomenon.

"The headlamps of a glossy limousine coming from the direction of Commercial Road East lighted up the dark, narrow street. I ducked back into the shelter of my alley as the car pulled up before the house indicated by Fong Wah. A uniformed chauffeur—some kind of Asiatic—jumped out smartly and opened the car door for his passengers. A light appeared in a lower window of the house. The street door was thrown open.

"A tall, dignified Chinese, wearing a fur-collared overcoat and a fur cap, alighted and walked in. He was followed by an Arab girl wrapped in a grey fur cloak. I had a glimpse of her features. She was like something from an Edmund Dulac illustration to *The Thousand and One Nights*.

"The door closed. The light in the window disappeared. The chaffeur jumped to his seat and backed out swiftly, as he had no room to turn.

76

"Minutes passed and I continued standing there in the grip of such excitement as I had never felt before. For a mere instant while the light flooded out from the opened door, I had seen the face of the man in the fur cap, and in that instant my imaginary monster came to life. His face—well, I needn't describe it. I have written of it often enough since, and you know it as well as I do.

"Was it 'Mr. King'? I don't know, and it doesn't matter. 'King' was only a nickname or a part of his real name, anyway. Whether or not it was the same man whom I saw ceased to interest me. I knew that I had seen Dr. Fu Manchu! His face was the living embodiment of Satan."

11

LITTLE TICH

THE TALL CHINESE WHOM HE SAW IN LIMEHOUSE PROVIDED THE LAST BIT
of inspiration which Sax needed to create the character of Fu
Manchu. He began writing the first story in the series, "The Zayat
Kiss," in the fall of 1911. However, work on the series was soon
suspended for a few months while Sax dealt with another commission.

Arthur Greening, the publisher of the book which Sax had
written on behalf of George Robey, now invited him to "edit"
(actually, to ghost-write) an autobiography for the comedian Harry
Relph, who was known as Little Tich. This meant that Sax's
second publication in book form, like his first, would fail to carry
his name. However, this did not trouble him. Little Tich was a
star for whom he had already provided a good deal of material and
who, like George Robey, had become a close friend.

Sax's friends were almost invariably people whom the world
would label as extraordinary. It was an essential touch of the
bizarre which attracted him—provided that it was accompanied by
intelligence and a genuine breadth of imagination. Little Tich was
certainly gifted with these qualities. The image which he created,
like that of Fu Manchu, has outlived its creator: the majority of
those who today employ the nickname "Tich" for anybody of
small stature have little idea that in doing so they refer back to a

78

popular comedian of the early 1900s. Physically, the original Little Tich was almost a midget.

Yet, strange though it may seem, this droll caricature of a man was a real-life Don Juan. Something about him—his brilliant wit, or his quietly authoritative personality—caused women not to see him as a quaint figure of fun but actually to fall in love with him. His retinue of girl friends looked like a line-up for an international beauty contest.

On the stage, Tich was more than a physical oddity. His comedy technique was peculiarly individual and all but indescribable. He did not deal in innuendo, but relied upon clever word-play and a sort of lunatic logic to secure his effects.

His material was most difficult to write. It presented Sax with the kind of challenge which he could accept with satisfaction. But there was one notable occasion when he succeeded in meeting it with rather too much success.

Afterwards, Sax often spoke with amusement of what happened when Tich asked him to create a number concerning a bargee. He wrote it, and also composed a rollicking tune which both of them considered quite good. Tich tried it out at rehearsal and perceived no flaw in it. (He had the unique habit of rehearsing his songs on a 'cello. Since the instrument was nearly as large as he was, this must have been something worth seeing.) Neither, apparently, was any weakness noticed by the man who wrote the orchestral score. But, on the first night that Tich sang the number, he visibly became purple under his make-up.

"Then the truth dawned upon me," Sax said. "I had written a tune in which, for some ten or twelve bars, there was no pause for breathing! I doubt if Gigli could have sung it!"

Little Tich was anything but lacking in education. He could play with equal facility in either English or French and, in fact, had already captivated audiences in Paris before appearing in London. Sax and his quondam partner once attempted the impossible assignment of translating some of his numbers into French for a projected revisit, and were saved from madness only by the comedian's final decision not to go.

But when Arthur Greening proposed the publication of an autobiography, the work fell naturally to Sax.

Greening further proposed that a preface should be written

by Bart Kennedy, a journalist who, at that time, had a big name in Fleet Street. Kennedy was another extraordinary character, but not one of those with whom Sax was likely to make friends. By all accounts, his boorishness and arrogance must have been unique in the annals of journalism.

It was Sax who first had the job of meeting him to find out what fee he would require. Kennedy demanded thirty guineas (which reduced Greening to a state of collapse) and then calmly observed that he had never seen Little Tich. Conquering his astonishment, Sax made an appointment to meet him at the London Pavilion at a quarter to ten the same evening. Tich appeared at ten o'clock.

But, at five minutes to ten, when Sax stood waiting in the foyer, there was still no sign of Bart Kennedy. Fearing that he might have missed him, though it was difficult to imagine how, he walked through to the back of the stalls. Perhaps, he thought, Kennedy might have come earlier and be already in the house.

He had, and he was.

Sax had no sooner entered than he became aware of a disturbance going on at the end of the fifth row, where a couple stood engaged in heated argument with a man from the box office. Farther along, in the sixth row, an attendant bent over someone who occupied one of two vacant seats in front—an unmistakable figure with a wide-brimmed black hat and a caped overcoat (neither of which he had removed) and leaning forward upon an enormous blackthorn stick. To the obvious complaint that he was occupying a stall booked by somebody else, Bart Kennedy's only reply was to raise the head of his blackthorn and wave the attendant away.

At that moment, the curtain went up and Tich appeared. The attendant, at the urgent behest of those members of the audience behind him, retired baffled. The indignant stall holder and his woman friend were rushed downstairs and along a corridor to a box which fortunately was empty. The office man and the sergeant waited grimly at the end of the fifth row.

Sax prudently decided to stay where he was and play the part of silent onlooker.

At the end of Tich's performance, Kennedy stood up ponderously and, stumbling over everybody's feet, made his way out to the side aisle, where the two men pounced on him. He shouldered

80

them aside.

"My name is Bart Kennedy," he said loudly, "and I don't care a damn whose seat I've sat in!"

He turned and stumped heavily in the direction of the exit. Sax, following hastily in his wake, caught him up in the street on his way to the stage door.

"Ah, there you are!" Kennedy growled. "I thought you'd missed me. Show me Little Tich's dressing room."

"Perhaps," Sax suggested, "you would wait a moment whilst I tell him you are coming. He is very sensitive in the company of strangers."

"Nonsense!" Kennedy said. "No comedian was ever sensitive!"

He followed on Sax's heels, giving him no more than time to bang on the dressing room door before he was in. Tich, who was changing and, at such times, hated intruders other than old friends, dragged a dressing gown from a hook and threw it over his shoulders. Kennedy slumped down on a settee, with no greeting, rested his hands on the top of his blackthorn and stared at him fixedly.

"Well," he said at length, "you're a funny little fellow! In fact, I think you're funnier off the stage than you are on!"

He stood up and walked out, leaving his two outraged principals breathless. Two days later, he walked as unceremoniously into Arthur Greening's office and threw down on his desk the half dozen sheets of the finished preface, a glowing tribute to the art of Little Tich which, for calculated insincerity, must surely be a masterpiece.

"My fee is thirty guineas," he said, "and I'll take it now!"

On such stuff reputations may be made—of a sort. But it is rather pleasing to think that the names of Little Tich and Sax Rohmer will long be remembered with affection, whereas that of Bart Kennedy has already passed into merciful oblivion.

Little Tich: A Book of Travels and Wanderings, by Little Tich, was published near the end of 1911, in the same paperbound format as Sax's previous book for Greening. It had a good sale, but neither Sax nor Tich ever got a shilling for it, due to the fact that Arthur Greening's business went into bankruptcy shortly after the publication of the book.

"What gives me the hump," Tich said, when Sax reported to him after attending the first creditors' meeting, "is that that impudent devil Bart Kennedy got *his* money!"

Sax was inclined to agree, but he felt no animosity towards the publisher. It was characteristically impossible for him to harbor ill feelings against anyone whom he had counted as a friend. Afterwards, he was wont to remark that in a purely financial sense Greening had more than paid his debt since, as it happened, it was through his good offices that Dr. Fu Manchu first came into print.

It happened in this fashion. During the preparation of *Little Tich,* Arthur Greening was living in Dulwich Village, at no great distance from Herne Hill. Generous in his friendship as he was improvident in his business, he rarely failed to commander Sax for the evening whenever the latter called at his office, and afterwards they would return home by the same train. After pausing at a convenient coffee stall, they would then usually adjourn to Sax's study there talking until almost daybreak.

It was on one of these convivial occasions that Sax, recalling the existence of an unfinished manuscript, hunted it out and showed it to his guest. Greening was impressed. Although his publishing business was doomed to failure through his poor health and his lack of financial ability, he had first class writers on his books and was closely acquainted with the top people in the trade. Sitting down at Sax's desk, he then and there wrote a letter to Newman Flower (later Sir Newman), editor of *The Story-Teller* and soon to become the guiding hand on *Cassell's Magazine* as well.

On the following day, Newman Flower rang up, asking to see the manuscript. This was the first portion of the series of connected short stories called *The Sins of Séverac Bablon*—"a story of a Jewish Robin Hood," as Sax characterized it. Encouraged by Flower, Sax finished the series, and it was published in *Cassell's Magazine* beginning in June 1912.

As soon as *Séverac Bablon* was finished, Sax had returned to work on the Fu Manchu stories. Newman Flower purchased these as well, and the first series of ten episodes was published in *The Story-Teller* from October 1912 to July 1913, under the over-all title *Fu-Manchu*. (It may be noted here that Fu Manchu retained the hyphen in his name throughout the first three books in the

82

series; thereafter, it was dropped.) The stories were an immediate success.

Sax had reached the turning point where he was at last able to dispense with song writing and concentrate entirely on fiction. His work was already so popular that Newman Flower was anxious to give him a contract to write exclusively for *The Story-Teller*. But, realizing that this would too seriously restrict his output, Sax wisely decided not to accept. At the same time, he had now reached the stage at which it was necessary for him to entrust further negotiations involving his numerous stories to an agent.

Not so wisely, as events turned out, he chose to put his business in the hands of a former editor at Cassell's who had left the firm and set up a literary agency. Sax had no means of knowing that he was beginning an association with a man who would conduct his literary affairs through such a maze of dishonest dealing that even down to the present day they could never be fully sorted out. The deception was carried on over a period of fifteen years and Sax himself was brought to the verge of ruin before, purely by chance, he discovered what was happening.

In the meantime, Sax and Elizabeth continued to live a frankly Bohemian existence. It was the way they had always lived, and the way they liked living. Accepting the basic insecurity of an artist's career as inevitable, they made no attempt to stabilize their position. Each new sale meant a burst of short-lived prosperity to be enjoyed to the full—a new dress for Elizabeth, or a trip to the Channel Islands.

Contrary to what might have been expected, Sax did not forthwith settle down to churning out a stream of Limehouse thrillers. With a little money in hand, he was able to devote the greater part of his time during 1913 to the composition of a long non-fiction work, *The Romance of Sorcery*. At the age of thirty, he was still sufficiently the dreamer to cherish visions of establishing himself as a serious student of the occult. Although perfectly well aware that the book would make little financial profit, he tackled it with energy and enthusiasm.

At one point, he carried his researches to the length of making a special journey to Paris, to see the house in the rue St. Claude formerly occupied by Cagliostro. Here, at the height of his colorful and adventurous career, the eighteenth century sorcerer

83

and alchemist had allegedly performed miracles for the entertainment of fashionable European society. Cagliostro was the type of historical character to appeal naturally to Sax. With his superb showmanship and boundless nerve—he claimed the ability to enlarge precious stones and to render sea water inflammable—he had won so great a reputation that at one time he enjoyed the protection of Louis XVI. Sax found the magician's house still standing, but converted into cheap tenements. Remaining, however, was the great stone staircase up which French nobility had passed to attend the mystic sessions in the gilded salon. Sax obtained a good photograph of it for inclusion in *The Romance of Sorcery,* but was rewarded with no further discoveries.

Meanwhile, back in London, the Fu Manchu stories had been submitted to Methuen's for publication in book form. They narrowly escaped rejection. E. V. Lucas, then acting as reader for the company, voted against them, and never tired of reminding Sax of the fact when, afterwards, they had become close friends. Fortunately, Lucas was overruled and, in June of 1913, while the last of the stories was still on the newsstands in magazine form, *The Mystery of Dr. Fu-Manchu* came on the market—the first book to bear Sax Rohmer's name on its cover. It was greeted by a success as striking as the stories had had in serial form.12

Readers who imagine that Sax and Elizabeth thereupon became millionaires overnight should learn more of the facts of authorship. They did have, however, what was to them an undreamed-of sum of money to spend: all of fifty pounds.

How did they spend it? Obvious enough: after more than four years of married life, they could at last take their long deferred honeymoon in Egypt.

12

THE FALSE PYRAMID

CAIRO TODAY IS LESS THAN HALF A DAY'S FLIGHT FROM LONDON, BUT FOR Sax and Elizabeth, in 1913, it meant two weeks on an ocean liner.

The excitement of preparing for that journey—the longest that either of them had ever made, and to the destination they had so long dreamed about—was something which they knew they would never quite recapture. They had little enough money on which to attempt it, but that they could attempt it at all speaks eloquently for the value of sterling in those far-off days of golden sovereigns.

For the inclusive sum of fifty pounds, Thomas Cook undertook to provide transport via Port Said to Cairo and Luxor, hotel accommodation for a month, and transport back to Southampton. However, as Sax and Elizabeth soon discovered, "transport" did not mean travel in luxury.

Aboard the one-class vessel—otherwise referred to by their sea-going friend, Frank Wyatt, as a no-class vessel—they found themselves in a cabin near to the hold with no porthole, and with a number of steam pipes decorating the ceiling. Further to her dismay, Elizabeth found the other women passengers so well dressed that she began to feel ashamed of the three new, home-made dresses of which she had previously felt so proud, and nearly developed an inferiority complex during the first couple of days out of port.

But the cloudless skies below latitude 40º soon dispelled doubts and fears. What the jet traveller has gained in speed he has lost in leisure, for there is no more pleasantly relaxing experience than to lounge about the sun-drenched deck of a ship plowing lazily through the limpid stillness of the Mediterranean.

By the time they reached Marseilles, the young couple had already achieved a popularity on board ship that was almost embarrassing. Sax, given suitable company, was a good talker, while the youth and beauty of Elizabeth more than made up for any deficiencies in wardrobe. In addition to that, entertainment was their business.

Elizabeth, who knew the rudiments of palmistry, whiled away the time reading hands with an uncanny accuracy that astonished her female victims. In their innocence, these wives and daughters of Indian Army officers and civil servants never dreamed that their husbands' casual conversations with Sax supplied the necessary details. Where Sax was concerned, they were dealing with a man who had the trained mind of a master criminal. Not only his fellow passengers but the forces of law and order at large were lucky that his innate honesty allowed him to use it "for amusement only."

The smoking cone of Stromboli slipped away northwards and westwards. Sax organized a treasure hunt, in which one of the clues involved buying a drink at the bar, to the marked satisfaction of the barman. Games on deck were not much in his line, but Elizabeth, who had learned stage dancing from her mother, daringly surpassed herself at a skipping competition with a hornpipe that drew a round of applause from the bridge.

Thus pleasantly employed, the days passed quickly enough till the ship anchored off Port Said and, leaning on the rail, they looked across to a long, dusty waterfront where the familiar civilization of Europe suddenly gave place to another and older world unaltered by time. The color, the tumult, the sounds—even the smells—fascinated. Sax was no less fascinated by the awesome warnings of the ship's officers; Port Said, at that time, bore an evil reputation which Elizabeth, for her part, found more alarming than attractive.

Once ashore, Sax's behavior might have been easily predictable. No sooner were they installed in the comfortably respectable atmosphere of the Eastern Exchange Hotel than, telling Elizabeth to stay where she was, he set out on his own "to buy something." Dusk was not far off.

Sax's solitary, and usually nocturnal, expeditions were not inspired by any distaste for Elizabeth's company. Rather, it was simply that he wanted to feel himself free to take any presented opportunity of penetrating into odd corners where he would have feared to take her. Not that this was very reassuring to Elizabeth. Never knowing where he had gone, or where he might be going—because, half the time, he himself did not know—she invariably suffered agonies till his return.

She suffered them now. The Moslem East was not then, and still is not, accustomed to consider unaccompanied young ladies as a natural phenomenon. In the course of the next twenty minutes or so, Elizabeth received so many offers of assistance that the lobby became untenable. She retreated upstairs, locked the door and, finding that the balcony communicated with the next room, closed and locked the long windows as well.

The temperature rose rapidly to that of an orchid house. Exasperated, Elizabeth got our her diary and wrote in it: "I think I have married the most inconsiderate and irresponsible man I ever met in my life." Then she snapped the book shut and sat down, disconsolately to imagine all the things that might happen to her husband in Port Said, and wonder what might happen to *her*. Later, she gave up keeping a diary. There was too much occasion to write the same things in it.

For a girl ostensibly on her honeymoon, Elizabeth's comment on the situation was fully understandable. Yet the seemingly offhand manner in which she was treated reveals nothing of the true state of relations which existed between this unusual couple. Their partnership did not, as so often happens, drift into a gradual cooling off of affection. In the latter years of his life, when the youthful urge to explore had been satisfied, Sax could scarcely bear to be separated from her even for a few minutes.

On this occasion, as usual, with twilight deepening into the purple wonder of Egypt's night, Sax reappeared, blissfully unconscious of being in any way to blame. He had not been searching for hashish or belly-dancers. He had been to Simon Arzt's for a box of Egyptian cigarettes and a fly whisk.

The short train journey up to Cairo was uneventful save that for two eager spirits making their first contact with the real Orient everything was an event. Biblical figures in flowing white robes or loose, nightshirtish garments striped like pajamas, crowded the wayside stations. Only the *pashas* wore European dress, crowning the effect with a red felt *tarbûsh* like an inverted flower-pot. Noisy children with phenomenally white teeth and huge, liquid eyes armed themselves for their journeys not with chewing-gum or boiled sweets but with sticks of raw sugar-cane as tall as themselves.

From the windows of the train, they watched ragged-coated camels plodding alongside the track, half hidden under loads the size of a small house. Squawking hens ran precipitately from the path of a long-legged Arab ridiculously seated on a short-legged donkey.

"Just look!" Elizabeth said, her eyes dancing. "When he stands up, he gets off—and when he gets on, he sits down!"

At Cairo station, they transferred to an *arabiyeh* drawn by a sleepy horse and endured a boneshaking passage Nilewards along a broad street splendidly bordered with tall palm trees. Past the luxuriant playground of Ezbekiyeh Gardens, they looked up enviously at the fabulous terrace of Shepheard's Hotel. The better part of twenty years was yet to pass before they should find themselves among that elegant company.

For the present, Thomas Cook had placed them at a modest pension conducted by two English ladies. The chiefly noteworthy point about it was the food. It was so awful that, before they left, Sax had grown visibly thinner. Nevertheless, it was here that they ran into an adventure unlikely to have happened to any but the Sax Rohmers.

On the evening of their arrival, they sat down to make the usual plans to do the usual things: visit the bazaars, the mosques, explore the Great Pyramid. And, while they were still so employed, in came the one man whom of all others in Egypt Sax might most earnestly have wished to meet—Rex Engelbach, the energetic chief-of-staff of Flinders Petrie. Diggings, of which he was in charge, were going on in the Fayyûm, and business with the Cairo Museum (where, afterwards, he became curator) had brought him up to town. But that he should have chosen that particular pension in which to spend the night was another of those fantastic chances peculiar to Sax.

Engelbach, burned dark brown by exposure to the sun, had a whimsical, mischievous face and the small, agile, muscular body of an acrobat. It was he (and the adventures which they subsequently shared) that later led Sax to write:

"Popular conception of a working Egyptologist is grotesquely wide of the mark. We must substitute a tough specimen of humanity with leather lungs and hardy frame, his skin baked by the sun to a dark copper color; brain, nerve and muscle ready for any emergency. An absent-minded, flabby Etyptologist would be lucky if he lasted three months."

It is hardly true to say that they became friends. Rather, they became friendly enemies. Professional Egyptologists are curiously intolerant people, respecting few opinions but their own, and possessed by a strange reluctance to admit mystery in anything. Such a man was Rex Engelbach. Sax's open-mindedness appalled him and, inevitably, it was not many minutes before they were hot in argument on the subject of the Pyramids. It is hard for all but Egyptologists to believe that these stupendous edifices were built simply to serve as tombs. But, for an Egyptologist, it is harder to contemplate a range of alternative possibilities, none of which can be tested.

Sax did not subscribe to the theories of mad mathematicians who claim the dimensions of the Great Pyramid as a record of human achievement, past, present, and future. As usual, he subscribed to no theory, but contented himself to maintain the true purpose unknown. What theory, he argued, could satisfactorily account for the apparently lunatic architecture of the passages? Why was the King's Chamber equipped with ventilation shafts?

Engelbach was not impressed. The chamber contained a stone sarcophagus (though nothing was found in it); therefore it was a tomb. The passages ran the way they did because they were built that way. There was no mystery.

But, to his exasperation, Sax persisted. The Egyptologist breathed hard. Then, slowly, his features relaxed into a devilish grin.

"The Great Pyramid," he said, slowly, "is famous only because it is the biggest and the easiest to approach. It is not the oldest, but the fifth. Leave it for another day. Come with me, and

89

I will show you a pyramid that will give you enough to write about for a lifetime. Meet me tomorrow morning at Rikka station."

Rex Engelbach's offer was prompted partly by generosity and partly by a dryly humorous intention to let these two romantic young idiots see what Egyptology off the beaten tracks was really like. The Pyramid of Meydûm is anything but a tourists' pyramid. It stands well out in the desert—no road goes near—and, lacking the assistance of a team working on the spot, is completely inaccessible.

Jogging along on docile donkeys through the rich crops of the Fayyûm, neither Sax nor Elizabeth had as yet much idea of what they were taking on. Rikka lay a mile behind. Engelbach, tramping stolidly alongside bare-footed like a *fellah* and brown enough to be mistaken for one, paused to exchange laughing greetings with a farmer waist deep in growing corn. Ahead, the fertile carpet of green and gold, the fruit trees, the palms, ended abruptly on the shore of a dry sea of desert shimmering in a haze of heat.

Three miles beyond, the pyramid stood out starkly on the skyline, a forbidding structure, like some weird freak of nature rather than anything built by the hand of man.

"The Arabs call it 'The False Pyramid'," Engelbach explained. "They believe it is a mere casing built around a natural rock—and they're not far wrong."

"They also believe that it is the home of an evil spirit," Sax replied, smiling, "and, according to tradition, it was once a stronghold of ancient Egyptian sorcery. I doubt if they're far wrong about that either!"

West of the Nile, they seemed to be riding backwards through time. Here, in that fertile stretch of land which has been the garden of Egypt since the days of the Pharaohs, the clock had moved back by a thousand years. Dogs barked distantly among mud huts roofed with palm leaves. A sullen creaking and splashing rose from a *shadûf*, where laborers worked a crudely mechanical dipper counterweighted with a large stone, to scoop up water from a well. Women, swathed from head to foot in heat-absorbing black, passed by with earthenware pots balanced on their heads.

Crossing a narrow wooden bridge and following along the bank of a small canal, they traversed the outer fringe of cultivation and came out upon the desert sand. Now, in the distance, the great ruin loomed up directly before them. With some surprise, Elizabeth saw that it was not, in the geometrical sense, a pyramid but a tower rising in three unequal stages from a sandy mound.

There was that about it which conjured up visions less of Memphis than of Babylon and the priests of Bel. From the lower part half buried in sand, the steeply sloped sides of the second stage shot up to an imposing height, surmounted by what looked like a small cupola. Elizabeth thought of the Dark Tower of Browning's poem and, despite the heat, shivered.

"Are we going inside that thing?"

Sax nodded. "We are—if it's humanly possible."

"It is possible," Engelbach said grimly. "First, we must climb the mound. The entrance is on the north."

At the base of the acclivity, they dismounted and began to scramble up amongst piles of rubble, fragments of broken masonry. In the vicinity work was going forward on prehistoric tumuli. The Egyptologist cupped his hands and shouted:

"*Ya Ali! Ta'ala hina!*"

Ali Mahmoud, the headman, came toiling up to them, carrying a rifle.

"What does he want with that?" Elizabeth asked.

"There may be snakes or scorpions at the foot of the shaft. They slip down."

The path became worse at every step, zig-zagging in a fantastic way. Close upon midday, a merciless sun poured down unchecked until they reached the welcome shadow of the pyramid. In front of them yawned a black hole, four feet square.

"It's much hotter inside!" Engelbach said affably.

Sax threw off his hat and stripped down to shirt and trousers. Had she known exactly what was coming, Elizabeth would have damned propriety and set a new fashion by coming in trousers too. Her light linen frock and tennis shoes were not suitable gear for this kind of work.

Ali Mahmoud lit a torch and plunged in, trailing his rifle. The passage descended at a sharp angle, the stone floor polished to a glass-like surface by generations of sandstorms. Other than by resting one's hands on the roof above, leaning forward and lowering oneself step by step on heels and bottom, safe descent was impossible.

The temperature grew hotter and hotter. With the dust created by their movements rose a unique smell like ancient rottenness, a decay begun when the world was young. Even breathing became difficult. To a distance of some two hundred feet from the entrance, the passage sloped down into the heart of the rock below desert level.

Bathed in perspiration and gasping for air, the explorers collapsed upon the floor of a small cavern hewn out of the rock, the roof still less than four feet high. Looking back up the tunnel, the entrance appeared as a square of azure light no larger than a postage stamp. But worse was to follow.

After a brief interval, Ali Mahmoud suddenly stretched himself prone on the rubble of the floor and wormed his way into an opening no more than sixteen inches high. In the reflection of his flashlight, Rex Engelbach's lips showed pursed in a quizzical smile.

"From this point, the passage runs level for forty feet," he said tonelessly. "But it's a trifle too tight for comfort."

Sax, without answering, followed on the traces of Ali Mahmoud. Elizabeth, watching his heels disappear into that impossible hole, felt sick with terror. Forty feet of that? But no one had ever yet dared her to anything that she hadn't done. She lay down and crawled in after Sax.

It was like crawling down a drain. The foul-smelling passage was so low that it was not even possible to employ one's knees—one just had to wriggle along it, literally like a snake. Raising her body too high, so that her shoulders pressed against the roof, Elizabeth felt a sudden dreadful sensation that the whole vast weight of the gigantic structure was bearing down upon her, crushing out her life.

Praying that she wouldn't faint, cursing Sax, cursing Engelbach, and cursing herself for being the silliest woman in Egypt, she dragged herself onwards. All at once, Ali Mahmoud halted, then lashed out with his torch. A bat had flown into his face. The torch went out, followed by a stream of muttered curses in Arabic.

Now there was no light but the dim glow of Engelbach's flashlight, somewhere in the rear. Elizabeth crawled on mechanically. Ahead, she heard Ali Mahmoud's voice speaking, apparently, to Sax.

"Take my hand, please. A little way and you stand up."

A match spluttered. Sax had disappeared. She struggled forward and a lean brown hand closed firmly on hers, helping her to haul herself over a massive stone partially blocking the opening of the nightmare passage. Thankfully, she stood upright and saw that they were in a kind of well. The beam of Engelbach's flashlight, directed upwards, was lost in impenetrable shadows.

"Up we go!" he said tersely. "I can never stand this hole for long!"

From being pot-holers, they now became mountaineers. Ali Mahmoud braced himself against one corner of the vertical opening and, using him as a human ladder, they scrambled up to a projection above his head. Thence it was dangerously possible to reach the lip of the shaft. They had entered the so-called "King's Chamber" of Meydûm.

Sax and Elizabeth stared up apprehensively at the frowning roof, which was upheld by wooden pillars, fossilized in some way by long contact with rock, but still recognizable as timber. They had carried part of the weight of the countless tons of stone between this chamber and the top of the pyramid for more than four thousand years. Save for litter strewn about the floor, there was nothing else to be seen.

Had this strange place, built during the reign of Sneferu in the Fourth Dynasty, been intended solely as a tomb? Sax was loath to believe so. His speculations on the original purpose of the Meydûm pyramid would, on his return to London, provide the basis for one of the episodes in a novel called *Brood of the Witch Queen*. In the "Bats of Meydûm" section of that novel may be found circumstantial accounts of the approach to the pyramid on donkey-back and of the traversal of the unwholesome passage leading to the "King's Chamber."

The journey out through this passage repeated its horrors in reverse—with the uncomfortable addition that the explorers were already exhausted and half suffocated from the inward trip. Somehow, the sixteen inch passage was negotiated.

Back in the rock chamber, with the distant space of azure beckoning tantalizingly from the mouth of the shaft, a new trial presented itself. To slither down that long, treacherous slide was

93

one thing, to hoist oneself foot by foot up it was quite another. Now there was no way to accomplish it but to lean *backwards* over the sloping floor, hands resting on the roof, and work laboriously up in a seated position.

Sax, not physically robust but endowed with a certain wiry stamina and driven on by that burning curiosity which supplies its own energy, managed it creditably enough. Poor Elizabeth, less fanatically inspired and less suitably clad, arrived at the top a shocking travesty of her trim self, scratched and bruised, with her neat linen dress scraped up to her knickers. Whilst she sorted herself out, the party rested six feet from the entrance. The temperature inside the pyramid was so high that to step out into the desert sunshine without cooling off would be to court pneumonia.

As they emerged, Rex Engelbach burst into a ringing laugh and, turning, seized Elizabeth's hand in a painfully cordial grip.

"Congratulations!" he said dryly. "You'll probably be interested to know that so far as history goes, you are the first woman ever to have entered the Pyramid of Meydûm!" Elizabeth smiled faintly. At that moment, she felt considerably more gratified at being the first woman to have got out of it.

13

CAIRO, LUXOR AND HOME

SAX AND ELIZABETH CAME BACK IN THE TRAIN FROM RIKKA TIRED OUT
and dishevelled as tramps, with fleas hopping from their clothing
all over the compartment. ("Native donkeys," Engelbach said
unsympathethically, as he saw them off at the station, "are always
covered in insects.") Once in Cairo, they dashed to their hotel
and a bath, and so to bed.

The remainder of their honeymoon passed more conventionally and less strenuously. The usual things remained to be done,
and they did them. They visited the Great Pyramid—child's play,
after Meydûm—and cudgelled their brains unsuccessfully for a
good answer to why any sane architect should place a gallery
twenty-seven feet high between two four-foot bottlenecks. They
visited Sakkara on camelback from Gizeh, saw the labyrinthine
Tombs of the Bulls and the six-stepped pyramid of Zoser, the
oldest in Egypt. (Meydûm is the second oldest.)

Elizabeth was pleasurably surprised to find that she had a
natural affinity for camels. The weird, loping gait of the beasts
disturbed her not at all. She could ride across the desert for hours
without getting camel-sick. But, with good reason, she continued
to detest donkeys.

In the company of a Mrs. Chope, whom they had met aboard
the ship, and her son who taught English in a Cairo school, they
were dragged off to a dance at Shepheard's. Sax, at least, was

95

dragged since he could not dance and firmly resisted all Elizabeth's efforts to teach him. As soon as they arrived, he disappeared into the bar with Bernard Chope, and was no more seen that evening.

It was a gala night at Shepheard's, gay and colorful, with music provided by the regimental band of the Gordon Highlanders, who were stationed at the Citadel. Out in the garden festoons of colored lanterns hung from the palm trees, and the stars in the clear Egyptian sky shone like silver lanterns set against a deep blue canopy. Sitting forlornly in an alcove alongside Mrs. Chope, Elizabeth thought wistfully of a handsome dancing partner. He turned up like a *djinn* out of a bottle—a tall Arab, spruce in a well-cut dress suit and *tarbûsh* of a deep Burgundy shade. Bowing ceremoniously, he addressed himself to Mrs. Chope, asking her permission to dance with her companion. Mrs. Chope gulped and looked bewildered. Elizabeth stood up quickly and said, "Certainly."

They danced, very decorously. The *pasha*—for such he undoubtedly was—behaved courteously and correctly, but kept his heavy-lidded eyes fixed on his partner's face in a fashion she found somewhat embarrassing. When the dance ended, he led her back to Mrs. Chope and bowed again with great deference to the elder lady. Then, taking out a card case, he inquired politely if he might call the following day, as he was deeply interested in her daughter.

Mrs. Chope dissolved into helpless laughter.

"She isn't my daughter!" she gasped, finally. "And she's married!"

The *pasha* stiffened. Only by the raising of one eyebrow did he signify his astonishment, but the movement was sufficient to show Elizabeth that he was on the verge of a gentlemanly heart attack. He bowed again and strode away, unspeaking. Dress suits and dance bands he could deal with, but how to explain the foreign madness of husbands who left their wives unaccompanied?

Thomas Cook's schedule put them next on the long train ride south to Luxor, the site of ancient Thebes. Here they were to see the wonder of Karnak, the Colossi of Memnon, Der el-Bahari, the Valley of the Kings—in fact, generally to sample the delights of Upper Egypt.

They sampled them, and were themselves sampled. Elizabeth

was the first to notice it. Waking from deep sleep midway through their first night in Luxor, she found herself itching all over. She got out of bed, switched on the light and turned back the covers. To her horror, the bed was alive with lice. In Cairo, she had learnt to endure fleas and mosquitoes, but this was too much. Abandoning the attempt to sleep, she changed hastily into a fresh cotton dressing gown, and spent the remainder of the night in a chair on the balcony. Sax slept on, untroubled—he could sleep through a bombardment—so she left him to be eaten. But, when dawn came, she wakened him and told him. If this was Thomas Cook's idea of a suitable hotel, it wasn't hers. They must transfer immediately.

Sax shook his head dubiously. A first class hotel would mean an expenditure that they simply couldn't afford, other than by cutting short their visit. Yawning, he retired to the bathroom-cum-lavatory to think it over. Two minutes later, he was back. pale-faced, to report it occupied by a nest of cockroaches, countless lizards, and two spiders of poisonous appearance.

They called the manager, who duly appeared attired in the inevitable white robe and *tarbûsh.* Sax's self-acquired Arabic was now fluent enough to make the position clear, but the manager didn't seem to understand. They showed him the lice still parading on the bed linen. He grinned broadly, flicked them off with his finger, and shrugged.

"*Ma'lesh!*"

Sax and Elizabeth agreed: "*Ma'lesh.*" Yes, certainly, there was nothing to be done. They packed their bags and moved over to the Luxor Palace.

So it came about that though they saw the Temple of Hatshepsut and the other marvels of Upper Egypt, the tour was a good deal more brief than they had planned.

Back in Cairo ahead of schedule, they now had little to do but kill time till their ship sailed. But their early return to the capital afforded them at least one more notable experience. It came in the shape of an unexpected invitation to a masquerade at the Semiramis, overlooking the Nile: no admission without a costume. They discussed the matter. Sax, who took a dim view of dancing, did not much want to go but, for once, he surrendered gracefully to Elizabeth's enthusiasm. But how were they to equip themselves with fancy dress? They had money neither to buy nor to hire.

They made it. Sax, falling into the spirit of the thing, borrowed his wife's eyebrow pencils, painted a hairline moustache on his upper lip and a short beard on his chin, substituted a wide ribbon for his tie, put on a red beret belonging to Elizabeth, and said he was a French artist.

Elizabeth, not to be outdone, promptly undressed to the skin, put on a flimsy silk nightdress, tied it around with a blue sash, plonked a large-brimmed leghorn hat on her head, and said she was Sweet Seventeen.

And off they went. The ball was a huge success, and no doubt they both enjoyed it. Sax enjoyed it by his usual method of vanishing into the bar. He emerged just in time to see his wife's costume awarded second prize.

"Yes," he said graciously, "you *do* look stunning in your nightie. But you'd have won first prize if you'd taken if off!"

Time was running short, along with funds. But no stay in Cairo would be complete without a visit to the Muski which, for penniless travellers, is at one and the same time a torment and a delight. They wandered through the narrow streets, feasting their eyes on the exquisite rugs and carpets, the brass and silverware, the delicate furniture of ivory and mother-of-pearl—all unattainable. Elizabeth looked longingly at unfamiliar but beautiful materials, and imagined them made up into dresses, which had to remain in her imagination.

But in the Souk el-Attarin, Sax yielded finally to temptation and plunged recklessly.

"Look here!" he said desperately. "You can't leave Cairo without at least a *small* bottle of the perfume of the East!"

To know the soul of a man, you should seek it in how he spends his money, not when he has much, but when he has little. This was the soul of Sax.

They passed under a striped awning into a diminutive shop, and sat down to the timeless, formal routine of making a purchase: coffee and cigarettes served by a charming old rogue; then half an hour of bargaining, casual and unhurried, till finally they emerged with a tiny flask of peerless oil of jasmine, at a price which nearly broke the bank.

"It was hardly more than a few drops," Elizabeth recalled,

"but on our next visit, when we could have bought the whole shop, it wasn't half so much fun!"

Though the tiny flask is long since empty, she still keeps it.

Sax returned to London in time to put the finishing touches to *The Romance of Sorcery*; the preface is dated 31st January 1914. The book was published in London early the same year and in New York in 1915. Compiled in less than a year by a young man of thirty, it was a remarkable work running to more than a hundred thousand words. In addition to two long sections on occultism in general, it contained short biographies of Apollonius of Tyana, Nostradamus, Dr. John Dee, Cagliostro, and Madame Blavatsky. The book was dedicated to Fred Winter, not a fellow occultist, but simply a French-speaking friend who had accompanied Sax on his visit to Cagliostro's house in the role of interpreter.

Harry Houdini, the illusionist who was keenly interested in occult matters, added the book immediately to his extensive collection and wrote a warm letter to Sax, complimenting him on the authorship and saying that he looked forward to a personal meeting. But war intervened and several more years had to pass before they met.

The Romance of Sorcery sold well among those for whom it was principally intended. Naturally, it failed to have the same wide popularity as Fu Manchu, yet it was more widely read by the general public than Sax had anticipated. Methuen's issued a cheap edition in due course, which, in common with all subsequent printings, was abridged and lacked the illustrations from the original edition.

After finishing *The Romance of Sorcery*, Sax returned to fiction. He combined his studies of the history of sorcery with his recent Egyptian experiences and wrote the novel *Brood of the Witch Queen*, based on the theme of the survival of ancient Egyptian sorcery in the modern world. The book was serialized in *The Premier* magazine, beginning in May 1914. Serializations in Canadian and American magazines appeared almost simultaneously. The novel did not appear in book form until four years later.[13]

Possibly as a spot of light relief, Sax next turned his attention briefly to a final, hilarious experiment in theatrical promotion.

This was an episode frankly intended more as a joke than as business. Still closely connected with his stage friends, Sax decided to launch a comedian under the extraordinary billing of "Charlie Green—the Man Who Doesn't Want Money." Green was supposed to be a wildly eccentric millionaire from Australia, and his publicity was to consist of walking about the streets of London, throwing money right and left as he went. When he appeared on the stage, he would likewise throw money into the audience. To make him suitably conspicuous, the promoters dressed him in green from head to foot. They found him a white dog, and dyed that green, too. Then they put him up at the Savoy in an attic. The mad millionaire was, in fact, so impecunious that he spent most of his free time steaming the stamps off the return envelopes which accompanied his voluminous mail of begging letters.

Duly according to plan, Charlie Green strolled lightly along the Strand, scattering handfuls of half-pennies and farthings carefully burnished to resemble sovereigns and half-sovereigns. He got his publicity. By the end of some twenty minutes, traffic was jammed solid from St. Paul's to Trafalger Square. Poor Charlie Green ended up under arrest.

In the meantime, publication of *The Romance of Sorcery* had aroused an unexpected interest further touching upon the theatre. The legendary Sir Herbert Beerbohm Tree conceived the idea of a play in which he should appear as Cagliostro. Sax was approached on the matter, and plans laid for a collaboration. Sax was enthusiastic. So, also, was his Fleet Street friend, Chance Newton ("Carados" of the *Referee*).

"My boy," he said (Newton had a voice which conjured up visions of *Maria Martin* and *Sweeney Todd*), "my boy, it will make your reputation!"

Fortunately, with Fu Manchu in print, Sax's reputation was already in the making, for he was not destined to write a play for Tree. A few weeks later, Britain went to war with Germany.

14

SAX AT WAR

SAX HAD THE GOOD SENSE NOT TO RUSH INTO UNIFORM, KNOWING THAT HE had neither the temperament nor the physique for creditable soldiering. Nevertheless, in actual fact, he was a man patriotic above average, and by that I mean patriotic towards England. Logically, perhaps, the reverse might have been expected. He came from southern Irish stock and Ireland, on the eve of War, was clamoring for Home Rule. But Sax was, by conviction, as much a British royalist as his supposed ancestor, Patrick Sarsfield. When, ultimately, in 1922, the Irish Free State came into being, he was horrified. "The fools!" he exclaimed. "What can they hope to gain by it?" And, to the end of his days, he never visited Ireland.

It was, then, just plain common sense which held him back from volunteering for immediate service on the outbreak of war. But when the call came he had no intention of attempting to evade it. Nor did he.

Meanwhile, some indication of his feelings is given by the fact that he did what he could do best. Unknown to Elizabeth he wrote a short story titled "The Crouching Man" and arranged for its publication in *The Story-Teller*, where it appeared in November 1914, under the printed announcement:

All fees accruing to the author will be devoted to the funds established for the assistance of those who must suffer from the Great War.

Then he turned back quietly to his regular work. The impact of World War I at home was very different from that of World War II. Civilians were not in the front line, and food rationing was not introduced until the final year. What the war meant for England was inconvenience, shortages, anxiety, the agony of loved ones lost on the Somme, and deadly boredom.

In these conditions, the drug traffic of Limehouse flourished. Sax wrote a masterly book, *The Yellow Claw*, which, under the guise of a popular novel was a revealing study of that traffic. In it, this time, he actually named the sinister "Mr. King" who had been Fu Manchu's prototype. (Mr. King was hardly in a position to bring action for libel.) The book was published on both sides of the Atlantic and, in 1921, became the first of Sax's stories to appear on the cinema screen.

Possibly inspired by the aura of violence which enshrouded all Europe, it was around this time that Sax had his third experience of a preternatural dream, set apart from the usual run of nightmares by peculiarly vivid details and an aftermath.

On this occasion, he found himself making his way stealthily along a narrow gallery, its style and appointments belonging to the period of Louis XIII. Moonlight poured in at lofty windows and reflected at certain points a crest in stained glass which decorated some of the panes. Ahead of him crept a man whom he recognized as an old personal friend, known since schooldays, but both wore the uniforms of musketeers.

As in the episode of the Egyptian Dancer, the mind of the person whose body he seemed to occupy remained closed to him. Approaching a window, he would crouch beneath the sill, seemingly with some idea of concealing himself from the view of anyone outside. But he did not know why. The friend in the lead behaved in the same fashion.

At the end of the gallery were double doors with painted panels and gilded lever handles. Arrived at these doors, they paused, listened a moment, then drew their swords and, simultaneously, threw open both leaves.

Beyónd was a small anteroom. A fire of logs blazed in an open hearth and some six or eight guardsmen lounged about the place. Hats, baldrics, swords, and cloaks lay discarded on tables and chairs. A door on the opposite side of the room was the evident objective of the two intruders. The guardsmen sprang to their feet as, side by side, the two intruders dashed towards it.

At the same instant that they had it open, Sax felt an excruciating pain between his shoulders and jerked upright, back in his proper person and in bed. But the pain was still there and continued, fierce enough to leave him gasping and physically sick for the next two or three minutes before, gradually, it passed off.

Ingenious explanations are no doubt to be found. But the simplest seems the most reasonable. Surely, the death memory of some remote ancestor?

In March 1915, thirteen thousand Allied lives were thrown away in the battle at Aubers Ridge. In May, the sinking of the *Lusitania* added a thousand civilians—men, women and children—to the debit of War. By the end of the year, British Army casualties had reached the staggering figure of three hundred thousand. There were many sorrowing hearts in England. A prominent figure in the House of Commons in those days was the Irish M. P. and journalist, T. P. O'Connor, who several years afterwards would become Father of the House. He came from Athlone, the home of Sax's mother, and had long been a friend of the family. Now, in addition to his parliamentary duties, he was publishing a *Journal of the Great War*.

Acceding to his request, Sax looked back to his experience as a lyric writer and, concealing his new identity under his old, contributed a mystic poem of consolation, in the name of A. Sarsfield Ward. To the best of my knowledge, it is the only piece of poetry that he ever wrote, so I think it worthwhile quoting the first verse.

> Dear one, I stand beside thee!
>   Dost thou not mark me here?
> Love, I am bending o'er thee—
>   Counting each falling tear!
> Mother, whose son hath left thee—
>   Wife, with the heart of stone—
> Woman of many sorrows—
>   Peace, thou art not alone!

Many who read those lines today may dismiss them as mere sentimentality. But there is a time when the sentimental rings true, and there are those who have need of it. A great many years later, Sax was startled when an old lady unexpectedly produced the verses from her prayer book and, not dreaming that he was the author, confided to him that she had derived much comfort from them.

In that same period, Sax continued to write tales of violence and cunning. The fame of the Fu Manchu stories had reached the point where he was virtually driven to write more. He wrote the second series in the fall and winter of 1914-1915 and a third series during the year following, back-dating them so that they referred to the same pre-war era as the first. The popular tendency toward escapism was such that he kept the war out of all the mystery stories which he wrote while it was actually going on. In due course the stories were published in book form as *The Devil Doctor* (1916) and *The Si-Fan Mysteries* (1917).[14]

Fame and a modest degree of fortune had done nothing to alter Sax's Bohemian way of life. When you find a man who will placidly sit down and turn out several thousand words at the drop of a check, you have found a hack writer. Sax, on the other hand, was happy with the misty imagery of his thoughts, but loathed the mundane business of getting them down on paper. If it had not been for the solicitous bullying of Elizabeth, he would probably have written nothing at all. In the first place, it was necessary for her to direct his imagination into suitably murderous channels, and this she could do only by deliberately picking a fight with him. When he finally reached the stage of readiness to wring her neck, he would go and work it off in a Fu Manchu scheme to wring the neck of a Prime Minister.

If words failed to do the trick, she resorted to assault. She threw things—and one remembers that Elizabeth had served her apprenticeship as a juggler. "She never misses!" Sax said, with doleful admiration.

But even that was not the end of it. Having achieved the initial stage of planning, she had thereafter to emulate Balzac's servant by locking Sax up in his study and refusing to let him out till he had produced the required quota. And then she would go around to the window and pull faces at him—also necessary, since otherwise he was quite likely to escape through it and make off to play golf. Those were lively days at Herne Hill!

At other times, when Sax had nothing definite to write, the wanderlust would take hold of him and he would disappear, completely without warning. Fortunately, for the time being, he could not get outside the country, and, to his credit, he never stayed away long without sending back a postcard to announce where he was. This gave Elizabeth a sporting chance, when she thought he had overstayed his leave, to summon him back by acrid correspondence or, in the last emergency, go out and get him.

On one such occasion, she decided to send him a telegram, cryptically addressed to "Sax Rohmer, I.B." This odd designation puzzled and disturbed the post office clerk, who refused to send it. Wartime restrictions were adamant, and he thought it might be a code.

"It's a decoration," Elizabeth said. "My husband is descended from Charles II."

This was another of Margaret Ward's fantasies. The birth of Patrick Sarsfield is unknown, and she presumably supposed him to have been among the unacknowledged progeny of the Merry Monarch.

"Well, then," the clerk insisted, "can't you write it out in full?"

Elizabeth said that she could—and did: "Sax Rohmer, Irish Bastard."

But the clerk still refused to send it.

In January 1915, the Zeppelins came and air raids on London thereafter developed into a regular feature of the war. Those who passed through the trials of the Blitz in World War II may smile bitterly to hear the night of October 8th, when thirty-eight people were killed, described as "one of the worst attacks." But to a population inexperienced in total war, the sight of those great, torpedo-shaped monsters drifting slowly through the searchlights must have been a psychological weapon of terror equivalent to the flaming horror of the flying bomb.

After *The Si-Fan Mysteries*, Sax had little further opportunity of writing before the war caught up with him and he went into the army. He applied for a commission, and joined the O.T.C. with the Artists' Rifles, in training at Gidea Park. Here, at least, he was in good company. His fellow Artists were actors, writers, musicians, painters—a recruiting sergeant's nightmare.

"Existence at Gidea Park," Sax commented, "was unlike anything to be found in the too extensive literature of the War. Everyday life was more like a musical comedy than an Officers' Training Corps."

He met some strange people, and people to whom strange things happened. Among the latter was a young man from Cumberland who saw active service, was shot through the heart, and lived to tell the tale. Then there was the Bensonian actor who reproved his sergeant for misquoting Shakespeare during a route march, and maintained his point by delivering the whole of a speech from *Richard III* while the platoon stood listening.

Those Artists whose homes were in London were lucky. They usually got fortnightly leave, from Saturday morning until first parade on Monday, so that they were able to spend every other weekend with their families. This they soon found methods of extending to an additional night out of camp. It became an increasingly common practice to send a telegram on Sunday night reporting sick and to appear on Monday morning after parade with a certificate issued by some kind-hearted medical friend.

Sax worked this very successfully, till one grim Monday morning when an ambulance with stretcher-bearers arrived at Herne Hill to take him to the Fourth London General hospital. Elizabeth said that he had already left for Gidea Park, and held them off while he escaped via the back door.

On the alternate weekends, the Artists' ornamental girl-friends and wives could come out to Romford, and accommodation at the local hotels was at a premium. Thus it happened that both Sax and Elizabeth were on the spot when the Zeppelin S. L. 11 was shot down at Cuffley on the 2nd September, 1916. It was a sight so awesome that neither of them ever forgot it.

The Zeppelin had already passed over the camp, circled but failed to detect it through the sheltering screen of trees, and was several miles beyond when, suddenly, it burst into flames. It broke in the middle, curling up like a dying scorpion. Two horns of fire sprouted out of the night; then, white hot, the S. L. 11 fell. Close upon its fall followed the sound which Sax has numbered among the more unpleasant of his recollections. It swelled from six or seven miles away, bearing down like a tidal wave—a sound of frantic cheering.

Sax did not cheer. His imagination showed him all too vivid a picture of the awful death of the airship's crew, trapped under

106

their blazing vessel. A dirigible on fire does not hurl itself into the earth like a stricken fighter 'plane, to the instant extinction of all within, it settles down ponderously, crushing the gondolas under a twisted mass of steel girders, and flares like a gas mantle.

Next day, when Sax saw the remains of the Zeppelin and the bodies of the men who had manned her, he remembered that wave of cheering. The men had literally been roasted. In the soft ground where their bodies had fallen were clear-cut impressions resembling the insides of mummy cases.

One item of equipment alone remained undamaged—the observer's car, trailed beneath the airship on a steel cable. It had fallen clear of the wreck and lay intact to a pair of Zeiss glasses. But there was no trace of the observer. All the evidence pointed to it that he alone had survived. Yet, though the neighborhood was combed, he was never discovered.

In contrast to the lightning advances and large-scale victories of the Second World War, the history of the First reads more like a stalemate extending from late in 1914 down to the final break-through of the tanks in August 1918. To the logical mind of Sax, the wanton slaughter of thousands in the occupation and re-occupation of a few hundred yards of mud seemed not only tragic but grotesque.

Such an absurd state of affairs was not to be tolerated without protest by a man of his imagination. "Would any experienced boxer," Sax asked himself, "spend his strength on blows to the shoulders and forearms of an opponent? Of course not. One well-placed uppercut to the jaw would achieve more than a hundred wasted punches."

War was a ghastly business but, once committed to it, why indulge in mutual massacre where judiciously selective murder might suffice? Convinced that any sane brain must reason like-wise, he applied himself to the task of working out fourteen separate plans for the assassination of Hindenburg, Ludendorff, and the key-men of Germany in general. What Fu Manchu could do with the backing of the Si-Fan could obviously be done with the backing of the British War Office. Naturally, it would be expensive. The agents employed would be subject to such risks that rewards sufficient to make them independent for life would be necessary. Yet, for an amount not greater than was squandered by the Treasury in twelve hours of indecisive struggle, enemy head-quarters could be silenced and the war shortened by at least a year.

But not one of Sax's friends possessing any official influence could be induced to have anything to do with the scheme. "It's hardly cricket!" they said.

Sax was indignantly astonished. Morally, the idea seemed to him unassailable. If it came to that, he was by no means sure that the other side had not already thought of it. He had more than a suspicion that the death of General Grierson, the officer originally in command of the British Expeditionary Force, and the subse-quent drowning of Lord Kitchener off the Orkneys had not been so innocent of intrigue as was supposed.

To the annoyance and somewhat to the alarm of his col-leagues, he insisted on going ahead, and beseeched his political friend, T. P. O'Connor, to obtain him an interview with Ian Mac-pherson, then Parliamentary Secretary for War, and later Lord Strathcarron. O'Connor sent back a reply, inviting him to lunch with them at his flat overlooking Westminster Cathedral. Sax hastily obtained a day's leave from his Colonel and went up to town. But O'Connor, though a valued adviser of Lloyd George, was fully as eccentric as the rest of Sax's friends, and notoriously absent-minded. Sax arrived to find a warm welcome and an excellent lunch, but no Ian Macpherson. O'Connor had forgotten to invite him.

Tactfully reminded that such had been the purpose of their meeting, O'Connor was contrite. "The good Lord forgive me!" he exclaimed. "Well, come over to the House with me. I know Ian will be there, and you can have a chat with him."

He shepherded Sax across to the House of Commons, left him in a waiting room, and went in. But before he found Ian Mac-pherson, something in the debate caught his attention and, for-getting his visitor completely, he stood up to speak. He was still speaking half an hour later, when Sax gave up and made his way disconsolately back to camp.

In response to a further letter, the eccentric M. P. sent a reply profuse in apologies and again promising an appointment. Again Sax obtained special leave and journeyed up to Westminster. This time, O'Connor had not only forgotten to make the appointment, but was not even at his flat. He was in Liverpool.

But by now Sax had had enough. Remembering his days in Fleet Street with Swinborne Sheldrake and his audacious interview with Lord Strathcona, he decided on direct action. Behind the back of O'Connor's embarrassed secretary, who knew nothing about any appointment, he abstracted a few sheets of notepaper from the great man's desk, slipped them into his pocket, and took a taxi to the office of O'Connor's *Journal of the Great War*.

The actual work of editing the journal was done by the same man who was Sax's literary agent. (It had been through T. P. O'Connor that they had met.) Sax browbeat him into the loan of a typewriter and hammered out a personal introduction for himself to Ian Macpherson. Then, to the horror of his agent, who foresaw them both locked up in the Tower or shot, he rubber-stamped it with O'Connor's signature and rushed off to the War Office.

Once again, audacity paid off. He got his interview and delivered his Fourteen Point Plan of Intensive Warfare into the hands of Ian Macpherson. But he might just as well have saved himself the trouble. Needless to say, it was not adopted.

"I was not actually arrested," Sax said, "but from that moment on, I was regarded as a menace."

Sax had long believed that his wife was gifted with latent psychic powers. She refused point blank to cultivate them, but a capricious sixth sense continued to manifest itself, sometimes aimlessly and at other times significantly, to the point where she could no longer doubt it herself.

At least one striking example occurred while Sax was in the army. During these latter days of the war, Ada, who had loyally assisted at their "secret" wedding, was back again with the Sax Rohmer household at Herne Hill, fulfilling her former position as "daily help." Ada likewise was now married. But her marriage had taken place only a little time before the war came to separate her from her husband. She had not seen him for three years and was desperately unhappy.

Elizabeth, coming into the kitchen to find her shaken with weeping, did not need to ask the reason. She paused an instant, embarrassed by the knowledge that she had no consolation to offer. Then, with a sudden, absolute confidence, she heard herself saying, "It's all right, Ada—Tom's on his way home!"

"Oh, madam!" the girl answered through her sobs, "it's kind of you—but I don't think so. I would have heard."

But Elizabeth, for no reason that she could define, was still sure that she spoke the truth. And she did. Tom arrived at 9:30 the same evening.

Meanwhile, though the main purpose of his visit to the War Office had not been accomplished, Sax had not been wholly disappointed. He had been granted a place in Military Intelligence. What he did in that highly mysterious field is, of course, unknown either to Elizabeth or myself. He kept his country's secrets as closely as he kept those of the Rosicrucians. We know only that he operated in the department known as M. I. 7b and continued to do work for them even after his official discharge from the army.

This, in fact, occurred not long afterwards. Though he was normally healthy enough, camp life in an English winter swiftly brought about a return of a lung weakness which had nearly killed him in infancy. He was removed to a military hospital, and invalided out of uniform a few months later.

Now it was possible for him to resume writing. But with the carnage going on about him, Sax felt in no mood for Fu Manchu. That yellow monster had provided his creator with a sufficiently substantial bank balance to do what he liked for a time. Sax used it to write what should, I suppose, be classified as a theosophical novel, *The Orchard of Tears*, expounding his ideas of a religion based on the esoteric truths concealed in the world's rival faiths, and the inevitable opposition of the powers of evil to any reformer who should seek to reveal them.

Readers who are anxious to know the kind of thing which the "master of villainy" was most honestly pleased to write should get hold of this book. How different it is from his usual material is, perhaps, demonstrated by the fact that, although it did reasonably well in England, it was never published in America.15 A well-timed work in more ways than one, it was issued in October 1918. In the same month, the long-disused church bells of Great Britain were rung with a joyous vigor that threatened to split the metal. The war was over.

15

HONAN

HARD UPON THE CONCLUSION OF THE WAR FOLLOWED THE SCANDAL
known in criminal history as the Billie Carleton case. Billie
Carleton, a vivacious London showgirl, apparently on the thresh-
old of a successful theatrical career, was among the more colorful
of the dancers at the Victory Ball held at the Albert Hall in cele-
bration of the Armistice. That same night, she died in her hotel.
Evidence produced at the inquest showed that she had been addic-
ted to drugs, and this pointed investigators towards Limehouse.

Sax's book *The Yellow Claw*, written some years earlier,
might now be seen as oddly prophetic.

As so often happens when a popular figure comes to grief,
the case, relatively unimportant in itself, was a spark to ignite a
powder barrel. A thorough investigation into the drug traffic of
Chinatown was demanded and commenced. But it was five years
before it was complete. In the meantime, "Mr. King," who was
certainly behind it all, packed up and left the country. His
manager, "Brilliant" Chang, was arrested.

In this sensational end of a pretty girl, Sax saw both the
opportunity and the need for another book to focus public attention on the traffickers. This was something which he could tackle
not only as a profitable assignment but also as a public duty. He
went to work immediately on the novel called *Dope* and, in his
determination to make it topical, worked at it so relentlessly that

111

before it was finished he became quite ill. Elizabeth had to take him off to Margate to recuperate.

She too worked hard at it. Sax usually wrote everything in manuscript, but this time he decided to dictate. He had a cousin Hilda, from his father's side of the family, who had just finished her wartime service with the St. John's Ambulance Brigade. Hilda and Elizabeth were drafted as secretaries. Neither of them knew shorthand, so they alternately scribbled down sentences in long-hand abbreviated to codes of their own invention.

The novel was completed in the late fall of 1918. When it was published in book form the following summer, it was a best seller—a thriller, and a warning appropriate to the times. The opium dens of Limehouse are now things of the past. Yet, ironically, recent events in all the great cities of the world have made that book equally appropriate today. Though fashions in drugs may change, the cynical trade of their purveyors and the misery of their victims remain the same.

True to form, Sax was no sooner through with this job than we find him once more turning his hand to a light-hearted experiment in commercial chemistry. This time he decided on the large-scale production of an Oriental perfume to be called "Honan" (the name of that Chinese province several times mentioned in *Dope*, and notorious for the cultivation of the opium poppy).

There are elements about this affair which remain mysterious, notably the motives of Sax himself. With what was now clearly enough an assured future ahead of him in fiction, why did he attempt the new project? One explanation may be simply that he was still seeking some source of income other than writing to furnish him with the independence to write only what he chose. But there may be an alternative.

The plot thickens around the slightly sinister figure of a man named Searle, about whom nobody seems to know anything. Searle was a sallow-complexioned individual, supposedly demobilized from the navy, previous to which service he had been a tailor. The latter seems likely enough, since he made a striking white coat for Elizabeth. Nevertheless, she always felt him to be an unlikable character.

The curiously inexplicable thing is that it was he whom Sax evidently intended to take charge of the business. Moreover, there is an impression that he instigated the whole thing solely to create an occupation for this man. Yet where they had first met, or what were the relations between them not even Elizabeth knew.

Apart from this odd detail, the Honan episode was less wildly unlikely than Sax's pre-war experiments. In fact, given slightly different circumstances, it might even have become a commercial success. Sax provided the formula from a book which reliably described the preparation of various Oriental perfumes and, for once, prudently refrained from trying to add his own embellishments.

Hilda, who was already a member of the British Pharmaceutical Society, was pressed into service again. She took the formula to a firm of perfume blenders and saw to it that they got it right. Sax, as always, wrote the advertising and subsequently had to change it, because sixty per cent of the people who answered thought he was selling dope. He also designed an attractive line in packaging.

This last was really the most interesting thing about the product. Each bottle was to be stoppered with a cork bearing a bright silk tassel and, to clinch the deal, be encased in a wickerwork frame of woven bamboo. Chinese labor would obviously be required, and it was forthcoming.

Honan—a properly constituted company, since Sax now had money enough to launch such a thing—had its office in Pelling Street, on the north side of Commercial Road. The "factory" where the bottling was done was the house of the duly appointed foreman, Ah Sin (which was not his name, but the name by which Sax always referred to him), on the south side, by West India Dock Road.

Ah Sin was a patient and long-suffering man. He must have been, since he had much to suffer. Sax, the perfectionist, was dissatisfied with the natural color of the bamboo, and wanted something darker. The difficulty here was to find a dye that would do the job and, at the same time, remain fast when accidentally spilt drops of perfume should fall on the basketwork cover.

After some experiment, this was accomplished. Then came the problem of finding a sufficiently commodious vessel in which to dye the bamboo lengths. Ah Sin pointed immediately to the baby's bath. They used it, with rather too much success. Their

113

dye not only resisted removal from the bamboo, it defied removal from the sides of the bath, and they had to buy him a new one.

, At the height of production, Honan employed a Chinese labor force numbering twelve or fourteen. Ah Sin cleared all the furniture from one room of his house, and they all sat around it cross-legged on the floor, weaving bamboo. Where the payment of wages was concerned, the company had to rely entirely on the honesty of Ah Sin. Only he could read the timesheets. These he dutifully collected each week and then, having totalled up the sums due, with the aid of a small abacus reported to Pelling Street for the money.

He took his responsibilities very seriously. Once on a foully wet night, rain descending as though the Yellow River had gone up in a waterspout and was coming down again to drown its children, Ah Sin once presented himself at the office, collected the men's wages, and departed. Sax and his compatriot Searle closed the safe, spent half an hour on the telephone, trying to locate a taxi for the return journey to Herne Hill, and were on the point of shutting up shop for the night when a tap came at the door and the Chinese foreman reappeared. He was a dreadful spectacle, like a water rat coming ashore.

"Make mistake!" he spluttered. "One too much!" He gravely handed back sevenpence-halfpenny.

Unlike Sax's more youthful endeavors, Honan actually came on the market and was sold. The sales campaign began with a well organized display week at Barker's department store in Kensington. One corner was rigged up to simulate a Chinese shop, the display was opened by that popular entertainer Helen Charles (who, at this date, still kept one foot in the door of the Sax Rohmer household), and the shop was presided over by a real, live "Chinaman."

The long-suffering Ah Sin was now called upon to become an actor. He had to be the "real, live Chinaman," since he was the only one of the native employees who could speak English. They decked him out in a gorgeous national costume (hired from a theatrical outfitters) complete with a false pigtail. Pigtails had gone out with the Dowager Empress—Sax was aware of that—but the shoppers would expect him to have one, so they included it. Then they brought him all the way up from Limehouse in an open car, making a kind of triumphal procession of it, through the West

114

End and twice around Trafalgar Square. Indeed, that naively honest little man who worked in the squalor of dockland must have achieved the bliss of an opium dream as he drove through the great streets of London like a prince on a state visit.

But, on the second day, Ah Sin failed to arrive. Hilda, in charge of the department store end, hurried down eastwards to discover what had happened. She found Ah Sin at home, but, "No can come, missie!" was all that he could say to her. He had been warned off. Low born, he was not entitled to wear a pigtail!

The incident throws a curious sidelight on the power of the *tongs* in Chinatown. Though, with the passing of the Empire, the formalities of caste privilege had become meaningless, there were still active in London those who enforced them.

Baker's had to do without their Chinaman, but sales of the perfume continued to be good. Elizabeth says, frankly, that she personally did not like the scent. Honan was heavy, cloying stuff reminiscent of the kind of thing that an entomologist uses to asphyxiate beetles. But Sax's cunningly devised containers were a decoration to the dressing table that few women could resist.

What happened after that is the most curious of all. Searle, for whose benefit the whole thing had presumably been started, literally disappeared. One morning he was just not there, and he was never heard of again. There is a hint of some trouble with the police, but no more than a hint. He came out of nowhere, and he went back there. Sax, if he knew, never explained.

With the manager gone, the business became strictly a family affair, the running of it falling entirely upon Sax himself and Hilda, the Chief Chemist. Elizabeth stayed resolutely at home with her cooking stove and declined to play. Bill Ward, unwise enough to pay a visit to Pelling Street, was so unlucky as to choose a day when, by some mischance, the perfume blenders had delivered supplies to the office, and found himself helping Hilda to shove a loaded handcart across Commercial Road to Ah Sin's "factory."

This was obviously not the kind of enterprise in which Sax was likely to take a lasting interest. He soon decided to wind up the company—fortunately, with no serious financial loss, since it was really a going concern. The bright silk tassels which had helped to provide the exotic flair to Honan were promptly appropriated by a rival firm, who added them to their boxes.

115

Had Sax ever seriously contemplated Honan as a business proposition? I have suggested that an alternative may exist, and the clue may lie in the fact that the whole operation was conducted in Limehouse. Sax had already become well known for his stories of London's Chinatown, and was currently working on another. He was still seeking information and local color. But his books could not have failed to bring him to the notice of potential enemies. "Mr. King" was still active, and Limehouse had become dangerous ground.

I think it possible that Sax may have envisaged Honan—in part, anyway—as a cover for his researches. It gave him an excuse for his visits to that unsalubrious quarter, and a base from which to operate, in addition to bringing him more closely into contact with the Chinese community.

In the vaguely suspicious character of Searle, there may likewise lie a clue. As a former seaman, he may have had some connection with drug smuggling, or at least known something about it. At a price, he may have agreed to impart those secrets to Sax. Which puts a new complexion on his ultimate disappearance. Who was responsible? Scotland Yard—or "Mr. King"?

The book on which Sax was working concurrently with the Honan episode was *The Golden Scorpion*. This was a further story of Chinatown, cleverly linked up with both *The Yellow Claw* and the Fu Manchu stories.

Fans of Fu Manchu should note that it concerns the activities of his temporary successor in the Council of Seven. (After being shot in the head by the fascinating Kâramanèh, the Doctor was in no fit state to resume control of the Si-Fan until some years later.) Fu Manchu himself actually appears in the book, but is not named.16

It is during the preparation of this book, whilst raking around Limehouse, that Sax had his last meeting with his old friend Fong Wah, and another curious incident took place.

The scareheads were piling up and, one by one, the mystery men of Chinatown were slipping away discreetly into the shadows. It was long since Sax had called at the crowded little store (of which Elizabeth retained poignant memories) and now he came only just in time. He arrived to find Fong Wah alone and the shelves bare. Fong Wah, too, was leaving. But he greeted his visitor with every evidence of satisfaction.

"I knew that you would come," the old man said, nodding like a china image. "It is fated that you and I, who have met in lives before, should meet once more in this."

He led the way through into the living room. It was partially dismantled—packed crates stood about the floor of the empty shop—but the black shrine in the corner, the thronelike chair, and the sword upon the wall still remained.

Fong Wah produced his special bottle of twenty year old Jamaica rum and ceremoniously mixed drinks, pressing the juice of a fresh lime into the glass and adding three lumps of ice. They talked—or, rather, Fong Wah talked, and Sax listened.

"I have saved some money, and now I shall return to Hankow."

"You were born in Hankow?"

"No—but I have pleasant memories of Hankow."

"You will find it much changed."

Fong Wah nodded gravely. For a while he said no more, than presently began to speak of memories which revealed his apparently advanced age to be greater even than it appeared. He spoke of Hankow under the old regime, and of a certain illustrious Mandarin, Governor of the Province, in a manner which showed that, even now, he retained something like reverence for that cold-blooded official. He told of a plague of river pirates and described with graphic detail how their heads were chopped off in the courtyard of the prison.

"But they were the more fortunate," he added benignly. "You know, honored friend, that my countrymen do not fear death. Other misfortunes must threaten the criminal. These lessons in correct behavior, under the direction of the Mandarin, were also carried out by the Public Executioner. In the West, such a person is looked upon with scorn. In the Hankow that I remember, he was a highly respected officer."

He went on to speak of the Six Steps of Wisdom—The Way of All Penetrating Truth—the Wire Jacket—and Sax began to feel the need for a second drink. Happily, it was available.

The conversation turned to topics less sanguinary. The second drink was followed by a third and a fourth. When at length Sax rose reluctantly to leave, it was close on midnight. Hesitating an instant in the now curtainless opening between living room and shop, he looked back, sweeping a final glance around the familiar appointments of that stuffy little back parlor in which his memories of Chinatown began, knowing that he stood there for the last time, and feeling a little sad.

"Wait!" Fong Wah said suddenly. He turned, unhooked the antique sword from the wall, and proffered it to Sax on the upturned palms of both hands. "We shall not meet again. Let this foolish toy serve to remind you of me, and of the China that was."

Public transport had closed down for the night. His mind hazy as much with his thoughts as with several ounces of pre-war rum, Sax walked absently westwards as far as Limehouse Town Hall and there, by great good fortune, came upon a taxi returning empty from the docks. In another half hour, he was opening the door of the house on Herne Hill.

Elizabeth, who never went to bed when she knew that he was on a visit to Chinatown, sat reading in an armchair. She looked up quickly as he came in, cocking an eye at the long, newspaper-wrapped package in his hand.

"What on earth have you got there?"

"Tell you in a minute," Sax said brightly, "when we've had some coffee."

While they drank it, he related his conversation with Fong Wah, considerately sparing her the precise particulars which that placid old gentleman had not spared him, but nevertheless giving her a picture of China which, if true, would have accounted for any revolution. Elizabeth listened, wide-eyed and unable here and there to repress a shudder.

Finally, with dramatic effect, Sax ripped off the newspaper and displayed his treasure, partly withdrawing the blade from its shagreen sheath. Well oiled and gleaming, it slid out smoothly.

"A family heirloom, sure enough. Sixteenth century Japanese workmanship, by the look of it. In the hands of an expert, an edge like this will cut through iron. With just such a sword as this, perhaps—"

Elizabeth sprang up abruptly, to the peril of the coffee cups. "Get that awful thing out of here!" she yelled. "Don't you understand? Fong Wah! *He* was the executioner of Hankow!"

"Good God!" Sax said slowly, "I believe you're right!"

16

TRANSATLANTIC ADVENTURE

LATE IN 1919, SAX MADE HIS FIRST VISIT TO THE UNITED STATES. IN New York, publication of *The Yellow Claw* and the Fu Manchu stories had proved popular—just how popular, Sax himself did not yet realize. The suggestion of a personal visit, made by his agent, was reasonable enough. The American publishers were naturally anxious to meet this hitherto unknown writer whose unorthodox work had created such a furor in their midst and, from this meeting, new contracts were bound to result.

For all their prescience, neither Sax nor Elizabeth could foresee that this same visit would also result in the beginning of an estrangement all but leading to the break-up of their marriage. The Other Woman was about to appear on the scene.

She appeared, not in New York, but on the quayside at Southampton. Sax had boarded the ship alone, for he always hated to have friends or relatives come to see him off. Leaning on the rail, watching the last-minute dockside activity while he waited for the gong to sound "visitors ashore," he saw her come aboard: a slim, blonde girl who strode lithely up the gangway with the assured gait of a seasoned traveller. And at the same instant that his gaze fell upon her, he knew that something would happen between them.

When Sax later confessed as much, he was not just trying to make a rather lame excuse. To assume that would be to ignore

119

the nature of the man. With his absolute contempt for the sanctity of marriage, he was convinced that he needed no excuse for starting an extramarital affair when and where it pleased him. He was, then, making only what he regarded as a plain statement of fact.

Sax believed implicitly in the reality of reincarnation. He believed that a rapport exists between individuals who have shared experiences in previous existences, an intangible link which not only draws them together but makes itself felt in an otherwise inexplicable sense of fellowship between strangers.

Be that as it may, this ready acceptance of an inevitable destiny was highly convenient for the young lady, who was no shy maiden to be lured into seduction. Rather appropriately, her name was Eve. She was very much a woman of the world, and enveloped in a certain cloak of mystery which no doubt gave her an added attraction where Sax was concerned. Clearly enough, he saw in her the embodiment of one of his own irresistible Circes of fiction.

We have, quite naturally, very little information about Eve. It appears that nobody had much. All that seems certain is that she made the Atlantic crossing frequently and may possibly have been concerned either in smuggling or espionage. She was a familiar figure to the ship's officers and regarded by them as some sort of high class courtesan. From independent sources, we know that on that occasion they laid bets as to whom she would leave the ship with when they docked in New York. She left it with Sax.

Amongst the Seven Wonders of the modern world, Sax willingly acknowledged the night skyline of New York City. As an impressionable man, he could not fail to be affected by the awe-inspiring spectacle of those unbelievable buildings with their millions of lights climbing up to mingle with the stars. Yet, oddly enough, when he first saw it, it failed to fill him with pride in the achievements of humanity. It chilled him with a sense of man's childish impotence.

A steadfast believer in the web of Destiny, Sax's premonition of impending doom was perhaps no less inspired by the helpless knowledge that his own cycle of fate was at last fulfilled. In Elizabeth he had found and recognized the eternal partner whom the artist must find before he can achieve anything. The woman

120

he held in his arms as he gazed on those fairytale, spangled towers was the consort of his other self.

But during the three weeks which Sax spent in America it is doubtful whether he had much opportunity for carrying on the intrigue which he had started aboard ship. To his astonishment, he arrived to find himself famous and from the moment he stepped ashore he was literally overwhelmed.

Here, for once, I have the chance of allowing Sax to speak for himself. The letter which he wrote to Elizabeth after his arrival still exists.

I am literally besieged. Reporters came aboard at quarantine, interviewed me and photographed me. Since reaching here I have had not one moment of peace. Photographers, newspapers, magazines ring me up at times like 8:30 a.m.! (There's a 'phone beside the bed!) I have so many engagements to lunch, dine and so forth that I'm going mad. McBride has made me an honorary member of the Players Club, and the editor of *Collier's*, of the Harvard Club. Al Woods has fixed me seats for every show in New York! I haven't a night off!

I'm going to be photographed to-morrow morning, lunching with editor of *Collier's*, going out to Street and Smith's offices in the afternoon, dining with Dr. Dillon and a rather classy diplomatic mob, and then proceeding to one of Mr. Wood's productions afterwards! It's incredible. If I sit down in the lounge, I find some fiend making a sketch at a neighbouring table. If I go out into the hall someone says "Which is Mr. Sax Rohmer?" and I bolt!

If they treat *me* like this, what kind of hell-on-earth must a really tophole writer suffer in New York? Honest Injun, I'm utterly and fearfully fed up.

My hair is a yard long. I haven't had time to get it cut. My clothes are all creases. I haven't had time to get 'em pressed. The day I leave New York I shall heave a great sigh of relief. Repose is not known in the American language.

Among the notables whom Sax met at this time was Harry Houdini, the stage magician who had earlier written to him in praise of *The Romance of Sorcery*. They took an immediate liking to each other. Houdini told Sax that he had himself visited Cagliostro's house in Paris and had obtained permission to remove a part of the panelling in his endeavors to find out how the self-styled sorcerer's miracles might have been produced. But he had failed to discover any clue.

For his friend's art as an illusionist, Sax formed the greatest respect. Houdini, the son of a rabbi, was, in certain respects, quite

Oriental. He had cultivated skills which, among Occidentals, might be regarded as impossible. He could use either hand with equal facility, could pick up a pin with his toes, could hold a needle between his lips and thread it with his tongue.

At the invitation of this uniquely gifted showman, Sax saw him appear at a "challenge night" in which the feat performed may seem literally incredible. Houdini had undertaken to free himself from a box deliberately constructed by a firm of packing-case manufacturers to prevent any such possibility. The box, some three feet square, was made of three-quarter inch oak, and after Houdini had coiled himself inside it, the lid was hammered on with a vast number of two-inch wire nails. It was then roped around, and the ropes securely knotted. A small screen, or tent, was lowered over it—and what the captive Houdini did beneath that cover no one knows.

Suffice to say that, at the end of five or six minutes, he not only stepped out, dramatically dishevelled, from the screen, but thereafter revealed to the astonished carpenters who had made the box and fastened him in it that every knot remained intact and every nail in place.

Unlike Cagliostro, Harry Houdini did not, however, claim that his feats were accomplished by magic. On the contrary, he most strenuously denied it. Far from being skeptical of occult forces, he gave much of his time to the defense of those whom he considered bona fide seekers after truth, by exposing the ingenious trickery of pretenders who brought the whole subject of occultism into undeserved disrepute.

To such a man Sax could give his friendship without reserve. Hitherto interested almost exclusively in the shadowy side of the mysterious, he now became fascinated likewise by the stage management of illusion and, encouraged by Houdini, entered on a deep study of the subject. At a later date, he was on close terms of friendship with Will Goldston and possessed the locked books of the Magicians' Circle (they actually were secured with brass locks welded to the covers), which Elizabeth very properly returned to them after his death.

In Sax's absence, Elizabeth had been busy at home, converting one of the larger rooms into a new study. She wanted him to return like a conqueror and enjoy the spoils of his victory. But she was sadly disappointed.

Sax did not come home after the ship docked, but remained inexplicably absent all night. Precisely why remains a mystery. It is not very likely that Eve had returned with him. More probably, I think, he simply tramped the streets haunted by guilt and unable to bring himself to face Elizabeth. When he did come home, he was a changed man. The gaiety had gone out of him. He showed no interest in the preparations made for his welcome and seemed to be dissatisfied with everything.

Before going to New York he had promised Elizabeth that they would visit the South of France together when he returned. But now he was strangely reluctant to go. Only her obviously bitter disappointment finally persuaded him.

There, too, he behaved oddly. Every morning, he would get up and walk down to the town alone. This was entirely at variance with his usual habits—in the mornings, Sax habitually went no-where. Elizabeth never found out why he did this and offers the suggestion that he may have been corresponding with Eve, via the local post office. If he was not, it is difficult to imagine what he was doing.

It was a holiday curiously symbolic of disaster. On the morning after their arrival at the hotel, Elizabeth broke her hand mirror. "Seven years bad luck!" she exclaimed. The superstition proved unpleasantly accurate.

Back in London, Sax continued to act in the same morose fashion. Elizabeth, as yet knowing nothing of the affair with Eve, could only suppose that the V.I.P. treatment he had received in America had left him with a distaste for suburban life—and, so far as it went, she was right.

Sax had been brought to face the great decision. He had seen the benefits which success could bring. He could content himself with doing the modicum of work to provide a simple standard of living and spend the rest of his time in an idealized dream world, or compromise whole-heartedly on the business of turning his ideas into cash and use the power of wealth to build his dream world in concrete form. His problem was one to which every artist must sooner or later find his own answer. To ignore material gain, seeking only to achieve artistic satisfaction may be one way, yet can he achieve even the half of what a man less gifted may do

123

on a sound basis of finance?

In the hope of providing Sax with the background he wanted—and which, if he wanted it, she felt that he honestly deserved—Elizabeth resigned herself to parting with their home at Herne Hill. They would move, now that they could afford it, into the heart of fashionable Mayfair. Through a friend, they obtained the lease of a property in Bruton Street.

Leaving her to officer the project, Sax set off on a second visit to New York. Whether or not he really had sufficiently important business commitments to justify it is obscure. There is not much doubt that the presence of Eve in New York occupied at least some place in his thoughts. But, as events transpired, he was lucky to get there.

The liner had been fourteen days out of Liverpool when they sighted the lights of Halifax. For twenty-odd hours in mid-ocean they had had to stand by an empty oil-tanker dragging her anchors. Fuel and rations were low. They reached Halifax only to find that a coal dump on the dockside had caught fire and now all available coal was either on fire or had recently been on fire. The night scene at the docks resembled Hell.

The coal was still smouldering when the gangs shovelled it into the bunkers, and on this dusty, devitalized rubbish the engineers had to get up steam enough to take the ship out into the teeth of a howling gale. An hour in the open sea and the appalling fact dawned on them that the gale was winning—they were being driven down onto the wicked coast of Nova Scotia.

It was decided that the best thing to do was to try to put about and return to Halifax harbor. This proved impossible. The attempt nearly capsized the ship, and there was nothing for it but to go on. But the lights of Nova Scotia were now nearer than they had been an hour before. A classic battle followed—engines versus sea—a desperate fight to get the ship clear of those beckoning lights. Somehow, they made it.

There is no record of what Sax did in New York, which, since he was probably doing it with Eve, may be just as well.

Elizabeth, meanwhile, was coping with the business of a major move. The Bruton Street property consisted of three floors above a bookshop, which they rented furnished. (Later, they bought the furniture.) The layout was peculiar. The first floor was one large salon with a recessed part at one end. This she curtained off and made into a study for Sax. The dining room and kitchen occupied the floor above. The third floor was devoted to bathroom and bedrooms—one, of course, for Bill Ward who continued to share the varied fortunes of the family.

None of them had any idea that they were moving into one of the worst haunted houses in London.

17

THE EXTRA INHABITANT

SAX AND ELIZABETH HAD BEEN IN RESIDENCE AT BRUTON STREET FOR NO more than a few weeks when the Extra Inhabitant announced himself by a peremptory double knock on the door of the lounge. But when they opened it, no one was visible.

Elizabeth was alarmed, Sax mildly intrigued. From his point of view, the possibility that the place might be haunted was an advantage rather than a deterrent. Little time passed before the suspicion became a conviction. During the several years that they lived there, the knocks were repeated on every door in the house.

"For the first six months or so," Sax recalled cheerfully, "we used to say 'Come in!' But nobody ever did, so we gave it up."

These, however, were by no means the only manifestations. Though nothing was seen, plenty was heard, and more experienced. First and foremost to sensitive guests, was an indescribable awareness of an unseen and malignant presence. Visitors less sensitive and knowing nothing of these odd occurrences, time and again remarked that on climbing the stairs after dark they had felt certain that someone was coming up behind them. They were not frightened, having no reason to suppose that they should be. They had simply thought that someone who had come out of the room below was following them upstairs.

The noises were more positive and not confined to rappings

on doors. The house, which was old, had been considerably altered in modern times and there was structural evidence that a staircase, now demolished, had once passed through the curtained-off space currently used by Sax as a writing room. Night after night, seated at his desk, he was acutely conscious of an almost constant sound of footsteps mounting and descending that stair which no longer existed! This, one might imagine, should have made the place impossible to work in—and, for a time, it did. But occult phenomena which led to no markedly sinister result had no terrors for Sax. Having admitted the footsteps and accepted them, he soon became unconscious of them, as one ceases to notice the ticking of a clock. But on certain rare occasions, he would still sometimes be startled from his work by distant cries and a muffled crash, apparently coming from one of the upper rooms. Curiosity soon prompted him to make an investigation into the history of the house. He found that it had been a gambling hell of Regency days, with a grim record of violence and suicides.

"Another sound, which never came until the small hours," Sax told me, "resembled that which would be caused by dragging a heavy burden across the floor. This was rather more difficult to get used to."

The ambitious move to provide Sax with an environment more closely in tune with his rapidly expanding status might be seen as a success. From their West End base of operations—with a nice assortment of ghosts thrown in for good measure—the Sax Rohmers had a grandstand view of high life in the 1920's.

In those days, Mayfair was still the Mecca of London society, where awnings and carpets appeared outside the houses to greet the arrival of soldierly-figured men, immaculate in white tie and tails, escorting women bejewelled and exquisitely gowned. Music filled the night and the laughter from opened, lighted windows was the laughter of real gaiety.

In that other world—so long vanished that few now even preserve it in memory—they saw a Cinderella coach with white horses, outriders and postillions draw up at the door of the Strathmore residence and carry off Lady Elizabeth Bowes-Lyon to Westminster Abbey to become Duchess of York and the future Queen of England.

Only a few days earlier, at the same house, they had witnessed another family scene not so properly belonging to history, when the Duke and his fiancée returned from a shopping expedition, accompanied by the present Duke of Windsor (then Prince of Wales, and the most popular young bachelor in English society). As the royal car pulled up, a footman rolled out the traditional strip of red carpet. But the Prince insisted on the others entering ahead of him. Then he solemnly rolled up the carpet and carried it into the house on his shoulder. A whimsical gesture, curiously prophetic . . . .

Without the gift of infinite adaptability, no woman could have lived successfully with Sax. Fortunately, Elizabeth possessed this gift. In the days of their secret marriage, she had lived with him the attic existence of an impoverished artist. Next, she had been an ordinary housewife in Herne Hill. Now she was called upon to preside over a gracious household among the *khans* of nobility.

All this she took in her stride. But, due to the malevolent tenancy of the Extra Inhabitant who resisted all attempts at eviction, servants were a problem at Bruton Street. None would remain in the house alone, or serve there for any length of time. None, that is, until the advent of a housekeeper whom I will call Mrs. Macgregor because she might have inspired the character of that name who appears in *The Golden Scorpion*. (Actually, she didn't. Sax had already written that story before he met her.) Mrs. Macgregor was the dourest of dour Scotswomen, and not in the least frightened of the Extra Inhabitant. Rather, I should say, the Extra Inhabitant might have been frightened of her.

Bill Ward, who in his seventies still insisted on getting up early every morning and going regularly to his office, was the only member of the family she regarded as sane. For Sax and Elizabeth, who often remained in bed till midday, she had undisguised contempt. Against all reason, she was firmly convinced that they lived on the old man's charity, and nothing would persuade her otherwise.

In the kitchen, Mrs. Macgregor was a law unto herself, and her law was strange indeed. When lamb was ordered, she served beef; when beef was ordered, she served chicken—all excellently cooked, but totally unpredictable. Her finest effort came when she dished up creamed cauliflower every night for two weeks. At the end of this period, Elizabeth ventured a timid protest.

"What's wrong with the cauliflower?" Mrs. Macgregor demanded belligerently.

In the end, it was not the Extra Inhabitant who expelled her from the house, but simply Elizabeth's determination to make a Christmas pudding. She had always made her own Christmas puddings. She liked them, and so did Sax. But Mrs. Macgregor would brook no intrusion into her kitchen. "If *you* make a Christmas pudding," she said, "I go!" And she went.

As if the house were not sufficiently haunted already, there was one occasion in the early Spring of 1920, when Sax introduced a phantom of his own. Such, at least, appears to be the only likely explanation of the affair ever afterwards referred to as the Mystery of the Black Cat.

Black, a tiny Manx feline, curled up in an egg-shaped basket, joined the Bruton Street ménage as an Easter gift. She thrived, grew to precocious maturity and, before departing this life, offhandedly presented the household with a total of ninety-eight kittens.

Cats are notably psychic, and Black was no exception. When the invisible Something rapped on the doors, she would look up sharply. But of all the strange happenings in that strange house, none disturbed her until one notable night.

It was about half-past eleven. Elizabeth was out at a theatre. Sax, seated at his desk, was hard at work on a story, with the curtains dividing the recess from the lounge left undrawn. Black lay sleeping in front of the fire.

Suddenly, and for no apparent reason, the cat leapt up, hissing furiously. Sax, startled, put down his pen and turned. As he did so, Black shot at high speed under the bureau between the windows, and crouched there, facing the study, her eyes shining like green lamps.

Such behavior in an animal normally so placid demanded investigation. Puzzled, Sax stood up and crossed the room towards her. As he did so, Black moved her head from side to side, as though he was obstructing her view of something—something in his study!

This was so clearly evident that Sax himself paused involuntarily in his tracks and looked back. But, so far as he could discern, there was nothing unusual to be seen in the book-lined recess. He stooped towards the cat and put out his hand to touch her. Without glancing aside, she snapped viciously and struck at his fingers.

She was insane with fright. Every hair on her body seemed to be standing on end and she was quivering with fear. Sax, who had thought himself case-hardened to phenomena, felt a chill run down his spine. What was the Something in his study, invisible to him yet all too clearly visible to Black?

At this point in the proceedings, Elizabeth came in from her visit to the theatre. Sax pointed to the cat and explained rapidly what had happened. Elizabeth, as puzzled as he was, tried likewise to approach the frightened animal but with the same result. Again Black ducked aside, continuing to stare fixedly into the study, and clawed at the hand outstretched to soothe her.

As nothing else seemed possible, they decided to wait and watch. Fully five minutes passed. Then Black crawled slowly out from the shadows and, with the infinite caution of a cat stalking a bird, crept inch by inch to the distant corner where the writing desk stood.

It became clear that Sax's chair, or his desk, or both, provided the focus of her interest. She approached the chair stealthily, hesitated for a long time—and then sprang on to it. From there, she leapt on to the littered desk (a liberty she would never have dreamed of taking in saner moments), stepped daintily amongst the loose papers, then sprang to the top of the bookcase which surrounded the recess.

Having crawled entirely around the bookcase, sniffing and searching, she finally came down on to a settee and seemed at last to become conscious of human presence. Elizabeth picked her up. The cat's heart was beating like a trip-hammer. What had frightened her?

The explanation—or the only half reasonable explanation—appears to have nothing to do with the fact that the episode took place in that much-haunted house. It lies in the fact of what Sax was doing at the moment when Black first showed alarm.

Absorbed in his work, his thoughts concentrated uniquely on the words flowing from his pen, he was writing a part of the book called *The Green Eyes of Bâst*—and the reader who has read it will probably need no further explanation. In this story, Sax had created the eerie figure of a woman influenced by the cat-worship of ancient Egypt and supernormally endowed with feline characteristics. This was the weird image which his thoughts at that moment conjured up—and Black *saw* it!

Despite the tremendous popularity of the Fu Manchu stories, Sax was too much the artist to tie himself down to one character. He was convinced, rightly, that he could write better stories, even within the framework of frankly commercial fiction to which he was now more or less committed. Consequently, for the next seven years, he wrote no more tales of the Chinese Devil Doctor and only one concerned with Limehouse.

By 1920, post-war trends in fiction already showed a marked difference from pre-war fashions. It was now practicable for Sax to get away from the rigidly episodic, "complete in one issue" type of serial which editors had formerly demanded, and to conceive a book-length novel as one coherent whole. This gave him a much better chance to prove his mastery, which he did very convincingly.

Sax kept his work strictly in character—otherwise, he would not have sold it—but he did not write to a formula. His methods of setting up a plot were extremely conscientious and often highly original. He was never content to accept that the easiest way of doing a thing was necessarily the best way.

It was due to this scrupulously honest approach that, early in his second year at Bruton Street, Sax ran into difficulties which drove him to the brink of a nervous breakdown. The matter began auspiciously enough, with a contract from *Collier's Weekly* of New York, desiring a tale specified simply as "a mystery story." The magazine editors had already so much confidence in the saleability of Sax's work that they were quite satisfied to leave further details to him.

Sax decided to write a mystery story in which the crime detection element would predominate. For the construction of this type of story, he had an ingenious procedure which was highly efficient in theory, but which few authors would care to put into practice. The best way to create such a story, he considered, was to begin by staging a crime under conditions which seemed to preclude any human agency. Thereafter, approaching the problem

131

from the point of view of the investigator, he would seek the solution in any clue that he himself had inadvertently left. Obviously, Sax reasoned, if the author does not know the answer when he sets the question, the reader has very little chance of discovering it ahead of him.

Applying these methods to the story in hand, which was to be called *Fire-Tongue,* he caused a celebrated medical consultant to be murdered at his own dinner table under circumstances which pointed to death from natural causes. By every means he could think of, he carefully eliminated any possibility of foul play. The result was a baffling problem, on the face of it susceptible of no solution, and he felt very pleased with it.

These opening chapters, totalling some 30,000 words, Sax showed to his agent, who was likewise pleased with them. The agent was about to leave for America himself, and said that he would inform the editors that a highly promising story was under construction.

Sax sat down to assume the duties of his detective, Paul Harley, and discover the fatal clue which he had missed, the key to the impossible crime. He read through what he had written. He read it through again . . . .

Several days, or rather nights, later the galling truth dawned upon him. It was close to 4 A.M., the writing recess was thick with tobacco smoke, and the level of the Jamaica rum bottle had gone down to below half when at last he had to admit it. There *was* no key! He had defeated himself. Cursing the waste of several weeks' honest toil, Sax ceremoniously tore up the manuscript and went to bed.

Next day, he started work on a completely new story. This one went according to plan. In fact, it went so well that he beat his own record. The novel was completed early in December, 1920, less than a month after he had begun it. (This story was *Bat Wing*, probably the nearest approach to the pure detective-story that Sax ever made, and another fine example of his ability to do first-class work in more than one field.)

The editors of *Collier's* would not, he thought, have any reason to feel dissatisfied with this. They had asked for a mystery story, and despite the fact that his first attempt had misfired, he had now written one. He despatched a cablegram to his agent,

132

who was still in New York, advising him of the date of delivery, and sat down to revise the final draft.

Two days later, a devastating three pages of cablegram came back from his agent. Unknown to Sax, he had taken a copy of the opening chapters of the earlier story with him to America and handed them to *Collier's*.

And they, in blind confidence that the rest would duly be forthcoming, had already printed the first installment.

18

HOUDINI TO THE RESCUE

IT IS NOT AT ALL DIFFICULT TO APPRECIATE SAX'S FEELINGS AT THAT moment. With no possibility of reprieve, he was obliged now to finish the story which he had already given up as impossible. If he failed, the price would be not only his own professional reputation, but also that of one of the leading magazines in America. Jointly, they would become the laughing-stock of two continents, and he would never sell a story again.

Under these dreadful conditions, Sax sailed for America by the fastest ship available. One installment of *Fire-Tongue* had already appeared; a second was about to follow. Only three were in hand. Concentrating on his notes the whole way over, he reviewed the problem from every conceivable angle, but when he reached New York no solution had presented itself.

His agent, who could scarcely have done otherwise, had confessed the situation to the editors of *Collier's*. Sax arrived to find his hotel apartment furnished with every stimulant to a writer's imagination that the anxious staff could devise. The walls were hung with beautiful black-and-white originals by Joseph Clement Coll, who had been commissioned to illustrate the story. Prohibition was rife, but a miniature cellar had been installed; a typewriter, a dictaphone . . . .

Sax set to work feverishly. Far from being in any respect simplified, the original problem was now aggravated by the fact

134

that, simultaneously with his unavailing search for a solution, he was compelled to write further material to keep up with publication. And he did not know where his writing was leading him! Nevertheless, a minimum of twelve hundred words a day had to be produced.

"At one stage," Sax said, "I was turning out copy, page by page, from my apartment to a team of messengers connecting with the printing press!"

Living the life of a hermit, attired in dressing gown and pajamas, he produced a fourth installment, only to find that it plunged him deeper into the mud, so far as the solution was concerned. His predicament was precisely that of a man lost in a labyrinth: he must go on with no means of knowing how many false turns conducted him yet farther from the light.

This state of affairs soon became cruelly apparent. The awful night arrived when he realized that the alteration of a single line of dialogue in Chapter Three would have provided him with a way out. But Chapter Three had already been printed!

Sax was afterwards convinced that, during this dire period, it was Harry Houdini who alone saved his sanity. Deeply concerned as much for his friend's health as for his reputation, Houdini insisted on hours of relaxation, at times almost literally carrying him from the building.

With his usual dogged stubbornness and complete disregard for his own good, Sax might well have refused to be pried loose, but if there was no means of confining the magician inside anything, there seemed equally to be no means of keeping him out. Regulations at this hotel were so severe that for any human being other than a resident to gain access to one of the apartments unannounced appeared nearly impossible. Yet, at all hours of the day and night—once, even, at 3 A.M.—Houdini came and went as he pleased, unseen either as he entered or departed. In those dark weeks of anxiety, Sax's knowledge of and affection for that strange man deepened considerably. Wearing a tweed suit over pajamas—for Houdini would brook no refusal—he ate a holiday dinner in the old house which harbored the wonderful library.

Houdini apparently possessed both the cloak of invisibility and the power to cast it over his companion. Together, they flitted like shadows, totally unhindered, through the dense crowds on the

135

congested sidewalks. Ignoring queues and box-office, they walked, ticketless, into a cinema, sat down and walked out again unchallenged and apparently unnoticed by anybody.

Nor did it rest there. Among the most singular and not the least alarming of his experiences, Sax later recalled the occasion when, grasping him firmly by the left arm, Houdini elected to cross Times Square against the traffic lights!

"The odds against success," Sax said, "are about the same as swimming the rapids of Niagara." Missing fast-moving cars by fractions of an inch, diving behind others, pausing momentarily, dodging forward again, they finally reached the opposite side of the street in perfect safety.

But these feats, as both Sax and Houdini insisted, were in no way supernatural. They were feats of the supernormal, such as might be performed by one trained in the Japanese art of *ninjutsu*. (The *ninja* renders himself invisible by the simple device of stepping behind you and, as you spin round to look for him, spins round with you.) They rest upon split-second timing and the agility of an acrobat, but there is not one in a million who could do them.

The peculiarly unique nature of Houdini's fantastic accomplishments rested on the fact that his mind was fully as alert as his body. Knowing the impossible situation in which his friend was placed, he had read every line in the story, approaching it as he would have approached the problem of escape from a locked box. And, in the end, it was he who found the answer.

Sax, by his own statement, had come near to cracking point and was pacing the floor of his apartment on the verge of desperation, when the door opened quietly and Houdini came in.

"I locked it," Sax said, grinning wryly, "but I might have known you'd have a key."

"I haven't. But I've got a hairpin."

Dropping into an armchair, the magician slipped from his pocket a copy of the magazine in which Chapter Three of *Fire-Tongue* had appeared. This was the issue including that maddening line of dialogue which, had it never been printed, would have enabled Sax to save the situation. Now, glancing over Houdini's shoulder, he was amazed to see that, although, thinking it useless to do so, he had never mentioned it, that line was underlined in pencil. Houdini had found it for himself.

"The character who said that has been dropped out," Houdini observed calmly. "Bring him back—think of a reason why he *lied*—make him change the words . . . and you're saved!"

It was true. By that masterpiece of simplicity the difficulties vanished like smoke. It was a device so simple and so obvious that, once pointed out, it would have seemed immediately apparent to the meanest intelligence. Yet, in the heat of battle, it is just such a detail which the most brilliant of strategists neglects—all save the rare cool-headed genius who sees it and gains the victory.

After his unsettling experience with *Fire-Tongue*, Sax evidently felt a not unnatural disinclination to tackle another book-length story for some time to come. Throughout the next three years, he wrote only a few short stories and devoted the greater part of his time to new adventures in the theatre.

Most of these never progressed beyond the planning stages. A project for a play featuring Matheson Lang as Fu Manchu was seriously discussed, but did not materialize. Curiously, although Dr. Fu Manchu has been employed in almost every other entertainment medium, he has not to this day appeared on the stage of the "live" theatre.

Sax, however, had at this period some justification for supposing that his work might be more profitably done in this field than in print. The cinema was now an established feature of life. Sax's novel *The Yellow Claw* had been filmed by the Stoll production company, and was released not long after his return from America. Two years later, it was followed by a series of fifteen two-reel episodes based closely on the Fu Manchu stories, starring Harry Agar Lyons as Fu Manchu.

Once again Sax was part of that glittering, slightly mad world of greasepaint and limelight which offered not very much in hard cash but a good deal in amusement.

Among his friends and compatriots at that time was an old schoolmate, Clifford Seyler (brother of the actress Athene Seyler), who was stage manager for C. B. Cochran during several seasons at the London Pavilion. In this capacity, he was working on a production in which Miss June appeared, at the same time that filming of *The Yellow Claw* was in progress. (Miss June, or simply June, was a well-known stage actress who was customarily billed only by her first name.) June had a small part in this film and, arriving late at

137

the theatre on three nights in succession, made the excuse that she had been kept working up to the last moment at the studio. In actual fact, the character which she played in the film came to a violent end at the outset of the story, and Seyler, remembering this, said coldly: "Nonsense! You were strangled a week ago!"

Clifford Seyler, whom Sax regarded as one of the most brilliant writers of humorous lyrics in England, was several times associated with him in abortive collaborations on musical shows. One, notably, was a three-act musical play based on the currently popular character of Captain Kettle, created by Cutcliffe Hyne. Nelson Keys was to play Captain Kettle; Sax and Clifford Seyler were to write the book and lyrics, in collaboration with the author, and the music would be composed by Herman Finck.

Despite this formidable battery of talent, it all came to nothing. Perhaps there was just too much diversified talent there to make any unanimous agreement possible. At all events, Cutcliffe Hyne wished to see his creation presented with at least the dignity of a light operetta, and could not at all see eye to eye with Nelson Keys, who regarded it as a desperately dull entertainment in urgent need of some bucking-up. So the whole thing was called off.

The year 1921 was altogether an unfortunate one for Sax. It had begun with the nerve-wracking business of *Fire-Tongue*. It ended with a major domestic crisis, the only serious difference between Elizabeth and himself which ever entered their lives. During the anxious weeks in New York, where Harry Houdini had been his only staff of moral support, Sax had not, as one might have anticipated, sought refuge in the arms of Eve for a rather pertrubing reason. Eve had already established herself in London.

She occupied a basement flat in Sloane Court where, after his return from America, she continued to receive semi-regular visits from Sax. Elizabeth, accustomed to the eccentric disappearances of her husband, suspected nothing. But it could not be long before the matter came to light, and when it did the shock was appalling. Sax had never made any secret of his contempt for marital relationships; she accepted that and was rather surprised that he embarked less on casual flirtations than she might have expected. But that he would go to the length of taking on a permanent mistress was something she had never contemplated.

The truth of the matter was that, by his basic nature, Sax was

138

the last person capable of carrying out his own philosophies. He could do nothing casually. Having once yielded to temptation, his sympathy was so easily aroused by the distress of the other party that he felt obliged to go on with it, whether he wanted to or not. Thus he became at once the victim of crossed loyalties.

Worse, perhaps, his almost pathetic honesty made deception unbearable to him. A past master of intrigue in his stories, he nonetheless hated the idea of carrying intrigue into his own life. In theory, he believed himself answerable to nobody; consequently, he was careless to the extreme.

For a few months, luck was on his side. Then Eve addressed a highly indiscreet letter to him and he did what anyone knowing him might well have expected. Absent-mindedly, he left it lying opened on his desk, and Elizabeth saw it. After her eyes had passed automatically over the first few words, she had no scruples about reading the rest and the secret was out.

Elizabeth was not the type who gives way to hysteria. She felt faint and physically sick, but the question now was simply one of what to do next. Being a marked degree more cunning than Sax, she promptly decided that a flaming row would do not the slightest good. It was no use saying that she didn't mind about his sleeping with some other woman—she did mind; but that was not the important thing. What really mattered was the way he felt about Eve, and about her.

She knew that she was useful to Sax, and knew that he knew it. That was the point which frightened her: was she, after all, no more than a useful commodity to him? This she had to find out. With a diabolical ingenuity which Sax might well have envied, she telephoned the number printed on the letter and, in the formal manner of a secretary, announced a visit from Sax at a time when she knew him to be safely occupied elsewhere.

Eve, attired in a suitably flimsy negligée, opened her door to find her anticipated visitor's wife on the doorstep. For the moment, she could think of nothing more useful to say than, "Oh!"

"Don't be frightened," Elizabeth said quietly. "I'm coming in, but I'm not going to hurt you."

Elizabeth's notoriously violent behavior was strictly for fun. In a deadly serious business of this nature, horseplay was not in her character. The interview passed off with the utmost decorum

139

on both sides. But, unfortunately for her, when confronted by a situation like this, Elizabeth was always seriously handicapped by her unruly sense of humor, which made her want to laugh, or by a ridiculous sympathy for the sufferings of her defeated opponent, which made her want to cry.

Eve, having discovered that she was not about to be murdered, put up a good show and, it must be confessed, won the first round on points. Elizabeth began to think that she might be sincerely in love with Sax, and even began to wonder whether Sax might not be in love with her. She could not fail to see that the girl was strikingly attractive, and her air of innocent fragility was convincing enough to brand any man as the aggressor.

Leaving Sloane Court no less unhappy than when she arrived, she tried to think of the future. She loved Sax too genuinely to stand in his way if this was the girl he really wanted, even though she was made desperately miserable by the certainty that Eve would ruin him. Her own feelings she dared not even consider. All that mattered now was how Sax felt. She had to know, and there was only one way to find out. Resorting to her usual, straightforward tactics, she told Sax that the game was up and demanded a meeting between the three of them.

A highly civilized but nevertheless harrowing scene followed. Eve, having the opportunity to prepare her campaign in advance, rather overplayed herself. This time she was discovered demurely clad in blue velvet, with one of Sax's books in her hand. Elizabeth, losing sympathy for her, insisted that Sax should there and then choose which woman he wanted—and immediately began to feel sorry for the indignity that she was inflicting on him. But she had to go through with it.

"I love my wife!" Sax said hoarsely, and spoke the truth, according to his own strange lights. They left the flat together.

Eve, however, was not to be disposed of so easily as that. At 2 A.M., she was at the door in Bruton Street, threatening suicide, and Sax had another distressing encounter to deal with. Eve eventually returned home and did not commit suicide.

Some correspondence followed. At the conclusion of it, Sax booked her a passage to New York and sent the ticket to her through the post, after showing it to Elizabeth. Eve left, with the mental reservation that she would nevertheless be back—and, very soon, she was.

In the following year, Sax's excursions into show business took a turn for the better, when his old friend George Robey came back into the picture.

The comic possibilities of Jules Verne's *Around the World in Eighty Days,* so well exploited in a recent film version of that novel, were both realized and exploited more than thirty years earlier. It was Sax who wrote the book and lyrics for *Round in Fifty,* in collaboration with Julian and Lauri Wylie, the show's producers. The show opened at the London Hippodrome on the 16th of March 1922, and ran for 471 consecutive performances.

Round in Fifty followed the fortunes of Phineas Fogg's spend-thrift son Phileas—played by George Robey—in his attempts to do in fifty days what his father had done in eighty. Described by the *Times* critic as "a musical adventure," it featured scenes ranging from London, via Boulogne, Brindisi, and Hong Kong to San Francisco and back again via New York to London. Events taking place en route included a Chinese ballet, a missionary revival meeting, and a mad song and dance by George Robey in Sing Sing prison.

In all this kaleidoscope of fast-moving action and laughter, the hand of Sax is plainly apparent. Originally, he had been charged only with the script, the music being composed by Herman Finck and James Tate; but, owing to the sudden death of the latter, he finished by having to provide a good deal of the music as well. It was Sax who likewise suggested the introduction of film sequences, one showing a motorboat pursuit of a liner missed at New York, another of a car dash from Portsmouth to London.

Audiences of the early 1920's had seen nothing like this before, and critics hailed the idea as "nothing less than a breathtaking triumph." George Robey is on record as saying that this was the most enjoyable revue in which he had ever taken part.

The enthusiastic reception of *Round in Fifty* clearly encouraged Sax to center his interests a while longer on the theatre. From being an acknowledged writer of highly successful novels and short stories, it began to look as if he might, after all, switch to the job of playwright.

19

ON WITH THE MOTLEY

THAT SOMEWHAT FEVERISH DECADE OFTEN REFERRED TO IN ENGLAND AS the Gay Twenties is too well known for any general description to be necessary. It was the familiar period of rapid change often running to extremes, socially as well as economically, which follows naturally in the wake of a major war and finds its most marked expression in the young. It was a time when, once again, values were re-examined, wartime and pre-war restrictions thankfully cast aside, idols overthrown, and new idols enshrined.

Some historians choose to regard that era as one of disillusionment and draw parallels with the aftermath of World War II. As a member of that so-called Lost Generation, I am disposed to doubt it. Our fathers honestly believed that they had fought and won the War to End Wars—there would never be another—so their gaiety was spontaneous and had little in common with the pessimistic "tomorrow-we-die" hedonism of a later era.

Sax had been born far too early to be a part of any "Lost" Generation. But, as a veteran of Edwardian Bohemianism, he now played the role both of an interested observer and, to some extent, a senior member in this resurgence of youthful ideals.

In 1922, the Hambone Club opened its doors. Situated in Ham Yard, off Great Windmill Street, in the middle of London's theatre district, this was a new center of *avant garde* activity, founded and presided over by the painter, George Hill, who accepted applications from no one who did not belong (at least remotely) to one of the artistic professions. Sax, needless to say, became one of the first members.

Approached by a steep wooden stair, the place had a bar with a sanded floor, where members sat around drinking Burton ale from the cask, and smoked long-stemmed clay pipes of the Pickwick style. Primarily, the Hambone Club was designed to be a rendezvous for the younger rebels, those who had not yet "arrived," but it was well patronized likewise by a "senior set." The latter included such names as Augustus John, E. V. Lucas, Herman Finck and Cedric Hardwicke. These were the associates who, during Sax's post-war phase of Bohemianism, occupied the place vacated by the Oakmead Road gang of his early youth.

Another visitor to that singular establishment was the notorious joker, Cole, chiefly remembered for the incredible feat of digging a hole in Piccadilly. Though that was undeniably spectacular, I think that for sheer humor I prefer one of his other exploits—when, persuading a passer-by to hold one end of a measuring tape, he nipped around the corner and gave the opposite end into the hands of another.

But that member of the Hambone Club whom, in later years, Sax best remembered was a certain Captain Ball. Short and stocky, Captain Ball had the knack of selecting garments so discordant that they hurt the eye. He was sometimes seen wearing a shirt composed of bright pink and white squares, with a dazzling yellow tie in which was stuck an emerald pin. Even "op art" painters would have grown pale at the sight of him.

At fancy-dress affairs—in which Captain Ball took a childish delight—he would appear disguised beyond recognition and (though nobody seemed to know where he had studied the art) so skillfully made up as to pass authentically for the part he represented. Speaking a sort of refined broken English, or (with apparent fluency) some unknown tongue, he appeared in the magnificently embroidered robes of a Chinese mandarin, or an Indian rajah, resplendent with glittering gems.

Yet there was nothing effeminate about this strange man. Out of disguise, he became a tough little ruffian, terse of speech and at times violent in language and behavior as the mate of a tramp steamer. For transport, he drove a single-seater Bugatti rac-

143

ing car, enamelled to resemble a magnified hornet.

At first no more than mildly amused by the antics of Captain Ball, Sax was astonished to learn that the ornate jewellery which he affected in his masquerades was, in fact, genuine. The Captain's habit of carrying a Colt revolver, which had previously appeared as a piece of Wild West exhibitionism, took on a new significance. It was rumored that he often had on his person precious stones to the value of some six or seven thousand pounds. Sax received direct evidence of this one night at the Hambone Club, when Ball contemptuously threw a heap of uncut diamonds on the table and invited him to bid for them. He declined. Captain Ball shrugged, gathered them up and, in the course of the evening, sold them to a later arrival for £3,250.

Here, then, was mystery backed up by something more solid than mere affectation. No one knew in what particular service Captain Ball was, or had been, captain; his truculently aggressive manner discouraged inquiry. Long absences from his usual haunts, punctuated by erratic reappearances, often with his features burned nearly black by the sun, suggested a seafaring occupation.

A considerable time went by before the truth finally came out. Captain Ball was one of those rare beings whose outward appearances more than justify their implications. He was a gun-runner. He supplied arms to the warring tribes of Africa and Arabia and had similar dealings with the Far East. He traded only on terms of hard cash, jewels or choice and marketable commodities.

On his death, he left a sizeable fortune and a large house in Regent's Park to his only relative, a little orphaned niece whom he had adopted. Sax, once again, found himself directly concerned. The house was purchased by one of the few surviving friends of his youth, Lionel Barton. He found the place marked with a weathered signboard which announced, "Any woman found on these premises will be shot!" and the cellars mined with dynamite.

Fu Manchu experts will, incidentally, find the name of Lionel Barton familiar. Sax had the occasional habit of conferring a friend's name on one of his fictional characters. In this case, it also made rather a nice paraphrase on Sir Richard Burton, the explorer and Orientalist on whose eccentric figure the same character was

144

actually based.

After an absence of only a few months from these gay scenes, the redoubtable Eve returned suddenly and dramatically to the attack. Something of a mystery, as I have already intimated, she seems to have had not only unlimited facilities for long-distance voyages but an efficient network of information. She arrived, unannounced, at Bruton Street precisely at a time when Elizabeth chanced to be spending the weekend in Margate.

Eve had evidently seen the film version of *The Yellow Claw* and noted the scene in which June, in a state of drugged collapse, burst in upon the apartment of a young writer, with her civet coat worn over the unexpected minimum of a nightdress. Resolved to improve upon this, Eve entered Sax's study wearing a long fur coat and as naked as her namesake beneath. According to her own statement, she had come non-stop from Paris. Imagination recoils before the prospect of what a Channel crossing clad only in a fur coat must have been like, so presumably she did not intend to be taken literally.

An appeal of this nature was more than Sax could resist and, for a time, Eve was restored to his good graces. I do not mean that he resumed the affair ardently. Though, throughout a period of several years, he never wholly got rid of her, their later adventures seem to have been rather a desultory business. Personally, I am inclined to think that, more than anything else, it rested on Sax's characteristic feeling of obligation towards anybody whom he had once admitted into his circle. In this respect, his ideas were purely those of the Far East.

This time, he was a trifle more careful. At least he had the good sense to tell Eve to write to him only at the Eccentric Club. But he soon became careless again. Having collected her letters, he left them lying around, with the result that Elizabeth found out about this new phase of the affair, exactly as she had found out about the first.

Elizabeth's feelings might better be described as disgusted than furious. She decided on a change of tactics. Obviously, she reasoned, it was no use challenging Sax with her discovery and forcing him to promise to break off the affair, since she would afterwards have no way of knowing whether he had actually done so or not. This—the thought that she could no longer trust him—

was the bitterest of all. Although she did not feel very humorous about it, her retaliation nevertheless had all the aspects of a Noel Coward farce. The tone of Eve's letter plainly revealed that it was she who was doing the running—she complained sadly about Sax's seeming neglect of her. Elizabeth therefore made up her mind to create further misunderstanding between them.

She could imitate Sax's oddly distinctive handwriting well enough to satisfy the man at the Eccentric Club. So, writing a note ostensibly from Sax, she sent her maid down to the Club to collect his mail. In this way, more of Eve's letters came into her hands. Elizabeth then sat down and answered them in person, informing her rival that Sax had turned them over to her because he wished to end the association. Eve wrote back furiously to Sax. Elizabeth captured that letter too and gave it the same treatment.

After a little of this sort of thing, the situation soon became confused to absurdity. Sax, a little piqued because Eve had apparently not written to him, finally roused himself to call on her. He was received with a slap in the face and a heated denunciation for having given her letters to Elizabeth. It was useless for him to protest that he had not; Eve simply declined to believe him.

All this he later confessed to Elizabeth. In the crazier days of Herne Hill, while they dodged the bailiffs and dreamed of a honeymoon in Egypt, they might have laughed over it together, and there the matter would have ended. But, sad to relate, the laughter now rang hollow. The seeds of mistrust had been sown, and Elizabeth was at a loss to know where and how it would all finish.

Yet, for all the unhappiness and uncertainty of those post-war years, I find myself most deeply impressed by the touching simplicity with which Elizabeth said to me: "We quarrelled often, but we always made it up before bedtime. I never once went to sleep angry with Sax."

Another of the old-school Bohemians closely associated with Sax was the popular composer Herman Finck, whose music accompanied many of the shows then staged in London. Though he never attempted to dig up Piccadilly, Herman Finck had his own store of practical jokes equally disquieting to the recipient. Friends who called on him at Drury Lane, where he was conducting the orchestra during the pantomine season, had particularly to look

146

out for themselves. If he could, Herman would ply the unsuspecting visitor with drinks and detain him in his room backstage till the call-boy came to announce the rise of curtain. Then, seizing the visitor by the hand, he would hustle him through the dimly-lit maze of subterranean passages in that warren of a theatre, finally to thrust him into a seat and disappear. Whereat a burst of applause all at once informed the bewildered man that he was sitting not in the stalls, but in the conductor's seat in front of the theatre orchestra!

Sax had worked with Herman Finck on the production of *Round in Fifty*. He was likewise teamed with him in a number of other ventures, none of which materialized. After *Round in Fifty*, Sax's next and only subsequent stage success was not a musical but a three-act melodrama, *The Eye of Siva*.

Presented at the New Theatre in August 1923, this was a play which had all the aspects of a Fu Manchu story, except that Fu Manchu did not actually appear. The leading character was the detective, Paul Harley, who had earlier appeared in the novels *Bat Wing* and *Fire-Tongue*, as well as in a number of short stories. Viewed in the light of later achievements, the cast was remarkable. The part of Harley was played by Arthur Wontner, who was later to become one of the most successful screen portrayers of Sherlock Holmes. Other members of the cast were Cathleen Nesbitt, D. A. Clarke-Smith, Forrester Harvey, S. J. Warmington, and Edmund Breon. There were other noteworthy performers, equally striking if less distinguished. Of these, certainly the most unexpected was a female known simply as Kali.

The Eye of Siva was what I would describe as a "stage manager's play," featuring every conceivable device, exotic and fantastic, up to and including a death-ray. When the truckload of assorted props arrived at the theatre and unloading commenced, Mr. Bronson Albery, the rather strait-laced manager, became visibly disturbed. The chain hoist to the scene dock operated in such a way that the loads went up past the window of his office. Having watched a succession of unlikely objects swung up, followed by a six-armed image and a Chinese coffin, he summoned Sax to his presence. More than a little severely, he made it clear that nothing like this had ever gone into his theatre before, and had he been warned in advance, it would not have gone in now. His was a

147

respectable establishment.

Sax did his diplomatic best to assure him that it would remain so. But he had not finished speaking when he became aware that the manager was no longer listening. Glassy-eyed and rigid in his chair, he was staring at the window. Sax turned his head quickly and looked. Thirty feet above Charing Cross Road, on a level with the office window, a large cage swung erratically back and forth on the loading chains. It contained Kali—a full-sized and highly enraged female leopard.

And, sure enough, so far as the smooth running of a theatre was concerned, that leopard was a thoroughgoing nuisance from start to finish. Unlike many females, she seemed to have no stage ambitions, and never became reconciled to theatrical life. The night watchman, convinced that she "had it in for him," declined to make his rounds. He said that whenever he came near, the leopard hurled herself at the bars of her cage and glared at him.

As the run of the play lengthened into months, the fetid atmosphere of the scene dock penetrated even to the dressing rooms, till the whole place resembled a menagerie, and actors and actresses began to ask indignantly whether they were working in a theatre or a circus. The staff put their heads together and considered asking the management for leopard-money.

Anxiety of a totally different nature was displayed by the animal's owner, Mr. D. Tyrwhitt-Drake, F.Z.S. Some weeks after the opening, he called on Sax at the theatre and announced that he had come to check up on the health of his cat. Sax escorted him backstage. The curtain had just fallen on the last act, and the place was swarming with stagehands busily engaged in reconstructing the day-set.

Mr. D. Tyrwhitt-Drake, F.Z.S., approached the cage and, before anybody had an inkling of his purpose, slid up the door, grabbed the snarling leopard by the scruff of the neck and hauled her out onto the stage floor, where, forcing open her jaws, he proceeded to an inspection of her teeth.

"I have never seen a stage cleared so quickly," Sax told me. "They went off right, left and center, down traps and up the fly-ladders."

In fifteen seconds flat, he found himself standing alone beside the zoologist and his cat. To his credit, let it be said that when all

148

else had fled he stood his ground. But he made a mental note never to write another play even remotely concerning anything larger than a fox-terrier.[17]

During this same period of theatrical activity came the never to be forgotten night when Elizabeth found herself alone with the Extra Inhabitant of Bruton Street.

At the theatre, D. A. Clarke-Smith had taken over the leading part, owing to the sudden illness of Arthur Wontner. Sax had thought it advisable to go along and see for himself how the audience reacted to this.

Elizabeth stayed at home. Owing to the reappearance of Eve, domestic relations were not going very smoothly just then. There were no fights. Elizabeth had come to the conclusion that fights with Sax served no useful purpose. If she persisted in attacking him on the subject of Eve, the logical result would merely be to strengthen his motives for concealing the affair. Instead, she had decided to register an indirect protest by making a show of her own independence. She would show Sax that, whether or not he could get along without her, she could get along without him. She began writing stories aimed at the women's magazines.

As an act of defiance, it did not work very well. Sax, with his usual naive innocence, failed to see it as such and, with his usual generosity, promptly offered to assist. And to her own surprise, Elizabeth found herself taking an interest in the job for its own sake. She not only wrote stories, but actually sold them.

So it happened that, on this particular night while Sax was at the theatre, Elizabeth had made up her mind to stay in the house and work on a story. After a leisurely bath, she changed into a nightdress and, with a light robe thrown over it, settled down at the bureau in her bedroom. The only other person in the house was a parlormaid, the latest of the sequence who, so far, remained blissfully ignorant of the ghostly goings-on. The Extra Inhabitant had remained tranquil of late.

It was about nine o'clock when the girl came in to inquire if she might go out to post a letter.

"Certainly," Elizabeth said. "But don't stay out too long, because there's no one to open the door or answer the 'phone."

Forgetting the incident completely, she went on with her writing. Some time passed before she was again disturbed by three

149

sharp knocks at the bedroom door.

"Come in!" Elizabeth said absently.

Vaguely it crossed her mind that the girl had come back. But there was no reply and, after a brief interval, the knocks were repeated. Elizabeth froze in her chair as the truth dawned upon her. The parlormaid had *not* come back. It was the Extra Inhabitant.

Staring fixedly at the door, she felt a wave of fear sweep over her. It was no good telling herself that it had happened before, that there was nothing there. The door remained closed. She was afraid to go and open it—yet, with an awful sense of conviction she knew that, tonight, if she didn't go and face it, there *would* be something there. Fear drove her to the attack. Elizabeth went at the door in a bound, wrenched it open and stared out. As usual, nothing was visible. But courage is expendable. It is not the first emergency which engenders panic but the same emergency too often experienced: there comes a last straw.

Elizabeth charged blindly down the stairs, checked her flight long enough to grab the telephone and send a frantic S.O.S. to the stage door of the New Theatre, ran down more stairs and slammed the door of the house behind her. Breathing rapidly, and conspicuously undressed, she stood on the doorstep and waited for rescue.

A policeman strolled by, cast a casual look at her lightly-clad form, looked harder, and halted.

"Waiting for somebody?" he inquired.

"My husband," Elizabeth said faintly. "I was alone . . . I got scared."

She added a half explanation, not too coherently. The policeman looked doubtful. His expression indicated that, of course, There Aren't Such Things, but he showed no anxiety to enter the house and prove it. Instead, he ranged himself alongside Elizabeth in the doorway and they both waited.

The absent parlormaid (having left her boy-friend in the shadows of a convenient corner) reappeared at the same moment that the taxi arrived, bringing Sax post-haste from the theatre.

"What happened?" he demanded.

Elizabeth told him.

"Oh, is that all?" Sax said, looking rather disappointed. "I thought the house was on fire!"

150

The London presentation of *The Eye of Siva* was followed by two successful tours. I am not sure exactly how long it ran in the West End, but it was long enough to be classified as a success and long enough for all concerned to get thoroughly tired of it. In the meantime, there were still more episodes which, if they could not be directly blamed on Kali, at least seemed to be in some way concerned with her.

The last which I remember Sax talking about took place during that period of over-familiarity when work backstage tends to become automatic. Sax had, more or less by chance, dropped in to watch the show from the prompt corner. The entire staff, he observed were carrying out their duties like sleepwalkers. The stage manager turned the pages of the script listlessly, his eyes scanning the typed words with the blank efficiency of a computer, his fingers moving mechanically over the signals board. Just behind the two of them, a stagehand sat on a chair with an empty wooden box at his feet and a trayful of broken glass resting on his knees. It was his job to simulate the crash when Kali was presumed to jump through the roof of a conservatory off-stage.

Listening to the dialogue with half an ear, Sax presently realized that some ten or twelve lines had been spoken since the cue, and no crash had been heard. He twisted around sharply, and saw the stagehand staring vacantly into space.

"No glass crash!" he hissed, furiously.

The stagehand woke up.

"Gaw!" he said. "I forgot!" He pondered the matter for a moment. "I'll do it now!"

He lifted the tray on high, but Sax and the stage manager dived on him together and got it from his hands just in time to prevent a second disaster.

20

BACK TO THE SINK

PLANS FOR FUTURE THEATRICAL VENTURES WERE IN THE AIR—AND remained there. They reached the stage of an impressive agreement drawn up between the Adelphi Theatre, Sax Rohmer, Clifford Seyler, and Herman Finck (and witnessed by other eminent names including E. V. Lucas and Tom Webster), for a musical play to be called *London's Sweetheart*. For reasons which are obscure, it was not fulfilled. I think that, this time, it was Herman Finck (though I may be doing him an injustice) who simply failed to come up with the music.

But if these old friends, somehow or other, could never manage to work together they could nevertheless play together as, perhaps, only the neo-Bohemians knew how. One never knew what they would do next, and trembled to imagine it.

A typical instance occurred when Sax, in a journalistic moment, came out with an article in which he suggested a connection between red hair and easy virtue. E. V. Lucas (who had never agreed with him on anything, since the days when he had nearly sabotaged *Fu-Manchu*) said that it was nonsense.

Sax insisted that it was not nonsense. Moreover, he said, he was ready to demonstrate it. E. V. Lucas invited him to do so. This was one occasion when he would be quite happy to be proved wrong. So they went to Drury Lane, where *The Three Musketeers* was playing, collected Herman Finck and three red-headed speci-

"Captured!"—as Elizabeth calls it—the first photograph
after their marriage.

"Curly" as Sax called her; Elizabeth as he first knew her.

Arthur Henry Ward, aged 4—the future Sax Rohmer.

William Ward, about 1880.

"Barrymore profile" of Sax Rohmer.

Sax and Elizabeth of Herne Hill.

Sketch made for the autograph book of his cousin Hilda, by Sax
Rohmer (then A. Sarsfield Ward) aged 18.

"Charlie Green" under arrest.

Postcard (with "I.B." decoration by Elizabeth) inviting Sax home from 6 months' absence in America.

Black-and-white study of a street in Damascus, by Sax Rohmer.

Sax Rohmer's study at Lovelands Way.

The roulette team lays plans for a session.

Lovelands Way—Elizabeth's cottage at Lower Kingswood.

Little Gatton.

Elizabeth's satinwood panelled sitting-room at Little Gatton.

A part of the lounge at Little Gatton.

The bar, adjoining the dining room, at Little Gatton.

The dining room, with the *Mauretania* panelling, at Little Gatton.

Sax and Elizabeth visit New York, 1935.

Sax and Elizabeth of Braemar House.

I wonder if any of your readers could explain a phenomenon (of today) which puzzles me? I refer to this sudden interest in the Russian language. Why does anybody want to know Russian?

French — yes. A knowledge of this beautiful language opens the door to a treasury of literary gems. German — yes. Germany, too, has a legacy of literature, particularly in the field of Orientalism and other sciences. Italian, Spanish are rewarding, more musical languages. But Russian? Why or Eskimo) Kham?

Not only is Russian an ugly language, but what has a knowledge of it to offer the student? Prior to the coming of Kruschev and his equally uncultured associates, I cannot recall that much interest was taken in Russia in this country. If we except two or three gloomy writers of no major importance, what do these new enthusiasts expect to learn from an ability to read Russian? Russia is peculiarly barren in great literature. Musically, she once produced giants, but music speaks every language; the output of contemporary Russian composers sounds to me like someone's music played backwards.

Can it be that these young earnest students are preparing themselves for a Communist America ruled by Kruschev?

mens for the experiment, and all went back to Bruton Street.

It was about 3 A.M. when Elizabeth, who had gone to bed early and fallen asleep at once, woke to find herself alone. There was no sound, but even the silence of that house was uncanny. She lay there, unable to go to sleep again, and beginning to feel rather worried. Sax, as she well knew, had a habit of working far into the small hours, but that haunted writing room bothered her. She was sure that, some night, something would happen. Eventually, she decided to go down and see if he was still working.

She put on her dressing gown and braved the dark stairs to the lounge. It proved dimly lighted and occupied not merely by Sax but by the most unlikely group she could have imagined. It was like an opium den. Lying back in an armchair was a mellow-looking gentleman whom she did not recognize as E. V. Lucas, not having previously met him. A redheaded girl was sitting on the floor beside him, her head on his knees. Opposite, in another chair, was Herman Finck. A second redhead had her arms about his neck.

Elizabeth blinked, looked around for Sax, and found him, through a haze of tobacco smoke, seated at his desk. Placidly smoking his pipe, he sat there thoughtfully contemplating a third redhead who reclined on an ottoman with her clothing revealingly arranged.

It was—or should have been—an awkward situation. As she stepped into the room, five heads jerked round and five pairs of eyes stared at her with something near to consternation. The sixth pair of eyes just switched slightly in her direction and remained impassive. "Hallo, darling!" Sax said cheerfully. "I thought you'd be asleep! Let me introduce Miss One, Miss Two, and Miss Three. Herman you know. E. V., this is my wife, Elizabeth."

What, in identical circumstances, a Mayfair hostess should have replied is somewhat difficult to suggest. But, for Sax and Elizabeth, the days of Oakmead Road had not quite died, nor did they ever.

"Delighted!" she said sweetly. "Do let me get you some sandwiches!"

But the guests seemed to have no appetite, and they all left rather quickly.

Despite the limited successes he had scored with *Round in*

153

Fifty and *The Eye of Siva,* it finally became evident, even to Sax, that a permanent career in play-writing was not going to be profitable. He turned back to the novel and, from that time onwards, never seriously considered any alternative.

In three years, the doubts and fears provoked by *Fire-Tongue* had evidently worn off, for the work which he now tackled was another 80,000 word effort, not a detective-story but a modern mystery inspired largely by his old interest in Cagliostro the alchemist. It was called *Grey Face.*

This story proved to be not only a commercial success but, from the literary point of view, quite outstanding. Readers in the mid-1920's liked plots which were complex, and that of *Grey Face* is so intricate that it requires the closest attention to follow it. As an example of fashions in popular literature during that period, I consider it one of the finest things written.

At Bruton Street, the domestic outlook continued to remain unsettled. On the short-term basis, relations between Sax and Elizabeth were generally amicable, often interspersed with bouts of sheer fun which made it seem as if no shadow had ever come between them. But, for the future, whether events would lead to a genuine reconciliation or a complete break, no one might predict.

Elizabeth, still grimly determined to assert her independence, decided to take up acting as a serious study. She became a pupil at Lady Benson's, and concentrated her endeavors on trying to learn something about the Shakespearean theatre. In the afternoons, while Bill Ward was away at the office, she appropriated his room at the top of the house and delivered Portia's summing-up over the rooftops of Mayfair. But later, when she attended an audition and received the offer of a part, she refused it.

Sax, in the legitimate course of his business, paid a visit to Berlin, where translations of his stories were now doing well. (The fact that he had once advocated the assassination of Hindenburg fortunately remained unknown.) He had no adventures with German *fräulein*—or, if he did, was not detected. According to the record, the most sinful thing that he did was to visit a nightclub equipped with the novelty of a glass dance-floor and hostesses accessible by telephone from the customers' tables.

At the same time, he found the personality of his official translator, von Bebler, startling enough to stick long in his memory.

Von Bebler was a heel-clicking Prussian, whom war had impoverished to the necessity of earning his bread by commerical translation. His English was faultless, but his contempt for any breed other than the Prussian remained unaltered. Goldmann, the publisher—who was both his employer and a Jew—he invariably referred to as "this fellow."

When going through numerous boxes of "foolish things" for the preparation of this book, we came across the printed programme of a Grand Concert held aboard the *S. S. Aguila* on the 18th of May, 1924. Sax and Elizabeth were on a Canary Islands cruise. The concert, by the way, featured three sketches and, needless to say, Elizabeth was in all of them.

Discovery of this item led to recollections of Sax's first meeting with Captain McPhee and the curious conversation which they had aboard that ship. Sax, who had a personal and professional interest in travellers' tales, always became friendly with the ship's officers on every voyage that he made. He had not been long aboard the *Aguila* before he found himself invited to take a drink in the captain's cabin.

McPhee rang for his steward, sat down at the table, and began to air his grievances. His principal grievance, it appeared, was that the steward was a Chinese who could not or would not understand English. With the arrival of Hop Ling, this presently became apparent.

"Scotch!" snapped the captain.

Hop Ling beamed, nodded, pointed his finger at him, nodded again and pointed to himself.

"Chinee!" he said, and pointed the finger hopefully at Sax. "You? Scot?"

"Whisky!" roared McPhee.

Hop Ling looked blank. Captain McPhee made strangling sounds; then, giving up the attempt at verbal communication, he lifted his thumb in the gesture of a man drinking. This seemed to work.

"He knows what to get—I think!" he said dolefully, as Hop Ling departed.

Sax smiled politely, and they began to talk of other things. McPhee was a tough little Scottish seaman, then in his early forties, with no great imagination and no nerves. Hardly the man, he thought, with whom to discuss metaphysics. For a while, he spoke of foreign ports, storms at sea, feats of seamanship—till, to his astonishment, the captain cut him short with a question.

"D'ye believe a man may look into the future?"

"Do you?" Sax asked quickly.

"I've read ye'r books," McPhee said slowly. "Time was, I'd nae ha' credited sich. But the now . . . ."

The story he had to tell was a strange one. Years previously, when still a young ship's officer, McPhee had once found himself in charge of a ship moored in an Indian port. Looking down from the bridge, he had all at once been surprised and enraged to see a tall Hindu on the deck, staring up at him. No one was allowed on board. McPhee lifted up his voice and said so, not over-courteously. The Hindu answered him in cultured English.

"Sahib, I am charged with a few words which I must say to you."

His "few words" consisted of an outline of McPhee's future from that moment to the day of his death. The ship on which he stood would be wrecked, but the disaster would bring him promotion. He would meet his future wife in a place he had never visited before. Oddest of all, he would "be suspended below water and receive reward."

"And these things have happened," McPhee said gravely.

He broke off as Hop Ling re-entered with a tray bearing a whisky bottle, two glasses and a bottle of soda water. The captain's face registered a half satisfaction, but only half. It happened that he, personally, preferred to take plain water with his whisky. But how to get this information across to Hop Ling?

"Water!" McPhee said, scowling.

Hop Ling stared at him.

"Water, ye daft ha'porth!" shouted the captain. He turned agonized eyes towards Sax. "Dear God!—what can I say to the moron?"

Sax thought for a moment. Then, with sudden inspiration, he traced out the Chinese character for "water" (one of the dozen or so that he knew) on the table top with his forefinger. Hop Ling nodded vigorously and went out.

Captain McPhee sighed profoundly, filled the glasses, and

156

took up his interrupted tale.

"It a' happened like yon black heathen said. Our ship was wrecked. They made me master of anither. I met the lass and I married her."

"And the bit about 'being suspended under water'?" Sax asked, intrigued.

"Aye. There's nae mystery aboot that." McPhee laughed. The ship had developed engine trouble, necessitating an adjustment to the propellors. Being the strongest swimmer aboard, he had gone over the side with a lifeline and fixed it. The owners had made him a gift in recognition.

"Congratulations!" Sax said.

The captain regarded him thoughtfully and at length. "Ye'll maybe no say that when I tell ye the rest. My wife will leave me. And then, a sickness that the doctors can find no name for. I'll be sick near to death, but I will no die."

"And you believe that?"

"I dinna ken."

There was silence. Then the door opened and the Chinese steward came in again. He was carrying a large and dirty bucket, filled to the brim with seawater. Captain McPhee's face became purple and he began to choke.

On his way below, Sax met Hop Ling at the foot of the companionway. He paused. "Tell me, my friend," he said softly, "are you really such a fool as you make out?"

The steward looked back at him unwinkingly. The ghost of a smile lingered on his lips. "Captain Mac not nice man!" he said confidingly. "Very rude!"

Following the enthusiastic reception of the first series of Fu Manchu films, the Stoll Film Company now released a second series of two-reel episodes. In the Underground stations, all over London, larger than life sized posters depicted the leering visage and clutching hands of the Devil Doctor. The fame of Fu Manchu had never seemed greater than at that moment.

But, in the face of all this apparent affluence, the Sax Rohmers found themselves up against a major financial crisis. Once again, they had no money and, worse, a terrifying accumulation of debts astronomically beyond the insignificant worries of their modest existence at Herne Hill. How had it happened?

Neither of them quite knew. In part, there is no denying that it was due to the wild extravagances of Sax. He loved luxury, and spent lavishly to obtain it, yet there was no one better entitled to have luxury, for he knew how to appreciate it. In all that he did, there was no trace of vulgarity. He loved good food and good wines; he drank as much as he could handle, and no more. He lived like a king but, with the instinct of a born artist (since he was certainly not educated to it), lived like a king raised from birth in the polished good taste of a noble court.

And, more than that, no small part of his extravagances went out in his open-handed generosity. Sax did not donate large sums to charitable causes—he was far too unselective for that. Simply, the urge to help, whether by money or advice, was so strong in him that he gave freely to the first who asked, never even pausing to consider whether or not help might be deserved.

A case in point (though, certainly, there were others) was that of the male secretary who had been in his service since the conclusion of the war. This young man's only acquaintance with Sax came about from the fact that, during one of their pre-war visits to the Channel Isles, he had once praised Elizabeth's rendering of Rachmaninoff's *Prelude* on a hotel piano. Later, discharged from the army, he had met them again and mentioned that he had a distaste for returning to his former employment. Sax promptly made him his private secretary, ignoring the fact that the man could neither take shorthand nor use a typewriter, and worse (in Elizabeth's opinion), was also a fool!

Financially, Sax was incorrigible because he was quite incapable of regarding his earnings in terms of money. To him, it was all childishly simple. He knew that his work brought him the means to enjoy luxury. Therefore, so long as he continued to work, there seemed to him no reason why he could not live exactly as he liked.

This might have been somewhere near reasonable had his affairs been in the hands of a trustworthy manager. Unhappily, they were not. With the rising fame of his client, Sax's agent had been quick to recognize the advantages of keeping the books in confusion. Deliberately refraining from either paying out or declaring the sums which came into his office, he affably encouraged Sax to ask for money whenever he needed it. In this way, both Sax and Elizabeth were led to believe that they were receiving advances which were, in fact, merely portions of cash already due! At the same time, under cover of this system, the agent could dispose of additional rights (such as foreign translations) with very little chance of the sale being discovered at all.

Thus it was that the crisis need not have occurred, had Sax known that money remained to his credit. But Sax and Elizabeth did not know that. The creditors pounced and Sax's agent remained silent. Feeling like criminals, they spirited the furniture out of Bruton Street into storage and retreated to a suite of cheap furnished rooms in Clifford Street.

It is a favorite remark of Elizabeth's, whenever some circumstance deprives her of hands to do the washing-up:

"Back to the sink!"

Life at Clifford Street may not, perhaps, have extended literally to that. The house was divided into service flats, with meals available from a kitchen downstairs. But conditions were far from comfortable. And the food in that house was abominable. Sax went back to living on cheese, onions and beer.

For her own sake, Elizabeth did not so much mind. They had suffered worse hardship, and soon, she felt sure, they would fight their way up again. But she felt keenly unhappy about Bill Ward, who had been forced to move into lodgings at Denmark Hill. It was the first time since the conclusion of their pact in 1911 that they had failed to provide room for him.

Sax's father enters very little into this story for the simple reason that he was a self-effacing man who complained about nothing. But Elizabeth's affection for him was second only to her affection for Sax himself.

In a way, she was glad to be rid of Bruton Street with its Extra Inhabitant. But, as they soon discovered, Clifford Street had extra inhabitants of quite another nature. The other apartments in the house were occupied almost exclusively by Ladies of the Town. Not that that worried Elizabeth. It was no concern of hers how anybody earned a living. When they met on the stairs, she gave them the same smiling "Good morning!" that she gave everybody.

Always at his best in times of emergency, Sax stuck grimly to his desk and set to work to write his way out of trouble. In a short space of time, he had produced *Yellow Shadows,* another story of Limehouse, featuring a dramatized version of Elizabeth's memorable quest and the mysterious house in Three Colt Street.

Sax's magnetic personality had a reverse effect on the maids at Clifford Street. For no explicable reason, they were all terrified of him. When he was alone in the apartment, not one of them would enter it or even answer the service 'phone. Elizabeth, returning from shopping to find the beds unmade and the remains of horrible meals cluttering up the table, was annoyed and bewildered. Why they should feel so frightened of him she could not imagine. Certainly, it was not that he made passes at them. The maids were a slatternly lot, and Sax's taste in women was fastidious. But frightened they were. However, the cook, a plain-faced but honest woman who seemed genuinely ashamed of the fact that the management would not provide her with the wherewithal to produce edible dinners, was not frightened. "I *like* him!" she confessed, blushing.

Fortunately, the Clifford Street period lasted only for a few months. At the end of that time, the situation had so much improved that they were able to move into a pleasant flat in Braemar House, at Lancaster Gate. Elizabeth was delighted. Often, when walking in Kensington Gardens, she had looked across at that house and dreamed idly of living in it. Now, by a lucky chance, it had become possible. They packed up thankfully and left Clifford Street. The cook who liked Sax packed up too, left with them, and remained in their service for the next seven years, till she got married.

TEENAGE ROMANCE

THE MOVE TO BRAEMAR HOUSE WAS COMMEMORATED WITH A HOUSE-warming party which warmed the place almost to the extent of setting it on fire. Far into the night, the serene atmosphere of Lancaster Gate shuddered ιo shouts, screams, laughter and a fusillade of champagne corks. The congregation consisted of the usual hell-raising gang of writers, artists and theatrical people. Elizabeth's already famous younger brother, Teddy, was there with his partner, Jimmie Nervo. So was her nephew, Tommy. Benrimo, who had produced *The Eye of Siva,* was there, Helen Charles and her lately-acquired husband, Air-Commodore Glynne, Vera Pearce, Clifford Seyler, and Sax's effete secretary. It was not quite the sort of gathering for old Dr. Watson Councell, the occultist. He was not there. But his son was.

All of them had come on the strict understanding that they would all be expected to *do* something. Two of the men did a step dance. Nervo and Knox staged a wrestling match. Elizabeth, fresh from Lady Benson's, tried a speech from Shakespeare, but left it too late in the evening and got it tangled up with "Albert and the Lion" from Stanley Holloway. Air-Commodore Glynne, whose only excuse for inclusion among these backstage notorieties was the distinction of being married to one, could think of nothing more striking to do than put on a false nose and a bowler hat, sideways. He got the bird and was thrown out.

Two impossibly good-looking girls from an internationally famous beauty salon gave a physical culture demonstration, attired in prototype Bikinis. No one seemed to know who had invited them. None of the men much cared. ("Come to think of it," Elizabeth said thoughtfully, while we were discussing this, "where did Sax get all that stuff about beauty salons that he wrote in *Seven Sins?*")

Sometime after midnight, the young man from upstairs arrived at the door in pajamas, dressing-gown, and rabid hysteria. They dragged him in and soon he was peacefully asleep in a corner with his dressing-gown on backwards and a bottle locked in a death-grip. The people downstairs beat on the ceiling. The guests beat on the floor till they left off.

Sax, for his part in their entertainment, staged a few of the tricks he had learned from Houdini. With the assistance of Tommy Knox, he put on the illusion of the Turk's Head. (This is particularly gruesome, because it is demonstrably possible to move objects *beneath* the table on which the apparently decapitated but talking head lies.) It went very well till Tommy (who was, in fact, upside down) got a rush of alcohol to the brain and passed out cold.

Nothing daunted, Sax next announced the staging of a seance, at which he would materialize an entity from the Beyond. Just how good he may have been in his bona fide experiments remains undisclosed, but in the dramatic presentation of an illusion he was undoubtedly very good indeed. Having marshalled the bemused guests into a group at one end of the room, he extinguished the lights and began to intone a solemn dirge in an unrecognizable and fearful-sounding language.

This, in pitch darkness, past 3 A.M., and with all the participants rather less than sober, produced a suitably eerie effect. Suddenly came the high-pitched note of a bell and then, at the empty end of the room, a snakelike, iridescent something appeared, wavered through the air some eight feet from the floor and vanished. It was followed by a hissing sound, a gust of wind, and the appearance of a tall, vague, flaky-looking figure.

Somebody screamed, "Oh, Bill! It's Becky!" And, at that point, one of the girls from the beauty salon conveniently fainted. The lights were put up hastily, to discover Sax, apparently ex-

162

hausted, mopping his forehead with a handkerchief. Elizabeth noted, a trifle skeptically, that the partner of the girl who had fainted was missing along with the materialized entity.

After that, everyone felt the need for more drinks, and disorder was soon restored. The two physical culturists came back into circulation and were persuaded to dispense with their prototype Bikinis for the third encore of their act. But at this promising stage in the proceedings, the people downstairs telephoned the police.

All things considered, it was an eminently satisfactory party. In the tastefully appointed entrance hall downstairs, there were eight flowering shrubs in ornate pots—and on the way out Clifford Seyler paused to be sick in every one of them.

Despite this light-hearted beginning, the first few months at Braemar House were not happy ones. Elizabeth had now reached the point at which Sax's on-and-off affair with Eve reduced her to a state of desperate uncertainty. She never really knew when the woman was in England and when she was not, and the mere fact that Sax seemed to be behaving himself only suggested to her that he must be successfully misbehaving without her knowledge. She felt shut out from his confidence and farther estranged from him than before.

Sax, likewise, was in a state of nerves bordering on illness. Though he rarely suffered, physically, from anything more serious than a cold, he had a habit of putting so much mental energy into his work that it sometimes brought him to the verge of a breakdown.

Seeing that he was in such a condition now, Elizabeth urged him to spend three weeks' holiday in the benign atmosphere of Madeira. This would well enough serve to relax the strain of overwork; unfortunately, it would do nothing to relax the strain of domestic relations, for Sax himself was now shaken by the idea that his own inexcusable conduct had destroyed his marriage. One does not, then, need to be much of a psychologist to realize that he was in a state of mind to respond naturally to the first offer of sympathy, and, believing himself already damned, commit indiscretions to make bad worse.

To the sun-starved Englishman, Funchal is an oasis of heaven-blessed indolence and an invitation to romance. From the wide

163

sweep of the bay, bordered with white-walled houses set among luxuriant vegetation, the town rises up steeply towards an awe-inspiring backdrop of mountains, the foothills crowded with terraced gardens, sugar-cane plantations, and vineyards. Midway between, the modern boulevards of the lower part give way to a prospect of narrow, cobbled streets fancifully negotiated by bullock-drawn sledges.

Into this tropical paradise came Nanette—whom I will call Nanette, partly for the reason that, for all I know, she may still be living, and partly for another reason which will later become apparent. Bronzed, swimsuited and reckless, eighteen-year-old Nanette was quite a different proposition from Eve. She came from a good family, the teenage product of a generation outside Sax's environment, self-possessed, lawless, and eager for sexual experience. It was inevitable that she should form an infatuation for this intriguing, darkly mysterious celebrity and equally inevitable that Sax, in his present mood, should respond.

Nanette's parents—she was on holiday with the family—acted as a help rather than a handicap. Her father spent the afternoons sleeping. Her mother, engaged in a rather more mature liaison with a tycoon in tailoring, profitably employed these hours in furthering the affair, with Nanette and Sax to make up an illicit foursome.

Having come to Funchal with the intention of staying there three weeks, he stayed six. If he had been content to let it rest at that, as so many are nonchalantly content to do, the episode might have been no more than a usefully healthful antidote to depression. But Sax was not like that, and never could be.

On his return to London, he promptly aroused suspicion by sending flowers to Elizabeth (which he never did unless he felt guilty about something) and then went on to make virtually an open confession of the whole business by starting work on a story featuring one "Nanette"—a character and a story so far removed from his regular work that it was obviously little more than an account of his own misadventures.

Elizabeth decided that she had had enough. Once and for all, her position must be definitely settled. She told Sax to go to America and stay away from her till he had made up his mind whether he wanted to go on living with her or not.

Sax went—almost, one might say, into exile. By all accounts, his six months' sojourn in New York was not exactly a joyous one. Although he later admitted that he had seen Eve there, he cannot have had much to do with her, for he had very little money. No clear break occurred between them, but the affair seems finally to have petered out; apparently, he never saw her again afterwards.

Though now directly in touch with the publishers most eager to secure his services, he acted with singular perversity. The first thing he did was to complete *Moon of Madness*, the story of Nanette. It was not the kind of tale to interest *Collier's* and though he soon sold it to *Liberty* (which catered largely to women readers) he did not get such a good price for it.

Moon of Madness lacks the ingenuity of plot which one expects from a Sax Rohmer story; all the same, as a character study, it is fascinating. More interesting, from my point of view, is the fact that in this story Sax accurately sums up what surely were his own emotions at that time, and gives the clue to his subsequent behavior. "I have placed independence above every other virtue in man. I have fought for it and suffered for it . . . independence and loneliness are inseparable . . . I don't think I could bear that lonely path any longer . . . and if I have to follow it, there won't be very much left."

Nevertheless, for the present, he appeared to have no choice but to follow it. In what I can only regard as an attitude of defiance, he lived a hand-to-mouth existence on the proceeds of a few short stories and gave the rest of his time to a work that he could not sell at all, the second (and, apart from *The Orchard of Tears*, the only other extant) example of the non-commerical type of thing which he really wanted to write. This was a mystic play called *Wulfheim* (described as a masque with music), a mixture of theosophy and demonology.

Aside from his own unorthodox concepts of religion, in writing this strange work Sax seems to have been thinking of a curious episode to which Elizabeth was actually a witness. Some time previously, a dear friend of hers, following a long illness, had died— or, at all events, been pronounced dead. Arrangements for the funeral were undertaken—Elizabeth herself being in the room at the time—when the "corpse" suddenly came to life, and, in a quite normal manner, asked for something to eat.

"But," Elizabeth said impressively, *"it was not the same woman!"*

Sax remained in America for six months. He would probably have returned sooner, but, according to the statement which he himself made to me, "I was marooned! I could never get enough money both to pay my outstanding hotel bill *and* the fare home!" In the meantime he lived cheaply at the Algonquin Hotel, then somewhat haphazardly managed by an odd character who allowed his guests (chiefly of the artistic fraternity) to run weeks into arrears on the pathetic belief that they would sooner or later sell something and be able to pay up.

Concurrently contributing to his support was another unbusiness-like personality, a publisher who, on receiving a visit from an author, would happily pay several hundred dollars for an option on anything he cared to propose.

"But," said Sax, grinning, "he never once asked you to write the story afterwards!"

During Sax's absence, Elizabeth had troubles of her own. On one point, at least, she could now feel happier. Although the new flat at Braemar House was not extensive enough to provide a room for Bill Ward, she now had enough money to fix him up with something better than his uncomfortable lodgings at Denmark Hill. She found an apartment for him within five minutes' walking distance, furnished it with the overflow of things from Bruton Street, and secured the services of a good housekeeper. So Sax's father was back in the family circle.

But, in the meantime, Elizabeth had begun to feel really ill. She could not make out what was wrong with her. Dr. Watson Councell, the twentieth-century alchemist, who continued to act as their unofficial medical adviser, diagnosed a deep-seated complaint, but was opposed to an operation because he was opposed to all operations in principle. (He himself died of cancer several years later. But as he was then well over seventy he may have known that surgery could not have saved him anyway.)

Elizabeth, thinking that her illness was most likely the result of her disturbed state of mind, decided to combat it with a little pleasure-seeking on her own account. She contacted Sax's cousin, Hilda, of the Honan episode, and now a fully-fledged research chemist, and persuaded her to come along on a Mediterranean

166

cruise.

It was a lively trip, no doubt rendered the livelier by their presence. Elizabeth recalls nothing very much of the historical spots which they visited, but retains a keen memory of their several misadventures en route. After calling at Nice, where Hilda stepped off the ship to exchange greetings with a brother, they presently found themselves at an Italian port (possibly Genoa?) which, at that time, appeared to be chiefly remarkable for a certain notorious night-club in which no respectable woman would dream of setting foot. That was enough for Elizabeth and Hilda, who determined to go there. They armed themselves dramatically for the expedition with knives thrust into their stocking-tops and, much against his will, cajoled a fellow-passenger named Bates into acting as escort.

They were rewarded by the spectacle of a girl dancing naked on a table, apart from which nothing very sensational appeared to be happening. So they decided to *make* something happen. Seated at a nearby table was a strikingly handsome young man, accompanied by an older man, both keeping their eyes turned interestedly in their direction. Elizabeth promptly made up her mind that now was the time to "ditch" Bates. She grabbed Hilda by the arm, shepherded her ostensibly towards the Ladies' Room, and flashed an audacious wink to the handsome young man.

The move went according to plan. They came out of the place (unseen by their escort) to find the young man and his companion waiting in the street with a car. A minute later, they were being whisked off, they knew not whither, with every prospect (they thought) of being raped or murdered, or both.

They were neither. To their chagrin, the unknown destination to which they were being carried off proved to be the Yacht Club, where their abductors (an Italian Count and his manservant) entertained them courteously till 4 A.M. with coffee and sandwiches. They never found any use for their knives and were bitterly disappointed.

However, they were somewhat mollified when they returned to discover the ship in uproar. Bates had rushed back, nearly frantic, to report their disappearance and there were search parties out all over the town hunting for them.

A day or so passed peacefully before Elizabeth distinguished

167

herself again. This time, it was at the ruins of Pompeii, in the celebrated Street of the Brothels. Elizabeth, ingenuously struck by the peculiar appearance of what she supposed to be rainwater spouts, rather conspicuously pointed them out to Hilda.

Hilda, medically-minded, frowned and hissed in her ear: "Penis!"

But the word was unknown to Elizabeth's innocent vocabulary. "Peanuts?" she demanded loudly, and the men went purple. So did Hilda.

If Elizabeth failed to find romance on her Mediterranean cruise, it was not for any lack of offers. At Naples, the British Fleet was in port and the lady passengers were at once commandeered for a party aboard ship. The paymaster immediately became infatuated with Elizabeth, so thoroughly that he followed her around for years afterwards, but without the slightest success. More strikingly but less credibly numbered among her conquests was the unfortunate Bates, who later committed suicide and was rumored to have done so "because he had fallen in love with a girl on the ship"—Elizabeth! If he had, he was less demonstrative than the paymaster, for this was the first she ever heard about his infatuation.

Elizabeth came back none the worse for her adventures, but, unfortunately, no better for them. Her illness persisted, and it soon became evident that something was very wrong indeed. Bransby Williams' daughter, a near neighbor and an old friend, insisted that she should disregard the mystic diagnosis of Dr. Watson Councell and consult a specialist. (Bransby Williams was one of the old-timers for whom Sax had written two notable monologues, *Orange Blossom* and *The Pigtail of Li Fang Foo*. In the professional theatre of today, the monologue is a lost art; but both pieces are still, I believe, popular with amateurs and were reprinted as recently as 1954.)

Not too willingly, Elizabeth consented. The specialist, with little respect for the ideas of his alchemical colleague, promptly diagnosed appendicitis and she was rushed into hospital. But, on the operating table, he made an appalling discovery. His diagnosis had been correct, but so had that of Dr. Watson Councell. Unprepared, he now found himself with two operations to perform at the same time. Elizabeth came out of the anaesthetic to find him bathed in perspiration, trembling, and apparently feeling worse than she did.

The subsequent weeks in hospital were miserable. Not only was Sax "marooned" in New York and unable to reach her but, just at this time—May, 1926—came the great General Strike which paralyzed transport throughout England, so that neither friends nor relatives could come to her without great difficulty. She was worried, too, as to how she could pay the surgeon's fee. Funds were low. Neither Sax nor his father had the necessary money. Sax's agent turned up and offered to meet the bill with another of his famous "advances." But Elizabeth, instinctively, had begun to distrust him. She refused. Somehow, without his help, she did pay, but she no longer remembers how.

It had been the most serious illness of her lifetime, and she had had to face it alone. But, with her natural resilience, she was soon back on her feet. Spring drifted into summer and, with the coming of August, Sax returned from America.

His return was not, however, followed by any dramatic or immediate change in their relations. The mere fact that Sax had not chosen to avail himself of his offered "freedom" proved nothing other than that he was content to let things stand as before. So, for the time being, the state of affairs between them continued to be an uneasy truce rather than a reconciliation.

22

THE GREAT UNDERSTANDING

EVER SINCE THE DISCOVERY OF TUTAHKHAMEN'S TOMB IN 1922, SAX HAD been following subsequent developments with the keenest interest. Not that he subscribed to the popular superstitions which for a time made newspaper headlines. Though Sax's ideas on Egyptology were often considered fanciful by archaeologists, the "awful Curse of the Pharaohs" is conspicuously absent from his stories.

The episode, recently rounded off in the winter of 1925, after a long wrangle with the Egyptian Government, by the eventual exhumation of the royal mummy, had, however, pointed the way to a story. Now, back from New York, Sax settled down to work on *She Who Sleeps*, set partly in America and partly in Egypt. A mystery but not a crime story, it largely featured the excavation of an Egyptian tomb and proved to be one of his best works. In this story also, he produced one of his "composite" characters. The flamboyant and fascinating Danbazzar owes his physical appearance and personality to Benrimo, the producer of *The Eye of Siva*: but, at the same time, Sax was actually thinking more directly of his old friend, Harry Houdini.

Sax had no sooner finished this story and had been only a few months in England when he received an urgent call back to New York. *Collier's* had now suddenly decided, after an interval of almost ten years, to commission a revival of Dr. Fu Manchu, but for obvious reasons they preferred to have him write it on the spot.

With no very comfortable memories of the six months he had just spent there, he decided that, this time, he would take Elizabeth with him. So they set out on their first long journey together since their pre-war honeymoon, and it was from this point that the tempo of their lives, never exactly slow, began to increase rapidly.

The excitement commenced (without their knowing it at the time) before they left London. They had just taken their seats in the boat train when a messenger came pelting along the platform, shouting "Sax Rohmer!" and handed in to them a sealed package which, he explained breathlessly, contained publicity photographs to be called for in New York. Sax, whose luggage already contained one batch of pictures thrust upon him by his agent, and who hated personal publicity anyway, could not at all see why he should be given another lot; rather disgustedly, he thrust the package into a corner and, for the time being, thought no more about it.

The voyage in the *Franconia* was pleasant but uneventful. Elizabeth noted it chiefly for the somewhat spectacular entertainment provided by a light-fingered conjuror who not only managed to remove one man's wristwatch, without his knowledge, but actually to abstract another man's braces! At the shocking thought of what he might abstract from *them*, the ladies turned modestly pink.

To Sax, the Atlantic crossing was now so familiar as to provide him with no particular interest. But, on their arrival in New York, his curiosity was aroused by the untoward invasion of a squad of Customs officers who searched the ship from stem to stern. He contacted the Purser and asked the reason for this unusual activity. The Purser told him, in confidence, that they anticipated an attempt at smuggling a consignment of diamonds from London. But they failed to find anything.

Several hours later, when he had duly handed over the despised package of photographs to the messenger who came aboard to receive it, an uncomfortable idea occurred belatedly to Sax, and he made some inquiries. The second messenger had not come from his New York agents; no one knew anything about the second consignment of pictures. Like a character in one of his own stories, he had been made the unsuspecting carrier of the smuggled diamonds!

Sax had come to New York to write a Fu Manchu story for serialization in *Collier's*, and the attentive reader may note from the internal evidence of dates that *Daughter of Fu Manchu* is the story which he then began. But, by a curious turn of events, he was not destined to complete it for another three years. The current state of family finances was still distinctly tricky. They had, in fact, started out with little more than the necessary funds to get them to New York. But the fee offered by *Collier's* should, Sax imagined, be quite sufficiently adequate to provide comfortably for their support while he did the work and pay their fare home afterwards. He dutifully wrote the first episode, sent it across to the office, and then discovered, to his horror, that the editors did not propose to pay him until the completion of the entire series. They were now confronted by a major crisis.

"There is only one thing for it," Sax said finally. "I shall have to hold up the Fu Manchu and write some short stories and make them buy them."

Despite their experience, both of them were too modest to think about asking for an advance. Just as in the old days of Herne Hill, with the bailiffs at the door, there seemed no way out but an immediate job on a cash-sale basis. With that aim in mind, Sax recommenced work on a totally new series on the old "complete-in-one-issue" pattern, later to become famous as *The Emperor of America*.

Having finished the first story, he sent it along to *Collier's* by the hand of one Bobbie Denby, who sometimes acted as his liaison officer with the New York publishers. Whatever other qualifications Denby may have had for the job (and I have no reason to suppose that they were lacking) he could certainly claim that element of the bizarre appropriate to an emissary of Sax, for Denby had once been a dead man. He had, medically speaking, died during an operation and been subsequently revived by heart massage. The majority of those who suffer this weird but not unique experience know nothing about it at the time and, when questioned about their feelings during the period of "death," are only able to report complete unconsciousness. Denby, on the contrary, maintained that he had felt a sensation of floating upwards and shortly

172

found himself looking down on the roof of the hospital, at which moment he noted the unusual spectacle of a Chinese funeral procession passing along the street in front. Needless to say, this information was duly checked and proved correct!

Such, then, was the young man who now took Sax's story to *Collier's* office and very soon came back with it. The editors, who had bargained for Fu Manchu, were in no mood to accept substitutes. Faced with a situation which appeared desperate, Elizabeth decided that it was time for her to take a hand. As a general rule, she never interfered in matters concerning her husband's business—but Sax's genius began and ended with the ability to write first-class material. When that failed automatically to produce cash, he had no idea what to do next.

"Take it back to them!" she demanded, wrathfully. "Tell them they're crazy! It's a good story, and they've got to buy it!"

Denby, nonplussed by this kind of frontal assault, went back meekly to *Collier's* and reported. The editors were equally nonplussed but adamant. For the second time, Denby returned to the hotel to confess failure.

Sax began to weigh up the pros and cons of various methods of suicide. Elizabeth played her last card.

"I'm certain it's a good story!" she insisted (though she wasn't). "Go and tell *Collier's* that if it isn't a success they can deduct the money from the Fu Manchu contract!"

Denby made his third trip to the editorial offices. Tom Beck, the editor-in-chief, who liked and respected Sax, was now notably embarrassed. This was his first experience of dealing with Elizabeth, and it was not quite what he expected. With rather a bad grace, he gave way. The story was accepted and paid for. Thus enabled to put his emergency scheme into effect, Sax followed up the episode with six more, and the balance of their finances was restored.

In the meantime, *Liberty* (which had taken *Moon of Madness*) contracted to publish *She Who Sleeps* early the following year. As there is quite a strong theme of romance in this story, it was perhaps naturally suited to *Liberty*, but it would more probably have gone to *Collier's*, except for the fact the editors of the latter were still hankering after Fu Manchu and smarting from the ignominy of being fobbed off with *The Emperor of America*.

173

Out of trouble, but still in no position to finance a stay of several months while he completed a book-length novel, Sax said that he would go back to London and write the Fu Manchu story there.

And so ended Elizabeth's first visit to the United States—as memorable for the editors of *Collier's* as it had been for her. For Sax it had been a period of hard work and anxiety, compounded with the sadness of a personal loss. In the preceding August, he had sailed from New York leaving his old friend, Harry Houdini, in every evidence of health and professional prosperity. Shortly afterward, as the outcome of an absurd accident, Houdini was dead.

Collier's having been more or less placated with *The Emperor of America* stories, there remained no immediate urgency for *Daughter of Fu Manchu*. Sax felt that he had earned a rest, and his return to the dubious welcome of an English spring swiftly decided him to set sail once more for Madeira. Though he went alone, it is unlikely that he had any hopes of finding Nanette there nor did he. The adventures which befell him during his second visit to that island paradise were of a totally different nature.

Reclining in a long cane chair on the terrace of Reid's Hotel, and feeling at peace with the world, Sax flipped idly through the pages of an Italian magazine, looking at the pictures, since he did not read Italian, and doing so merely because it chanced to be the nearest thing lying around. Suddenly, to his astonishment, he saw his own name and realized that he was looking at a translation of one of his own stories for the sale of which he had neither been paid nor informed. All at once it was clear to him that Elizabeth's dark suspicions were well founded in fact. His agent, whom he had so long trusted implicitly, was playing a double game. These were matters which would have to be taken up when he returned to London.

But, in the interim, came other diversions to distract his thoughts more pleasantly. Came the day when, staring out across the bay, he saw a Yeoward Line vessel coming in to anchor, and recognized the *S. S. Aguila*. It was almost exactly three years since he had been aboard that same ship with Elizabeth, and listened to the strange story of Captain McPhee.

Was he still captain? Had other items in the Hindu's prophecy been fulfilled? The *S. S. Aguila* had barely dropped anchor before

174

Sax's boat was alongside. As he mounted the ladder, a familiar face looked down on him: Hop Ling. The Chinese steward nodded vigorously in answer to his inquiry.

"Yes, yes! Captain Mac have got. He velly glad look you, I t'nk." But, as Sax moved in the direction of McPhee's cabin, he laid a restraining hand on his arm. "Please—I telling you. You wise fl'end. What head t'ink face not say—alee same Chinee."

"What are you talking about?"

"You see Captain Mac, you not knowing him," Hop Ling said gravely. "Captain Mac long time velly sick."

Sax stared at him in an amazement not unmixed with horror. The words with which McPhee had last parted from him rose into his mind, stark and shocking, like lines graven on a tombstone. He would be gravely ill, his wife would leave him. . . .

"When—when did this happen?" he asked, a shade hoarsely.

Hop Ling considered. "I t'ink one year, maybe. He sick on next voyage, after missy run away."

Waiting to hear no more, Sax nodded tersely and hurried towards the cabin. He knocked, heard himself answered by a voice curiously dry and high-pitched, and thrust open the door. From the table opposite, a very old man rose unsteadily to greet him, a man of forty-five or six, who appeared to be at least eighty. Rather than lined with age, his skin was stretched taut over the bones like dried parchment. There was not a hair on his head, and his smile exposed not the uneven, tobacco-stained teeth of Captain McPhee but the ugly whiteness of dentures.

"I'll nae be needin' to tell ye," McPhee said tonelessly. "Like yon black imp o' Satan foretold it, in every cursed parteecular, it ha' come aboot."

His hands shook as he mixed the drinks. Somberly, as though relating the experience of some other person, he gave the details. On the bridge, one night, he had been all at once stricken by an unaccountable feeling of dizziness and, a moment later, collapsed. The following morning, he was in a delirium of high fever. The chief officer had taken the ship into Lisbon, where McPhee was hurried to hospital. The Portuguese doctors confessed the case to be outside their experience and, under medical care, he was shipped to the Liverpool Hospital for Tropical Medicine. There he had lain semi-conscious for three months with a temperature fantastically

175

above the hundred mark. Specialists had come from all over Europe to see this unique case—but none could give a name to it. Apart from the murderous temperature, which nothing could reduce, there was nothing identifiably wrong with him. But it was more than enough. Only McPhee's iron constitution saved him. All his hair had fallen out and all his teeth, and when the malady left him, as suddenly and inexplicably as it had struck, he was a human wreck.

"'Tis the blessed unsairtainty of life that gives a man hope," the captain said darkly. "That Indian deevil ha' taken it awa' from me—'twas his curse, I reckon, though I dinna ken why he did it. God help me!—for I ken His will down to the day of my ain death."

"Even *that*?" Sax asked quietly.

"Aye—the hour and the day and the manner of it. But I'll nae tell ye that."

Sax left the ship in a more sober frame of mind than that in which he had boarded it. To a student of the occult, he supposed, his friend's fate should have been interesting, even satisfying, but he was too much the humanist not to be oppressed by a sense of tragedy.

Hop Ling accompanied him to the rail.

"Look after him!" Sax said fiercely. "He needs it. No more of your tricks, now. Understand?"

The steward nodded. "Yes, yes. Me savvy. Long time velly solly for Captain Mac. Bhobbery all finish now. Captain Mac no more curse Hop Ling. Hop Ling no more spittee in whisky!"

"What?" Sax gasped. "You mean, you . . ."

But Hop Ling had vanished.

Three weeks later, when he came back to London, Sax did not immediately return to Braemar House, but moved into a service flat in Piccadilly. This was due to rather peculiar circumstances in no way connected with his marital difficulties. Like almost every other writer of international standing, he was now having trouble with the tax authorities. It is no news to anyone that the tax collecting machinery of any government, democratic or otherwise, operates, at best, with a complete disregard for humanity and, at worst, with very little regard for common sense. In the late 1920's, particularly, it was by no means unusual for celebrities whose income varied precariously to find themselves faced with demands for substantial back-payments on sums long since spent, during lean periods in which they earned nothing. Not a few had been driven to leave England and take up residence in France.

At the same time, Sax's position was being aggravated by underhand dealings, the full extent of which he did not yet suspect. Almost incredulously, he was only just then coming to realize that, apart from all the rest, he was being pursued for taxes on sums of money which his agent had pocketed. So far as the American side of his business was concerned, the negotiation of his stories had, luckily, been in the hands of reputable agents from the beginning. But, having not the slightest idea how otherwise to cope with questions of taxation, Sax had, in addition, entrusted his financial affairs to two separate advisers, one in London, and one in New York, neither of whom, as it now appears, carried out his duties with notable honesty.

From these worthies he had been given to understand (incorrectly) that he was liable to simultaneous taxation in two countries and, to avoid this, one or the other (I am uncertain which) had come up with the slightly lunatic suggestion that he should declare himself officially resident in Madeira and, for the time being, keep clear of his own property in London.

This, then, was the reason for Sax's temporary occupation of the Piccadilly apartment. Romantic motives were lacking—but, with the opportunity to hand, temptation was not far distant. Once again, Sax's fatal inability to accept sex without involvement betrayed him, and he was no sooner in the new apartment than he renewed the holiday affair with Nanette.

Moon of Madness, the story resulting from that brief encounter, was currently on the bookstalls; Nanette was no doubt suitably flattered, and the fire of her earlier infatuation easily fanned into flame. Lacking evidence, I hesitate to allot the responsibility to either, but it is equally likely that, prompted by the appearance of the story, it was she who was the prime mover. At all events, clandestine visits commenced and, as usual, were very soon discovered.

This time it happened simply that Elizabeth, in all innocence, had gone one afternoon to the flat in Piccadilly to deliver correspondence addressed to Sax at Braemar House. Obtaining no answer to her ring, she supposed him to be out and would have gone away again, leaving the letters with the hall porter, save for the chance that, just then, a chambermaid came down the passage. Struck by what seemed to be a good idea, Elizabeth asked her to open the door with her pass-key, so that she could leave the letters inside. But, when the chambermaid tried to do so, the door proved to be fastened from within. It was now evident enough that the place was occupied. The chambermaid, scarlet with embarrassment, made a hasty retreat. Elizabeth stayed where she was, repeated her ring and announced, calmly but forcefully through the closed door: "I know you're in there, so you might as well come out, Sax!"

Sax, knowing that she would quite likely call the fire brigade if he didn't come out, had really no option. After a short interval, he appeared at the door, fully dressed but artistically untidy.

"I was in bed . . ." he said defensively.

"I know!" Elizabeth said grimly. "What I want to know is who with!"

She thrust her way through towards the bedroom. But she did not have to enter it, for at that moment Nanette came out, likewise fully dressed to the ultimate, hopefully innocent limit of having her hat on. One glance at her was sufficient to assure Elizabeth, to her secret relief, that this time she was not dealing with a professional seductress. She did not dignify the affair with the serious consideration that she had given to the case of Eve. She put Nanette to flight with one well-directed slap, told Sax she would divorce him, slapped him too, and stalked out.

The outcome was somewhat ironic. Actually in less danger of divorce over Nanette (whom Elizabeth refused to take seriously) than he had been during his long-drawn-out dalliance with Eve, Sax jumped to the conclusion that he had at last gone too far—she really meant it. After spending some hours working himself up to a crescendo of panic, he arrived at Braemar House sometime past midnight, where it was now his turn to clamor at a locked door, feverishly seeking admission.

Elizabeth let him in and was deluged with a flood of pleas for forgiveness. Sax, brought to face the reality of a final parting, was desperate. He was so far overwrought that he literally went down on his knees to her. This was altogether too much for Elizabeth's sense of humor. She burst out laughing, and said: "Would you like a glass of beer?"

Sax said that he would and, in this mundane manner, some semblance of sanity was restored to the conversation. Nevertheless, he continued to protest his willingness to accept any terms she cared to name for the continuation of their partnership. Recognizing that he was in earnest, Elizabeth seized her chance to strike a hard bargain. She agreed to a fresh start on the understanding that, in future, she should receive half of everything that he earned—and, unhesitating, Sax accepted.

Coming from Elizabeth, who cared so little for worldly wealth, such a demand seems unexpectedly shocking. In actual fact, it was a demand dictated not by any mercenary motives, but by the unselfish good sense of a woman in love. In later years, Sax must often have thought of a certain episode in his favorite book, *The Thousand Nights and a Night*. It was the story of a wise and virtuous girl who, falling in love with a spendthrift young man, demeaned herself to extort money from him on every occasion, with the unique object of supporting him when, inevitably, he became ruined. Elizabeth knew her man. Over the next ten years, while Sax spent every penny that came into his hands, she saved twenty-five thousand pounds and spent the lot to keep his dreamworld alive though the grim years of the Second World War.

Extravagant as were his promises to reform, Sax was sincere. Although it was long before Elizabeth could really bring herself to believe it, he never again strayed from the path of moral rectitude. Spendthrift and unpredictable he remained—such was his character—but in deed as well as in heart he kept faith with her. Understandably, perhaps, they never regained the passionate relationship of their youth, yet, as the years passed, understanding and affection deepened to something finer and more enduring, so that, today, Elizabeth can still say, gently but firmly, "I wouldn't have had him any different from what he was. I could never have lived with anybody else."

Coincidentally or significantly, as you please, the seven years' bad luck of the broken mirror had expired.

23

THE JACKPOT

ACTING UPON HIS CHANCE DISCOVERY OF THE UNAUTHORIZED DISPOSAL of Italian translation rights, Sax duly took up the matter with his agent. The latter could give no satisfactory explanation, and furthermore declined to hand over the cash or any other sums outstanding. Judged by his later behavior, when the case ultimately came to court, he appears not only to have acted dishonestly but even to have become a trifle irrational.

Sax shelved the dispute for the time being, hating the idea of litigation and hoping that some more amicable settlement might presently be achieved. But, naturally enough, he thereupon terminated the agency; and so ended a fifteen-year partnership which, if it had seemed to bring him some profit, had likewise brought him losses impossible afterwards to assess. How much his work really earned during that period, neither Sax nor anyone else ever discovered.

Some months later, the British side of Sax's literary affairs was put in the hands of A. P. Watt & Son, and this firm subsequently served as his agents for more than thirty years.

With a little time still to spare before recommencing work on *Daughter of Fu Manchu*, a second visit to Berlin came next on the program, and this time Elizabeth went along. Henceforth, she was to accompany Sax on all his travels.

They had a fairly boisterous time in the German capital. At

a sizeable party of dignitaries in the Adlon Hotel, Sax was introduced to General von Secht, former head of the Kaiser's military intelligence service. The two veterans who had fought in opposite camps took an instant liking to each other. They were still swapping reminiscences when the party broke up, and once again Elizabeth was left with a double bedroom to herself. True to form, Sax and the General disappeared into the nightclub district and kept up their tabletop warfare till dawn.

Partly for pleasure and partly for business, Sax and Elizabeth investigated the current state of the theatre in Germany. The offerings included one show in which every girl in the company was nude. This proved too much for Elizabeth, who walked out. Sax, apparently, found nothing to object to. He was, however, devastated on a later occasion by the act of a male comic who, with his face set in a mask of misery, intoned his lines in an interminable monotone, while the audience howled with laughter.

"I went out to the bar and had a drink," Sax said, "and when I came back, some twenty minutes later, he was still at it!" The Teutonic sense of humor remained a mystery to him ever after.

The purpose of Sax's visit to Berlin was chiefly theatrical, for he hoped to negotiate the staging of *Wulfheim* in a German translation. This strange play (or masque, as he preferred to call it) had a theme largely concerned with the forbidden topic of incest, for which reason alone it was clearly not acceptable in England or America. Sax hoped that the Germans might display a broader outlook.

They did. Max Reinhardt, who had already gained a notable reputation for the production of remarkable plays, found *Wulfheim* intriguing. Sax left Berlin with the script under translation and a contract for presentation seemingly to follow.

Several weeks passed, at the end of which some of the Germans came over to London for a return visit, among them Reinhard Rijke, who had done the translation. This meant a special, top-level party at Braemar House which Elizabeth had some cause to remember. The cook got roaring drunk on champagne and, instead of playing the gracious hostess, Elizabeth found herself preparing the dinner with her own hands and the assistance of the ex-cook refugee from Clifford Street. Back to the sink!

Prospects continued to look bright for *Wulfheim*. Yet it was

181

not destined to reach the stage. The Weimar Republic was already crumbling. Adolf Hitler had thirty thousand uniformed storm-troopers on parade at Nuremberg. Amid the political chaos and civil unrest of those times, the nation had no leisure for artistic experiments in the theatre. Max Reinhardt never got around to producing *Wulfheim*; only a few more years were to pass before he himself would become a fugitive from the Nazi terror.

Since the date of her operation, now some eighteen months distant, Elizabeth's life had been anything but restful, so that she found herself still suffering the after-effects. It was suggested that she should return to Germany and take treatments at Baden-Baden. Sax, who had not previously been in that part of the world, readily agreed to accompany her and preparations for their trip were under way in the spring of the next year (1928) when a rather strange interruption took place.

Sax once told me the story himself, so I am able to give his version of it authentically, without having to deduce it from the several newspaper accounts which followed. He was, he said, alone in the flat and making himself a cup of tea in the kitchen when the doorbell rang and, answering it, he was considerably surprised to find himself face to face with Kenneth Littauer, the fiction editor of *Collier's*, whom he had last seen in New York. He was even more surprised when Littauer told him that he had been instructed to cross the Atlantic for the purpose of inducing him to recommence writing *The Emperor of America* stories. These stories, which Elizabeth had virtually forced on them against their will, had proved so popular with readers that the editors were now snowed under with letters asking for more.

On the face of it, this might appear gratifying. Sax, however, was far from delighted. Personally, he thought the series was rubbish, a mere piece of hack writing that he had been compelled to do in order to escape from a difficult situation; he had no desire at all to continue it. Ironically, the position was now directly reversed: it was he who wanted to write about Fu Manchu and *Collier's* who preferred *The Emperor of America*.

"All right," Sax said, after some argument. "I'll do it if you pay me £400 for each story!"

This was just double the amount offered, and he felt confident that they wouldn't rise to it. Littauer blinked and asked if he might use the telephone. Evidently determined to show the recalcitrant Englishman how business was done in the States, he put in a call to New York and waited there till it came through. Then he spoke briefly to his fellow-editors and turned back triumphantly to Sax.

"We will pay it!" he said. "When can you start?"

A battle for the face-saving last word followed.

"In that case," Sax said, "I'll start now."

"And I'll stay till you finish!" said Littauer.

Elizabeth came home to find the Baden-Baden trip postponed and her husband confined to his desk. Littauer had gone off to the Savoy, where he was registered. But, in due course, he turned up again to see how the work was progressing. Falling an easy victim to Elizabeth's culinary skill, he thereafter scorned supper at the Savoy and came in every night to read over what Sax had written—and eat kippers.

Sax worked rapidly, but the magazine was in a fever of impatience to feature the resumed series, and the close deadline required left no margin for delays in the post. When the first episode was completed, he and Littauer took the six-thousand-word manuscript to the Western Union office, and sat there all night while the entire thing, including paragraphs and punctuation, was sent out over the Atlantic cable. It cost *Collier's* a further £130 in cable charges, but the publicity which they obtained was probably worth it. Such a thing had never before been done in the history of either fiction or the telegraph. I should also imagine that it was never done again.

It was in this fashion that *The Emperor of America* series, extended by five more episodes, became a book-length novel subsequently added to Sax's imposing list of hard-cover publications. What is more, Sax—notorious for his lack of business sense—had innocently put over a deal (by trying to avoid it!) which made him for a time the most highly-paid fiction writer in the world.

The unwelcome but lucrative commission carried out, and the appearance of Fu Manchu's daughter again indefinitely put off, Sax and Elizabeth set out for Baden-Baden. It was a healthy, open-air holiday which they both needed, and from which both of them profited. They went almost daily for long walks in the aptly-named Black Forest, deeply impressed by the somber grandeur of that vast, funereal solitude. Here, as never in Berlin, Sax felt the legendary touch of Gothic horror; the trees whispered to him with the eerie voice of tradition. Here, as in Egypt, he rubbed shoulders with pagan deities and myths older than Christianity—Wotan and Siegfried, the Erlkönig, and the huntsmen who ride through the sky. His imagination was stimulated and stirred. Vaguely, the beginnings of a story began to take shape.

Elizabeth, in the meantime, was having adventures of her own—or, rather, trying not to have them. In accordance with medical advice, she had put herself in the hands of a certain Dr. Schacht, who prescribed a series of injections. But it was not long before she discovered that he had taken a fancy to her. He was not in the least reticent about it. He openly proposed an affair, and was greatly incensed when she refused.

Dr. Schacht was a wild-looking character who, evidently, was used to getting what he wanted. Elizabeth became afraid of him, and insisted that Sax accompany her whenever she went to his surgery. This enraged Schacht to the limit. "Why do you bring your husband?" he whispered furiously, giving her a particularly painful jab with the needle. Then he added, dramatically, "I am not a man who forgets insult!" And, indeed, he was not. Later, when the brother of the same Dr. Schacht became Hitler's Finance Minister, the German editions of all Sax's books were taken off the market, and the plates destroyed.

Although Sax's occult practices were mostly restricted to the kind of parlor magic which his friends expected of him, he nevertheless felt a sincere curiousity about the Unseen which time did not diminish. True, he was no longer inclined to turn his home into an alchemist's workshop with experiments to make sea-water burn, but Elizabeth had ample evidence that, even at Braemar House, he had not entirely given up his explorations.

She recalls, with some vividness, a night when, waking to find herself alone, as so often in the past, she had got up to look for her missing husband. This time she discovered him not in the company of Bohemian friends but alone in his study, with the Egyptian *Book of the Dead* open on the desk before him. He was holding aloft a peculiarly-shaped instrument and muttering some kind of conjuration.

"Sax!" she exclaimed. "What *are* you doing?"

He did not tell her, but afterwards she concluded that he was probably trying to establish contact with the departed Houdini.

"Go away!" Sax said fiercely. "You'll break the spell!"

"I will not go away!" Elizabeth said, with equal ferocity. "If you carry on like this you'll go barmy!"

Sax conceded that the spell was broken and ungraciously allowed himself to be conducted back to bed.

In twenty years of married life with Sax, Elizabeth had gained enough personal knowledge of such practices to be scared of them. During the early days, she had often entertained company, telling fortunes by the cards, and though, for the most part, such exercises had been no more than play-acting, there were times when she had displayed inexplicable glimpses into the future. Sax, greatly intrigued, tried to encourage her by a gift of Tarot cards—at that time, I believe, their sale was illegal in England—as a substitute for the ordinary playing cards.

Elizabeth made an occasional use of these cards for some years, to the alarm and stern disapproval of Dr. Watson Councell, who urged her to throw them away. Eventually she did, but not until she had frightened herself so badly that she wished she had taken his advice sooner. In five successive runs of the cards, she had seen the death of Sax (exactly as it later occurred), the war in Vietnam, and her own end.

Sax's attitude towards success was refreshingly different from that of many writers today, who seem to want to push opportunity to the limit. For Sax, a financial coup meant, as always, a breathing space in which to satisfy his creative urge on something more interesting, even if potentially less marketable. Although there could be no question of the fact that he could best make money as a novelist, the theatre continued to attract him strongly. On the stage, he might have the satisfaction of seeing the phantasmagoria of his imagination brought to life in a way that the printed word could not achieve, for the printed word, eminently satisfactory as it may be to the reader, gives back little to the writer.

It is not, then, surprising that the summer of 1928 found him once more at work on a stage play. The projected work was a three-act drama called *Secret Egypt* (not connected with the short-story collection *Tales of Secret Egypt*) and Sax began work on it in collaboration with Leon M. Lion. They started off well enough, and in very short time had achieved a breathtaking first act. But thereafter they stuck. Somehow, they could think of nothing strong enough to follow up that promising beginning. Finally, Leon M. Lion retired from the struggle.

"There's only one act!" he said. "And I make you a present of it!"

Sax, however, remained stubbornly determined to finish it. The Q Theatre, which had been closed for redecoration, was shortly to open and he had the offer of the first week for a try-out performance. As best he could, but still with misgivings, he completed acts two and three.

In his eagerness to get the thing staged, he even took a hand in the details of production and personally painted some of the scenery. As usual in the world of the theatre, it was a race against time, and one of his clearest recollections afterwards was of crawling about on a backcloth, outlining the enormous shapes of Egyptian gods and goddesses with a stick of charcoal, while the Q Theatre's man-of-all-work followed him up with a paintbrush. Elizabeth thinks that he probably spent too large a proportion of his endeavors on that kind of thing, and may be right. It is not uncommon for a writer to get bogged down by irrelevant details when in trouble with the main framework of his story.

At all events, *Secret Egypt* opened. D. A. Clarke-Smith, who had nobly acquitted himself in *The Eye of Siva*, was again playing a leading role. So far as Sax could make it so, the piece possessed all the required elements of exotic mystery and dramatic violence. He had done all that he could to inject interest into it, even to the extent of having the heroine flogged.

When the first interval arrived, visitors from the West End managements were enthusiastic. They assured him that the play would be a success. Sax smiled wryly and reserved judgment till they had seen the rest of it.

Towards the close of the last act, set in an excavator's hut, there was a minor stage disaster when, in the course of a fight, Ion Swinley (who had served with Sax in the Artists' Rifles) fell upon a camp bed which collapsed, apparently trapping him in the ruins. He got out of it, but Sax, viewing the mishap from the wings, felt it coldly symbolic. The enthusiastic visitors did not come back, and the play was not transferred to the West End. Surprisingly, perhaps, *Secret Egypt* nevertheless had good notices from the critics. Unfortunately, no copy of the script seems to have survived.

The year 1928 was packed with activity and no small degree of success for the Sax Rohmers. Having washed his hands of *Secret Egypt*, Sax settled down to write the story inspired by their visit to the Black Forest. Possibly the most far-ranging piece of fantasy that he ever attempted, this took shape as *The Day the World Ended*, a nice synthesis of crime detection with the apparently supernatural, giving way finally to an exotic exercise in science-fiction.

It was, beyond doubt, one of his best works. The tight, neatly dovetailed construction of the plot previews by some five or six years the polished, fully integrated type of novel towards which popular fiction had gradually been tending during the 1920's and which, in general, would become the literary achievement of the mid-1930's.

This precocious book, if I may so term it, has always been a favorite of mine and I have pleasant memories of finding my room decorated with John Richard Flanagan's black-and-white drawings, during the long period that I spent under the Sax Rohmers' hospitable roof. Flanagan illustrated all of Sax's stories for *Collier's* from 1929 to 1935, and Sax thought highly of his work. He never lost an opportunity to acquire the originals, and they formed a notable item of furnishing in his household.

In 1929 Paramount Pictures began work on the first talking film of a Sax Rohmer story, *The Mysterious Dr. Fu-Manchu*. It starred Warner Oland in the title role, and featured a young lady destined to achieve screen distinction in the 1930's: Jean Arthur. For the first time in their lives, Sax and Elizabeth actually found money coming in faster than they could spend it.

Over the years, Elizabeth had formed a nostalgic affection for the countryside, the kind of yearning for trees and verdant spaces that most keenly affects those whose lives have been mostly spent in the noisy hustle of a great city. At Braemar House, her appetite had been whetted rather than satisfied by their view over the pleasant prospect of Kensington Park Gardens.

Once, rising early on a spring morning, she had felt herself so irresistibly drawn that she had dared to go for a stroll along those sunny, well-kept paths, attired in bedroom slippers and a dressing-gown. Needless to say, she had not gone very far before a policeman appeared. Elizabeth agreed that her costume was unconventional, but politely inquired if it was in any way illegal. The policeman admitted, rather unwillingly, that it was not.

"Then I'm going for my walk!" Elizabeth said firmly.

"Oh!" said the constable; and, unable to think of anything else to day, added, "Mind if I come with you, then?"

"Not at all!" Elizabeth said sweetly.

So they walked round the park together, chatting idly, and finally a very puzzled policeman left her at her door.

Now, with money to spare, Elizabeth had a brilliant inspiration. She would build a cottage in the country, where she could lounge about the garden, clad or unclad as she wished, without the escort of officers of the law. It would be her special retreat, not that Sax would be barred from joining her there whenever he felt like it; but Sax, she imagined, would probably want to keep his finger on the pulse of the great metropolis, and prefer to spend most of his time in town.

Sax, with his usual unselfish co-operation on any project that he thought she wanted, readily agreed. Mrs. Wyatt, their erstwhile neighbor at Herne Hill and mother of the notorious Frank, had property at Lower Kingswood, outside Reigate, a convenient hour's journey from London. They leased the adjoining land from her and then, with no training in architecture but a wealth of natural talent, sat down to plan Elizabeth's dream cottage. Sax, brilliant in imagination and skilled with charcoal and crayon, conceived the exterior, and Elizabeth gave full rein to the flair for interior decoration which she had already displayed in their various premises in London.

When it was finished, the proposed cottage had the grace and warmth of a fairy tale, with that hint of the exotic inseparable from any work of Sax. They had a troublesome time finding a professional architect to translate the scheme into bricks and mortar: the majority of the professionals were sworn adherents to plans drawn from stock, and said that it could not be done. But eventually they found a man who was delighted by the challenge, and it was done. Unobtrusive yet unique, Lovelands Way was an exquisite gem set in the Surrey hills. And, while the finishing touches were being added, Sax and Elizabeth set off again on their travels to seek new adventures in their most ambitious journey to date, a three months' tour through the Middle East.

24

THE SYRIAN ADVENTURE

ON THIS MEMORABLE OCCASION, EGYPT WAS TO BE NO MORE THAN A
starting point. Leaving Cairo for a more leisurely re-exploration
on some future occasion, Sax and Elizabeth moved eastwards to
Port Tewfik. Here they paused to visit an old friend, Captain
George Winter, brother of that same Fred Winter who had accompanied Sax to Paris so many years before, during his researches for
The Romance of Sorcery. Captain Winter was a pilot in the service
of the Suez Canal Company, and from him Sax learned a number
of interesting and sinister facts concerning the slave traders of the
Red Sea.

The slave trade in the Middle East, said Captain Winter, was
not extinct. It had, in fact, been modernized. Slaves no longer
followed the weary trail across the desert from Darfur into Egypt;
nowadays, fast motorboats shipped them across to small ports in
the Hejaz, running without lights and dodging the naval patrols
maintained to intercept them. Thence the captives vanished into
the arid emptiness of Arabia, to be disposed of at the slave market
in Mecca or other secret places.

Sax noted the information and in due time put it to use in
writing *Yu'an Hee See Laughs*. The fact that such medieval bar-
barities could continue to exist, unchanged from the time of *The
Thousand Nights and a Night*, was no fanciful invention of his.
Not only did that despicable trade exist then, but it exists today.

Not long ago an adventurous team of cameramen using telescopic equipment succeeded in obtaining visual evidence of it.

East of the Suez Canal, Sax and Elizabeth knew that they would be venturing into a region where, under a shaky framework of quasi-European civilization, anything could still happen. Skirting the coast, the train brought them to Haifa. From that point, Nairn's transport service—in those days, virtually an armored caravan—carried them on to Damascus.

Damascus, the earlier capital of the Caliphs, retains altogether more of the perfume of the past than one can hope to detect in Baghdad. Seen from the Lebanon Hills in its setting of orchards and gardens, with the cracked domes and minarets of its ancient mosques made whole again by the healing sunlight, it is a city from an Arabian Nights fairytale, with justice retaining its proud title, the Jewel of the East.

Apart from mere sightseeing, Sax had a particular reason for his visit. One of the projects for which he hoped one day to find time was a biography of the Caliph Haroun al-Rashid. (Unfortunately, although he amassed a formidable pile of notes, he never did find time for it.) In the interests of this work, he was anxious to obtain access to the library of the Great Mosque, which was said to contain a number of records relating to the Caliph's reign.

Some of the information he wanted he obtained, but not all. The Moslem custodians were loath to supply an unbeliever with any information which, in their opinion, might be damaging to Haroun's character—and there was a good deal which undoubtedly was.

"Understandable!" Sax said dryly. "One might as well ask the chief librarian of the Vatican to produce the private diary of Alexander Borgia!"

In the pursuit of his inquiries, he secured an introduction to a rich and influential dignitary who lived in a sumptuous palace on the outskirts of the town. This was his first opportunity to visit such a household, and even if nothing else came of it, he felt that the visit would be worthwhile for its own sake. Aware, however, that it would offend Islamic custom to go there accompanied by his wife, he discreetly left Elizabeth at the hotel.

Presenting himself at a suitable hour of the morning, he gave his letters to the *bowwab* and was at once conducted into a small,

191

square courtyard pleasantly shaded by palm trees and enclosed on three sides by cloistered arches. Here the man indicated that Sax should wait, and vanished into the house, saying that his Excellency the Bey would appear shortly. That, at least, was what Sax thought he said (for Syrian Arabic differs from Egyptian to about the same degree that Spanish differs from Italian). After half an hour had passed, finding himself still alone, he was not so sure. Sax decided that the time had come to seek further advice. Either he had misunderstood the instructions of the *bowwab*, or the invisible Bey was as absent-minded as his old friend T. P. O'Connor.

Not a sound disturbed the stillness of the courtyard, save the gentle whisper of the fountain at the center; the place had the appearance of being deserted. Sax looked around, but could find no bell or any other means of attracting attention. Clapping his hands in what he supposed to be the approved fashion produced no result, and he felt it undignified to shout. There seemed, then, nothing for him to do but to explore until he came across some servant or other member of the Bey's no doubt sizeable entourage.

Striking off at random through the cloisters to his left, he entered a large salon, chiefly furnished with cushions and little inlaid coffee tables. It had the look of a room used for meetings, but at present it was unoccupied. So were the several smaller rooms beyond. A long corridor succeeded and, traversing this to the far end, he came to a ponderous door with ornate facings in brass. Knocking upon it to any useful effect would have required a hammer. He tried the handle, found that it turned smoothly to his touch, and thrust open the door.

Curtains of some diaphanous material billowed out in the draft, confusing and half enveloping him. He shouldered through them, took two steps beyond and halted—frozen by sheer horror. He had entered the *harem*!

The place was appointed and occupied in a manner which would not have disappointed a Hollywood scenic artist. Sax had a vague, turbulent impression of draped archways surrounding a circular pool the size of a hotel swimming pool—a flittering vision of brown-skinned female forms clothed in gauzy draperies, or not clothed at all. There seemed, to his startled eyes, to be at least fifty of them—though, later, he conceded that there were probably no more than a dozen.

192

A chorus of screams, yells, and giggles greeted his entry and the group split up like the seeds of a pomegranate dashed against a stone wall. Some vanished through the archways, some dived under the cushions. Splashes went up like shell-bursts, as four or five plunged into the pool. One, nearer than the rest, whose only apparel seemed to consist of an embroidered vest, snatched up the round brass top of a coffee table, scattering cups to perdition, and held it before her like a shield, regarding him from above it, open-mouthed and round-eyed.

For once, Sax felt no urge to appreciate the unveiled charms displayed before him. Seconds passed while he stood paralyzed by the enormity of his offence. Then he turned tail and bolted, slamming the door shut after him, and blundered unceremoniously through the intervening rooms to the courtyard, his only thought, now, to escape.

He arrived there precisely at the same moment that his dignified, white-bearded host entered from the opposite side.

"*Ahlan wa sahlan, ya khawagah*!" ("May joy be with you, sir!")

With no suspicion of the unforgivable dishonor to which his household had been subjected, the Bey greeted him warmly and, resting his hand on Sax's shoulder, led him into a room furnished in European style. Profuse in his welcome, he yet made no reference to his tardy appearance. The East remains timeless, in more senses than one.

The ensuing leisurely routine of coffee and perfumed cigarettes was the longest and most anxious half hour of Sax's life. His mission forgotten, he could think of nothing but scimitars and bowstrings. Straining his ears for the first outcry—the commencement of the uproar which he anticipated with every passing moment—he was scarcely conscious of what his host was saying. Yet nothing happened. A sense of sportsmanship was evidently not lacking among the other enviable attributes of the *harem* ladies, for it seems that they never told on him.

With time enough to explore Damascus at will, Sax and Elizabeth formed a particular affection for the bazaar quarter. Less tailored to the tourist than Cairo's Khan Khalil, The Street Called Straight retains to this day something of the authentic atmosphere which came into being with the first Caliphs. In those distant times, Damascus was already old. When and by whom it was built, no one knows; but it is believed to be the oldest continuously inhabited city in the world, dating back perhaps six thousand years.

Recent events which have brought the turmoil of revolution and war to that ancient capital would have saddened Sax immeasurably, for here, he felt, he first became conscious of the real meaning of peace. Even in the busy activity of the bazaars there was, paradoxically, a sense of repose. Afterwards, he could always go back there in spirit, remembering with delight the interplay of sun and shade in the alleyways of little open-fronted shops protected by striped awnings, the sweet, musky odors in the Street of the Perfumers, the gurgle of the water-pipes smoked by the leisurely shopkeepers, the metallic chatter of tiny hammers in the Street of the Coppersmiths. Sax and Elizabeth visited the bazaars often and made many purchases.

"In Damascus, you run less risk of being palmed off with a British-made fake than you do in Cairo," Sax told me. "But there is only one way to be certain. Have the man make it for you, and watch him begin!"

One of the pieces which he thus obtained was a magnificent wooden coffer, intricately inlaid with ivory and white metal, which occupied a prominent place in his study. Sax was amused when I priced it in hundreds of pounds. Those were still the days when almost incredible differences in the world's currencies made princes of European travellers. He said that it had cost him four pounds and ten shillings.

When at length the scheduled time of departure arrived, it was Sax's intention to strike northwards to Aleppo, returning to Europe by the long overland route, via Istanbul. But the plan included a detour en route, westwards to Baalbek.

For more than twenty-five centuries, Baalbek held the curious distinction of being a religious center sacred in turn to Greeks, Romans, Christians and Moslems, and founded on the ruins of a faith yet more remote, that of the Phoenicians. The great court with its vast flight of steps flanked by an imposing colonnade marks the site of the Roman temple of Jupiter Ammon, but it was originally the site of the little-known rites and ceremonies of the god Baal.

194

Sax arrived to find a German team of archaeologists actually at work there, and was fortunate enough to make the acquaintance of a local historian whose theories, unexpectedly, proved to be at least as colorful as his own. This man believed not only that the place had been the principal center for the worship of Baal during the splendor of Babylon, but maintained that an uninterrupted line of priests and priestesses had preserved the secret traditions of the ancient worship throughout the ages, and that it still existed. Founded on fact or fancy, this was obviously material for a story. Shortly afterwards it emerged as "Fires of Baal," one of Sax's more notable short stories.

From Baalbek, they had planned to make their way to Aleppo by train. It chanced, however, that during their short stay they became acquainted with a young Syrian who said that he himself was going there by road and suggested that they might like to accompany him. It was an attractive offer. From the train, coming from Damascus, they had been able to obtain some slight idea of the beauty of the landscape, so that the prospect of motoring through those lovely valleys and hills had an irresistible appeal. The Syrian assured them that his chauffeur knew the route and that, by starting early, they could reach Aleppo before dusk. Sax and Elizabeth accepted—and thereupon entered into one of the strangest and, at times, most alarming episodes of their career. The journey began auspiciously enough. Following the half-obliterated traces of an ancient caravan route, for there were no proper roads, the way lay across a wilderness of wild flowers so dense as to resemble a vast prayer carpet, extending as far as the eye could reach to the snow-capped mountains. Villages occurred at rare intervals, little enclosures of mud huts invariably built on mounds, surrounded by cultivated land.

The party halted for a picnic lunch by a small stream near a prosperous-looking cornfield. While they ate, from somewhere amongst the corn, there appeared a small Arab boy. He said nothing but lay motionless, elbows on the ground, his chin in his palms, only three yards from the car, watching them with great interest. Elizabeth gave him a slice of melon, which he accepted and ate without comment. When lunch was over and preparations for departure commenced, he disappeared as unobtrusively as he had come. And, for the time being, none of them thought further of

195

the matter.

As the afternoon wore on, the varicolored expanse of wild flowers gave way to a deep red carpet of poppies, then to grazing land. Save for the figure of an occasional shepherd, the whole of Syria seemed to be unoccupied, for whenever they passed a village on a mound, not a soul was to be seen.

In the shadow of a ruin, apparently Roman and mantled in flowers, they made a second break for tea. An hour later, still many miles south of Aleppo, they forded a stream in which the water came above the axles, and failed to find any continuation of the track on the other side. Following a hurried consultation with his Syrian master, the chauffeur turned the car about and, having driven them back across the stream, admitted with reluctance that he had lost the way.

"It was," Sax observed dryly, "a situation of some interest."

The road or bridle-path—for it had never amounted to anything more—had vanished; but several miles to the east might be discerned the telegraph poles which marked the course of the railroad. With commendable logic, Sax pointed out that it must merely be necessary, so far as the nature of the country allowed, to keep it in sight and follow a parallel course.

This worked very well until they came to a gulley through some low hills, which proved perilous going for a car. They managed it, but emerged to find themselves looking down upon another red carpet and no further sign of the guiding telegraph poles. This was more than a little disquieting. Nevertheless, it was clear that the railroad must lie somewhere to the east, so the obvious thing to do was to bear eastwards till they came across it.

Several minor mishaps interfered with the smooth execution of this plan. Owing to the character of the route, a suitcase fell off, unnoticed, and they had to go back two miles for it. By the time they found it, dusk was drawing near.

In another half hour, with little hope now of finding the railroad unless they should chance directly upon it, they sighted a mound more imposing than any they had passed hitherto. Upon it clustered a considerable township. There was a high tower, and what looked like the minaret of a mosque. The place was apparently surrounded by a strong stone wall. This appeared promising, but a quick conference with the chauffeur, whose knowledge of the district now seemed, at best, dubious, produced only vague and disturbing replies. He said he *thought* it was the headquarters of a powerful sheikh. But in view of recent disturbances in the neighborhood, and knowing nothing of the sheikh's sympathies, he advocated a wide detour.

Westwards, around the fringe of cultivated land, a sketchy path led presently to the semblance of a road. Along this they headed north again. Now the sun had already begun to sink below the snow-caps of the western mountains, to be followed by a quick curtain of darkness. Simultaneously, Elizabeth's fingers closed hard on Sax's arm.

"My God! Look!"

Fifty yards ahead, a tall, dusky man stood, rifle in hand, barring the path. A second and a third man sprang out right and left of him.

"It's a hold-up!" Elizabeth gasped.

Sax glanced anxiously at their host, raising inquiring eyebrows.

"I am not too sure she is not right!" the Syrian said mournfully. "These men wear French uniforms, but it may be a trick. I know nothing of this sheikh."

Alarming from the outset, the situation became increasingly so in its immediate developments. The uniformed men appeared to speak no language but Turkish, with which no member of the party was acquainted. By signs they indicated, clearly enough, that they had orders to intercept and escort them, whither or for what purpose remained obscure.

There was nothing to do but acquiesce. An armed man on either running-board, and the third man leading the way, they drove slowly eastwards, mounting a steep path towards the walled town. Elizabeth moved closer to Sax, her hand clasped tightly in his. Similar raids, which sometimes resulted in travellers losing all their belongings, were not uncommon.

"That little Arab boy—" she whispered. "You remember? He sent the news ahead! They were *waiting* for us!"

A cordial and impressive reception awaited them at the great gate, where they arrived to find the principal citizens of the town assembled, gravely seated on Victorian chairs upholstered in red plush, not that even this latter detail of unanticipated respectability did much to allay the fears of Elizabeth.

"They're going to hold us to ransom!" she declared.

To their considerable relief, a young French officer suddenly appeared. (Syria, formerly a part of the Turkish Empire, was at that time a mandated territory, under the administration of France.) This, he explained, was Sherak al-Oman, the last military outpost south of Aleppo.

The mystery was swiftly elucidated. When Sax and Elizabeth failed to arrive on the train by which they had originally intended to travel (but which they had expected to outdistance), the hotel manager in Aleppo had communicated by telephone with Baalbek, and thus learned that they were coming by car. Allowing time for their arrival, he had presently grown anxious. Though misplaced, Elizabeth's fears of a hold-up by bandits were far from illusory. There *were* bandits out on the road. Knowing such to be the case, the hotel manager had finally got in touch with the French commandant, and orders were promptly dispatched to the officer in charge at Sherak al-Oman to send out men in all directions and intercept any car proceeding north.

Having explained this much, the young Frenchman saluted punctiliously and departed, leaving them to the care of the Sheikh, a portly man, black moustached, wearing a frock coat and a fez. Seemingly delighted at this unique opportunity of entertaining distinguished visitors, he gave them a royal welcome.

Poetic justice was done. The Arabian Nights fantasy which Sax had so long courted and exploited had finally caught up with him and, for the remainder of the night, he enjoyed and suffered by turns the varied fortunes of a hospitality worthy of his beloved Haroun al-Rashid. Through the courtyard of the Sheikh's house, a dreamlike vision of twinkling lights, now that dusk had fallen, the party was conducted up a long open staircase to the guest rooms. Sax and Elizabeth found themselves in a room with two beds upon which, in anticipation of their arrival (and despite the heat of the night) had been spread an assortment of coverlets ranging from eiderdowns to leopard skins.

Elizabeth, travel-stained and weary, had to bow to the fact that, in the thirsty desert, ablutions were religious rather than hygienic. She was invited to hold her hands over a silver bowl held by a fierce-looking person robed in white, whilst his opposite num-

198

ber poured water from an ewer.

Afterwards, they sat down to a dinner party of sixteen (at which she was the only woman present) in a long, narrow apartment, one side of which was entirely occupied by latticed windows overlooking a main street of the town. The Sheikh took the head of a huge table, with some white-bearded celebrity, possibly the *imam* of the mosque, to his right, Sax and Elizabeth to his left. The service was carried out by men ceremonially robed, with daggers in their girdles.

There followed what was, for Sax, a terrifying experience. Sax was not gastronomically adventurous. If the truth be told, his youthful hardships had left him with an incurable preference for cheese and beer. Now he was to be confronted by a banquet of exotic delicacies, served in quantities to appal the staunchest appetite. The Sheikh, a monstrous trencherman, served his distinguished guests with his own hands, and Sax knew that to refuse anything offered would be regarded as a gross insult. His despair growing greater as course succeeded course, he plowed his way through a meal which, afterwards, he could only liken to a promiscuous sampling of face cream, perfume and toilet soap. The local bread had the consistency of clay. Cheese there was, but not of the kind that he knew. Made from sheep's milk, it appeared as a glutinous substance to be wound around the forefinger and lowered into the mouth. Pieces of meat, apparently goat, floated in a thick gravy, intensely flavored with something like saffron.

They ate to the accompaniment of a subdued buzz of voices. Scores of curious eyes were peering in at the latticed windows. Later, Sax learned that not only were they the first European visitors to enter the town in four years, but that no Englishwoman had ever been seen there before. Elizabeth was the chief exhibit.

When the meal was at last over, succeeded by excellent coffee and cigarettes, the Sheikh took them on a tour of his strange capital, escorted by eight or ten local notabilities and four lantern-bearers. They visited a house of entertainment, where a dancer danced for them. The ancient watchtower, inspected by moonlight and lantern light, proved to be of Roman origin. They shed their shoes and entered the mosque.

Back at the premises of their host, Elizabeth was invited to the *harem* for an interview with the Sheikh's favorite wife. In the meantime, Sax strolled round the courtyard, accompanied by the efficient Romanian woman who had been attached to them as interpreter, and a ceremoniously-robed young man, the son of some neighboring and wealthy sheikh, who was engaged to marry a daughter of their host. Sax found him a handsome fellow, but, in character, completely Oriental: he had never seen his future wife. Elizabeth, returning from the *harem*, reported that she had met the daughter, who had been educated at a French convent in Damascus and spoke perfect French. Tolerant as he was, Sax could not help but see something slightly barbarous in the situation so complacently accepted by both parties. After her seemingly liberal education, in tranquil obedience to the ancient precepts of Mohammed, the Sheikh's daughter had calmly returned to the *harem*, to be affianced to a man who had no Western culture and whom she had not even met.

In Sherak al-Oman, the manners and customs of the Caliphs continued to reign undisturbed by time. And ere they retired for the night, it was Elizabeth's lot to encounter yet another homely example. Irrespective of persons, there comes a time when human necessity must be served and, nothing having been previously said on this important subject, Elizabeth was finally compelled to inquire the whereabouts of the Ladies' Room. Though the language of the household was principally that of the old empire, Turkish, Sax's Egyptian Arabic was luckily adequate. Her wishes made known, one of the white-robed men lit a lantern and beckoned her to follow. He led her down the staircase, through the courtyard and out upon a patch of wasteland. Here, lifting the lantern on high, he nonchalantly revealed a noisome hole dug in the sand, and stood waiting. No amount of persuasion could induce him to go away until he had escorted her safely back to her room. Elizabeth decided that she liked Syrian toilet habits as little as Sax liked the cooking.

Protected by netting, and eschewing the surplus of exotic bedding, they spent a peaceful night under the roof of Islam. Their Syrian friend, doomed to sleep on a divan in the saloon adjoining, paid his penalty for losing them in the desert: he was nearly eaten alive by mosquitoes.

Someone has remarked that "an adventure is never an adventure while it is going on." Once again, Sax had encountered

200

experiences which, considered in retrospect, he would not have wished to miss. Once again, chance had given him an opportunity to penetrate the veil, which so few before him had done, and fewer still who were able to relate what they saw to such good effect.

"I salute the Sheikh of Sherak al-Oman!" Sax wrote. "He upholds the green banner of Islam in a land surrounded by infidels."

Aleppo was reached the next day with no further mishap. Thence the Sax Rohmers embarked on the long and tiring journey via the Taurus Express, through to Istanbul. They found this former capital of a shattered empire rather a sorry sight, already half submerged under a wave of Europeanization. Neither was much impressed.

But before they left, Elizabeth managed to get herself into mischief again. Not even the brilliance of morning sunlight in Turkey could induce Sax to early rising so, greatly daring, Elizabeth ventured forth into the old city, unaccompanied. Here she presently came upon the disgusting spectacle of a ragged urchin belaboring a diminutive donkey with a thick stick. Elizabeth hated donkeys, but not as much as she deplored cruelty. Unable to register an effective protest in the language, she forthwith snatched the stick from the boy's hand and smacked *him* with it.

In seconds, she was surrounded by a vociferous crowd, some cheering, some shouting abuse, and the uproar swelled rapidly to the dimensions of a riot. It required the intervention of a policeman to extricate her. Worse was to follow. The officer of the law was bewildered and displeased. Their lack of a common language did nothing to detract from the eloquence of his hands, and Elizabeth soon gathered that, far from being rescued, she was on the verge of being arrested. With the arrival of a second policeman, the situation deteriorated—for, though this one spoke English, he was evidently a fanatic in the direct line of descent from Barbarossa.

On hearing Elizabeth's explanation, he became so excited that the waxed points of his moustache seemed to emit sparks. Even if the boy had assulted his donkey—and why not?—it was his, wasn't it?—it was clear that she had assulted the boy, and incited a major disturbance of the peace. For any local girl, that would mean a quick visit to the lock-up, skirt and panties off, and a damned good hiding. There was no good reason why a foreigner shouldn't be treated likewise.

Elizabeth thought that he looked as if he meant it, and if he did mean it, indignant protests to the British Consul would not much interest her afterwards. She began to feel scared. But at this promising moment, an enterprising bystander stole the first policeman's revolver and, in the renewed bedlam, Elizabeth discreetly vanished.

Sax was rather disappointed. "In the interests of experience," he said glumly, "*I* had to bolt down the eye of a sheep!"

From the inchoate, half-world of Turkey, as yet struggling to impose a new culture on the ashes of the old, they moved on to Venice. Here nothing untoward happened, but Sax did not lack for atmosphere. The only complaint that a writer may make of Venice is that, factually reported, it presents a picture less credible than his wildest imaginings. The short story, "At the Palace da Nostra," resulted from this visit. The same visit also contributed the Venetian settings for a part of *The Drums of Fu Manchu*, written some years later.

Sax had now driven as far eastwards as his wanderlust would ever take him, a fact which may surprise readers who tend, erroneously, to associate his work with the Far East. But a more careful examination shows that, in fact, he rarely stepped outside those borders within which he had personal knowledge and experience. Fantastic as some of his stories' backgrounds may appear, Sax knew that they existed. He had seen them.

Rewarding as the journey may have been, Elizabeth was no doubt grateful for a spell of peace and comfort in her Surrey dream-cottage.

25

CARIBBEAN AFRICA

BOTH FINANCIALLY AND ARTISTICALLY, THE NEXT TEN YEARS WERE TO constitute the peak of Sax Rohmer's writing career, with the curious consequence that there is little to say about them. Henceforth, turning out book-length novels at the rate of rather more than one a year, he had not so much opportunity for lengthy adventures abroad and none at all for amusing digressions in other directions.

After their return from the Syrian adventure, Sax still hoped for a time that he might be able to settle down to the projected biography of Haroun al-Rashid. For his further researches, he sought the assistance of Charles Beard, an antiquarian and noted authority on ancient armor, who proved to be no less eccentric than the rest of his friends.

Elizabeth had her first meeting with him one evening when Sax brought him home to continue a discussion and, the hour growing late, pressed him to stay for dinner. Charles seemed loath to accept, but eventually did so. He then sat down at the table, still wearing his topcoat and seeming even more loath to remove it. Further persuasion followed and when, more or less by brute force, they finally got it off him the reason for his hesitation became plain. Beneath it he was wearing neither jacket nor shirt but only an undershirt.

Acting the perfect hostess, Elizabeth made no comment, but,

supposing the poor man to be a poverty-stricken genius, afterwards urged Sax to do what he could for him. She might have saved her sympathy. Charles Beard's deficiencies in wardrobe, if they were not occasioned by personal choice, were due to a scholarly absence of mind about laundry.

Beard's first impression of Elizabeth seems to have been equally unjust. Some few days later—Charles evidently having observed that she wore no ring—she was surprised to receive a gift from him in the form of a beautiful antique wedding ring of George III period. Embossed with roses and oakleaves, it carried an inscription on the inner side, "Let virtue guide thee." Elizabeth said that she doubted whether *that* would be much use in the twentieth century, but she liked the ring and wore it long afterwards. Due to her habit of throwing her rings at Sax in moments of stress, she possessed several. (I asked her which one she now wore. I was surprised and no little touched when she told me it was the same cheap ring that Sax had put on her finger in 1909 at the Lambeth registry office. "I only pretended to throw *that* one away!" she said, smiling.)

The same period began for Sax with a distressing piece of business which all his efforts had failed to avert—the hearing of the case against his literary agent. By what I have been able to gather from reading the evidence, it seems probable that the agent had no dishonest intentions when he first entered upon the association, but he simply had not the character to become the business representative of a worldwide celebrity. In 1913, he could little have dreamed that such a thing might happen, and when it did happen, he swiftly became intoxicated to a condition not far short of megalomania. Unable to deny that he had deliberately represented assets as deficits, he baldly declared that he had done so in order "to keep Sax Rohmer working." This somewhat novel line of defence prompted the judge to inquire whom he regarded as the principal, Sax Rohmer or himself. The agent replied "Myself!"

There could hardly be much doubt about the result. Judgment was awarded in favor of Sax, and he emerged from the courtroom the richer by some £1,600. This was all the money actually known to be owing at that date; what may previously have vanished without trace is anybody's guess.

Concurrently, Paramount Pictures were rapidly following up

the success of their first Fu Manchu film with *The Return of Dr. Fu Manchu*, again starring Warner Oland.

Elizabeth now spent most of her weekends in the country. Lovelands Way was an unqualified success and she could go there with an easy conscience, leaving Sax to be looked after by Edith Britten who, having originally joined the Braemar House staff as an assistant to the cook, had since proved herself a competent and devoted housekeeper. Courageous of character and scrupulously honest, she belonged to that vanished class of admirable women to whom service was a career, for which reason alone no record of the Sax Rohmers would be complete without mention of her. In the end, war parted them, but the bond of affection and mutual respect which had grown up between them was never severed and, through all their later adventures, it was always Edith whom they would find patiently waiting for their return home, to serve them again.

In the quiet loveliness of her Surrey garden, Elizabeth found peace and contentment, but she could never remain long inactive anywhere. Very soon afterwards, we find her a prominent member of the local Women's Institute, organizing drama classes and later extending her activities to producing plays and staging parties for the Personal Service League of the Windmill Press. Thanks to Elizabeth's stage experience and close connection with show business, these were no commonplace village entertainments but sparkling affairs graced by such unexpected visitors as Clarice Mayne, Jack Warner, Bransby Williams, to say nothing of Nervo and Knox and a host of less well-known but eminently professional artists.

Among the novel ideas which Elizabeth brought to her parties was to write and produce a play which ran throughout the evening in serial installments. In between them, there was dancing in the hall, following which no less a person than Sax himself (specially conscripted for the event) would appear on the stage to read a synopsis of the last episode before the next began. This was a night talked of long afterwards.

The pattern of Sax's working life at Braemar House was perhaps better ordered than it had been in previous days, but it could never be dull or even predictable. At one time he found the upper floor tenanted by a fanatic pianist who installed a full-sized concert grand in a direct line ten feet above his desk. Sax liked music,

205

but at the seventh consecutive rendering of the "Moonlight" sonata, he rebelled. Some acrimonious exchange followed, and Sax took a just revenge by putting his neighbor into his next short story, "The Squirrel Man," subsequently published by *Collier's*.

The much-delayed *Daughter of Fu Manchu* had now been completed, and the re-appearance of the fiendish Chinese doctor marked the commencement of both a new decade and a new era in popular literature. In all Sax's work there is an integrity that is all too often wanting among best-selling authors. He scorned to endow his characters with Peter Pan qualities, and after their long absence they returned to the scene aged by the appropriate passage of years.

The book was scarcely out on the stands before Paramount had issued their film version, *Daughter of the Dragon*. For the third and last time, Warner Oland played Fu Manchu, and the role of his daughter went to yet another screen personality of the immediate future, Anna May Wong.

It also happened that one quite undistinguished person was involved. Away in a country town, and still wearing a grammar school cap, the writer of these lines went to see that film, and first noted the name of Sax Rohmer. In my mind's eye, I pictured him as a man of mystery and, at that time, the staff at Braemar House would probably have agreed with me.

To them, with the sole exception of the indefatigable Edith, he was not only a mystery but a nightmare. His habit of fixing his regard absently on some point apparently behind the head of the person whom he was addressing, his tendency to ring for coffee at 3 A.M. (believing the hour to be somewhere around 9 P.M.) and, worst of all, his inexplicable behavior, not only irritated but terrified them. Long after the event, one of the maids once confided tremulously to Elizabeth: "I saw him come out of his room all peculiar, and he didn't seem to see me. He went and picked up the phone, and put it down again without speaking to anybody. Then he opened the door and went out into the hall, and came in again. And then he went back into his room and shut the door." Whereat the alarmed maid said she had retreated hastily to the kitchen and locked herself in. Elizabeth burst out laughing. These seemingly lunatic antics were no mystery to her. Sax had simply been timing the moves in a story.

Haroun was postponed and finally abandoned. Obstinate idealist though he always remained, it was impossible for Sax, in his current position, to devote the necessary time to such a work. As a serious historical study, it would have been as formidable and as little profitable a job as *The Romance of Sorcery*, and he no longer had the leisure for such exercises.

As one of the most popular writers of his day—a distinction which he had not sought deliberately to achieve—he had become more than ever the servant of his public. But even at the peak of his popularity, Sax remained artistically unspoiled; he could never resign himself to a regular stint at his desk like a businessman dealing with daily correspondence. Before he could write anything, it was still necessary for him to be prompted by an emotional stimulus.

This he could now usually obtain with the passive assistance of his so-called secretary who, illiterate so far as typewriting and shorthand were concerned, could at least play the part of a sympathetic listener. Closeted in Sax's study, they would embark upon diatribes against the weather, crime, the police, ministers of state, ministers of the church, women who wore too much, women who wore too little—anything and everything, till the very fabric of Braemar House trembled to their indignation and Sax finally reached the auto-induced catharsis which enabled him to write. Elizabeth, amused by this pose of universal cynicism, changed her earlier practice of addressing letters to "Sax Rohmer, I.B." and, in her postcards from Lovelands Way, saluted him as "Acidus." And then in a fair play spirit of self-accusation, she signed them "Little Bo-Pest."

Even at Braemar House, there were still times when these methods failed to produce the necessary result and Elizabeth had to revert to her former role of *agente provocateuse*. On such occasions, she usually began by going to the kitchen and warning any uninitiated maids.

"There's going to be a flaming row. But don't worry. It won't mean anything!"

Nowadays she was rarely called upon to go to the extent of throwing things, but if absolutely required, she could still do it and did. Her finest effort probably occurred over the dinner table when, all lesser attempts having failed to arouse him, she concluded by hurling a dish of curry full into his face, to the consternation not only of Sax but of the astonished maid who witnessed the event. "Oh, sir!" she gasped. "The rice is hanging all over your eyelashes!"

To borrow a line from one of Sax's own stories, "This circumstance was objectionably obvious, but the solecism passed without comment." Sax's abundant and phenomenally long eyelashes had been a bitter trial to him from the hour of his birth. In his early infancy, it had been necessary to cut them, to prevent them from entangling and sealing the eyelids. At school, they had lent to his youthful features a wholly misleading touch of effeminacy which provoked many a bout of fisticuffs. There was nothing he could do to get rid of them. True, they later added something to the dark mystery of his eyes, but at times they still tended to interfere with his sight and, over the years, he acquired a nervous habit of bushing them up with his forefinger.

In his next serial for *Collier's, Yu'an Hee See Laughs,* Sax produced a work which, in my opinion, most fittingly represents the highest in pre-war novel writing (though *The Day the World Ended* and *The Bride of Fu Manchu* are close runners-up). Tentatively, for such selections must always be more personal than objective, I chose this as the best of his stories. Sax conceded that it might be—he had no opinion of anything he wrote—but said he thought he had given it an inadequate title. Certainly it is a title which does not well suggest the exceptionally fine novel which it covers. Elizabeth, I should add, disagrees. Understandably, perhaps, she prefers *The Orchard of Tears*, which Sax wrote only because he wanted to write it.

Something like one in every three issues of *Collier's* now featured either a short story or a serial installment by Sax Rohmer. Vacations, these days, were necessarily restricted to short visits to the Continent or trips around England. And it was on one of the latter that Sax had another brush with the supernatural or, as he would rather have described it, the supernormal

"To speak of the supernatural," he declared, "is ridiculous, for nothing can exist outside the laws of Nature. But it is quite equally absurd—and pretentious—to suppose that all the laws of Nature are known to us."

On this particular occasion the Sax Rohmers had come to

rest at a country inn, during one of their English tours. It was a rambling, half-timbered place, obviously of great antiquity. What happened is soon told. Midway through the night, Elizabeth opened her eyes and, glancing sideways, saw that the adjoining bed was occupied not only by Sax but also by the vaguely luminescent form of a priest in full canonicals stretched alongside him. Either she was dreaming or extremely tired, for, on becoming aware of this singularity, she declares that she merely thought "Oh!—it's only a ghost!" and went back to sleep again.

But, in the morning, Sax complained of having felt bitterly cold all night. Elizabeth told him of his strange bedfellow. Intrigued, they contacted the innkeeper and asked him if he knew anything of the history of the place—if, for example, some dignitary of the church had died there. The man looked rather startled. "No," he said slowly. "Nobody died, that I know of. But they say that the body of Cardinal Wolsey was laid here on the night before his funeral!"

It is on record that Sax and Elizabeth made their next major trip abroad in the autumn of 1932, when they revisited America. Elizabeth remembers nothing about it, so it was obviously no more than a business trip probably concerned with the future of Fu Manchu. The second of the resumed series, *The Mask of Fu Manchu*, was currently appearing in *Collier's*, and the editors were pressing for more. The Chinese doctor's "come-back" had proved no less sensational than his debut.

Prohibition then being rife in the United States, they made an all-night train journey across the Canadian border which Elizabeth insists that they did for the sole purpose of getting a drink. They must have been very thirsty. However, while they were getting their drink they also had an opportunity to view that spectacular showpiece of the western world, Niagara Falls.

This was another natural "location" which impressed itself inevitably upon Sax's memory, and although he found no immediate use for it, it sprang at once to his mind when, some three years later, he placed Fu Manchu in an American setting. The temptation was too strong. He ended the story with the villainous doctor drifting to disaster on the brink of the Falls and, as he subsequently confessed to me, without any idea of how he could conceivably get him out of *that* one. There the sensational Fu Manchu stories might have ended. But the story had scarcely appeared in print before a Canadian fan living in that area wrote triumphantly to Sax: "I know how you are going to save him. It happened to me!" And he went on to give details of his experience.

Sax wrote back: "I assure you that I didn't know. But I do now. Many thanks!" Information rarely came his way so fortuitously.

But all that was still in the future. On the present occasion, business concluded in New York, Sax and Elizabeth moved on to take their first look at Jamaica. Here they were promptly entertained to dinner at King's House where Elizabeth made a notable entry. In the act of descending the grand staircase, a heel came off her shoe and she finished up in a disorderly heap at the bottom. Everyone was very polite about it, but she was sure that they all thought she was drunk. In retrospect, she would have felt much better about it if she had been.

Sax, too, had his memories of that dinner, which conjured up recollections of Sherak al-Oman. In his special honor, they were served liberally with the local delicacy, soft crabs. Sax had nothing against oysters, but all creatures with eight legs horrified him. He regarded lobsters as sea-scorpions and crabs as sea-spiders, and would eat neither, if he could help it. It was another meal which he long remembered.

An experience better suited to his taste was a visit to the world-famous Myers rum distillery. Jamaica rum was Sax's favorite drink. In company with Mr. Myers and several members of the staff, he spent the pre-luncheon hour helping to invent the Fu Manchu cocktail. This proved rather difficult, for Sax insisted that it ought to be a mysterious shade of green, but, short of dyestuffs, there is not much which will impart such a color to rum. At the fourteenth attempt they did eventually get it right, but none of them wanted much lunch afterwards. (I understand that this mixture was actually added to the official cocktail list, but I have not been able to find the recipe.)

But Sax had come to Jamaica neither to dine at King's House nor to shake cocktails. As usual, he had an axe to grind: here he hoped to extend his knowledge of occult matters to include some details of native magic. In the book *Bat Wing* he had already touched briefly upon the subject of Voodoo, but he freely admitted that the source of his information was second-hand. Characteristically, he could not be satisfied till he had passed judgment on the evidence of his own eyes.

In Jamaica he was near to the source, but still slightly off course. Everyone assured him that Voodoo was, and continued to be, confined exclusively to Haiti. Sax soon discovered, however, that a local offshoot of Voodoo practices—officially frowned upon by the British authorities—was secretly observed in a district west of Kingston. This was a curious religion known as Pocomania.

"I have no idea from what the name was derived," Sax said. "But it strongly suggested some kind of mental disease."

In the pursuit of these inquiries, he made the acquaintance of Michael de Cordova of the *Daily Gleaner,* an acquaintance which later became a close friendship. A member of the staff, who was reputed to be a specialist in matters concerning the native underworld, was placed at his disposal and was able to furnish him with some further details.

The cult, he said, was headed by a man known as the King Shepherd, whose authority resided in his knowledge of the Unknown Tongue, a divine gift miraculously conferred during a state of trance. Some devotees, thus anointed, claimed the power to make prophecies, cast out evil spirits, and to leave the flesh for as long as seven days during which period their bodies were certifiably "dead." Several missions existed and here meetings took place (nominally banned), sometimes for faith-healing, sometimes for the more sinister purpose of slaying an enemy by remote control.

Sax determined to attend such a meeting, undeterred by the information that white visitors were not encouraged. This, aided by his friend from the *Gleaner,* he finally managed to do. On the first Saturday of the following month—a night reputedly auspicious for manifestations of the Holy Ghost—they drove out of town until, presently, they encountered the procession of the Shepherd on its way to the mission. Parking the car, they joined the throng.

It was a weird company, made up of all sorts and conditions of natives, male and female, all marching, all singing, some carrying lights. Ahead of them, a man in robes and a turban—the Shepherd—led the way, waving his arms and capering madly, like an

211

African witch-doctor, his dancing becoming more and more wild the nearer they approached to their destination. This proved to be a large courtyard, where an impressive crowd already awaited them. The place was ringed round with tiers of wooden benches, and a black dwarf, attired in red and brandishing a sword, seemed to be performing the duties of usher. Relieved to find their entrance challenged by nothing more potent than glares, Sax allowed himself to be sardined into the crowded benches.

In lieu of an altar, an odd centerpiece known as the Table occupied the middle of the yard. Set out upon the ground, and composed of all sorts of local produce, it formed a strange geometrical pattern, presumably of some esoteric significance, the exhibits ranging from bread to a goblet covered with a white napkin, a small book and seven white candles. Around this Caribbean version of a wizard's pentacle—if such it was—the Shepherd and the black dwarf began to dance. One after another, members of the congregation ran in to join them. The chanting had increased in volume till now almost everyone was taking part.

Sax's companion leaned over to whisper in his ear. "White candles mean that this is a ceremony for curing somebody who is sick. For a Death Table, they use blue candles—the number of them represents the number of days which the victim has to live. Seven saucers are smashed and the candles extinguished."

The chanting and the dancing mounted to a frenzy. Suddenly the Shepherd halted and flung up his arms. His face upturned, eyes rolling and froth upon his lips, he babbled out a string of words in the Unknown Tongue. Shouts of acclaim rose from all sides. Others sprang forward to join the dance till the center of the court was a madhouse of leaping, cavorting bodies. On and on it went for fifteen or twenty minutes. Here and there a black body folded up in collapse, to the accompaniment of cries of joy from the worshippers. In the eyes of the Pocomaniacs, these were they who had received the Holy Ghost. Eventually the bizarre ceremony ended.

Sax was interested but not impressed. In Egypt he had seen the Whirling Dervishes hypnotize themselves into an ecstatic condition by similar means, but he very much doubted whether such inspiration really attended the antics of the Shepherd and his flock. In this melange of native superstition with rites usurped from the

212

Catholic Church, he saw only ignorance and deceit. He decided that the claims of Voodoo would have to await investigation until he could get to Haiti.

26

FAITES VOS JEUX!

WHILE THE MASK OF FU MANCHU WAS STILL RUNNING IN COLLIER'S, Metro-Goldwyn-Mayer Studios went to work on a film version under the same title. This time, the main part fell to the sinister Boris Karloff, and I am inclined to think that he may have been the best suited to play it. Warner Oland probably looked more convincingly Chinese, but Boris Karloff had the necessary gaunt height and more closely corresponded to Sax's descriptions of Fu Manchu.

Once again, other famous names were involved. Lewis Stone played Nayland Smith. Films of Sax's stories, from the silent days onwards, usually provided excellent vehicles to launch little-known artists on a distinguished career. On this occasion, the little-known actress who played Fu Manchu's daughter was Myrna Loy.

For a change, this film did actually have some resemblance to the original story, though not much. Like its predecessors, it was successful and MGM planned to make more. They were curiously obstructed by urgent protests from the Chinese Embassy in Washington. The Chinese diplomats took a humorless view of Fu Manchu, whom they considered damaging to their "image." At this time, the West in general, and America in particular, was becoming alarmed by the rapid expansion of Japan in the Far East, and rather inclined to encourage China as a potential ally against this threat. Consequently, the protest received closer attention

214

than it might otherwise have done.

The Chinese were unable to influence the publication of the Fu Manchu stories (at that time; later, they were able, and did) but they were successful in holding up the production of further films. Sax's rather questionable financial advisers were furious, and actually suggested bringing an injunction against the Chinese government for "loss of revenue." But Sax, who considered the complaint understandable, even if absurd, refused to give his consent to any such proceedings.

The name of Fu Manchu had now become a household word, to the extent that many people had a tentative belief in his physical existence. The same kind of phenomenon attaches, of course, to the name of Sherlock Holmes. Even at this late date, the British Post Office is annually embarrassed by letters hopefully addressed to Mr. Sherlock Holmes, at 221B Baker Street. No one ever wrote to Dr. Fu Manchu, since no one knew his address. But, at this peak period of the doctor's notoriety, there were some who did as well, or better. One humorist having, presumably, some grudge against a member of the American State Department, sent him a threatening letter, warning him of his forthcoming demise, and signed it "President of the Si-Fan." The F.B.I. was quite alarmed and, failing to find any information anywhere about this organization other than in Sax's stories, wrote and asked him if he thought there might be anything in it. Sax replied, politely subduing his mirth, that a Chinese society known as the Si-Fan *did* exist, but he doubted whether it would concern itself with American politics.

Down in Surrey, Elizabeth continued to make local history with her amateur dramatics. As a professional, she blankly refused to submit to the bugbear of all Women's Institute drama groups— the absurdity of women dressed up as men. Some way of inducing the members' husbands and boy-friends to take part had to be found, and she soon found one.

Contrary to all existing traditions, she introduced cocktails at rehearsals in summer, and hot Scotch and baked potatoes in the winter. After that there was no difficulty, excepting from the scandalized Committee, which had a special meeting on the subject and asked her to desist from this evil practice, since the hall belonged to the church. This, however, led to a concerted revolt of the members, who promptly retorted that the same hall was often hired out for wedding receptions at which the champagne flowed freely. So the evil practice was continued; Elizabeth got her male actors, and her society won the County championship at the next drama competition.

Somewhat unexpectedly, not only Elizabeth but Sax also was now spending a good part of the time in the country. He still did most of his work in town, but when he was not actually writing anything, was more often to be found at Lovelands Way. London was already beginning to show those symptoms of overcrowding which, even before the Second World War, would make it less a city of convenience than of hindrance.

From this time onwards, Sax showed an increasing tendency to withdraw from society—if, indeed, he had ever really been part of it—until he finally gained almost the reputation of a recluse. As a young man, he had sought intellectual companionship chiefly among older persons, many of whom were now dead. Of the young hopefuls in his own age-group, some had failed to make the grade, others had found their success in widely-separated parts of the world. At the same time, the nature of Sax's own work was essentially solitary, keeping him apart from his fellows rather than bringing him into contact with them, so that he had little opportunity to make new friends.

At Lovelands Way, the Sax Rohmer family formed a closer unit than it had done since the days of Herne Hill. Reluctantly, old Bill Ward had eventually retired from the office at the age of eighty-two. Now he came down to the country every weekend; his tastes were simple and direct, his joy and appreciation of everything childlike and touching. A deeply religious man, Bill Ward saw the hand of God in every work of Nature; his admiration of the color of a wild flower was an act of worship. Elizabeth never forgot the awe and humility with which he drew her attention to the symmetrical wonder of a simple daisy.

Two years later he died, and even that he managed to do in the grand old Victorian manner, reaching out to take Elizabeth's hand and join it to Sax's across his bed, while his eyes entreated her "Look after him!" Elizabeth nodded mutely. She always had, and she always would.

216

Thus the well-loved figure passed from the world of men. Few have shown the worldly wisdom to play the difficult role of a father-in-law to so great an effect. Without interference or criticism, he had followed their lives through their early struggles, through the precarious years of their marriage, avoiding the temptation to proffer unsought advice or to side with one against the other. Content to remain an onlooker, he had achieved his reward. He had lived to see them drawn together in a new companionship, and his son elevated to the pinnacle of his chosen profession.

In 1933 came the publication of *The Bride of Fu Manchu* which, beyond any shadow of doubt, was the best of the Fu Manchu stories, a neatly-constructed, sophisticated novel. Having given the preceding stories an Egyptian setting, Sax switched this one to the French Riviera. But he had no need to make a special journey to obtain the background. This was a part of the world which he knew very well.

Over the past ten years, he had made frequent visits to the Côte d'Azur. Hitherto, I have refrained from mentioning them, because they were too numerous and too brief to be listed separately. Even without travelling by air (which he never did) the Riviera is scarcely more than a full day's journey from London. That spectacular stretch of coastline, with its tunnels through the rock, ruined towers, hairpin bends and precipitous drops to the limpid depths of the Mediterranean, could not fail to appeal to Sax's sense of the dramatic. It would not be fair to say that he was less attracted by the more conventional features which have made Monte Carlo a world-famous resort for those in the higher-income brackets.

But in these days when so much time and energy seems to be spent on the attempted justification of ignorance and vulgarity, Sax's attitude towards wealth and luxury is likely to be misunderstood. Paradoxically—since he remained essentially "the artist" and unworldly—he loved luxury but was indifferent to wealth. Luxury, judiciously employed, he regarded as the highest practical expression of cultured living; lack of wealth he saw as a handicap of the same order as a lack of colors in the equipment of a painter. This, consequently, was the basis of his profound respect for the world of the "English gentleman."

In the favored 1920's and 1930's, the distinction still held sufficiently true that when one spoke of the Riviera as a playground of the "best people" there was no need for quotation marks—they really *were* the best people. Reasonably enough, therefore, it was in such circles that Sax liked to spend his leisure time, to wine and to dine.

Earlier, I have mentioned that he was fond of good food, and elsewhere I have seemed to contradict this by saying that his tastes were simple. But both statements are true. Sax had a lively appreciation of what good food was but, often, to his chagrin, was unable to enjoy it. Where aspects of cultured living were concerned, his ideas were those of the artist, not at all related to his own physical limitations; frequently, then, he exasperated his companions by ordering some celebrated local delicacy and subsequently finding himself unable to touch it when it arrived on the table.

One of the better-known establishments in which Sax carried on this kind of fun and games was the Colombe d'Or, in the hills above Nice. Artistically, the Colombe d'Or must have been particularly satisfying to him, for the fame of the place largely resides in the fact that the walls are hung with works donated by the world's best-known painters. In addition to being a restaurant, it is a museum of contemporary art. Apart from the paintings, the management preserves (or did) a kind of autograph book, to which top-ranking authors (whose works may be priced in guineas per word) have contributed full pages in manuscript. Sax once mentioned to me that he had visited the Colombe d'Or so many times before he was invited to add his contribution that, when at last he was, he felt as if he had been granted a royal distinction.

Here also it was—in passing—that he once saw the outset of a strange procession—the participants strangely robed, devil-masked and bearing flaming torches—en route to a Witches' Sabbath in the enshrouding mountains. These, admittedly, may not have been numbered among the "best people." But Sax, with visions of blasphemous orgies under the horns of the Goat, beautiful girls stretched naked on Satanic altars and similarly naked worshippers dancing back-to-back, wished earnestly that he might have followed.

In Monte Carlo, Sax stayed usually at the Hotel de Paris, and dined at Quinto's. Some understanding of his respect for French

218

(or should it be Monegasque?) cuisine may be gained from the fact that when Victor Quinto later opened his restaurant in Arlington Street, Sax added his financial support.

The history of Monaco, which consists uniquely of Monte Carlo and its environs, is curious and interesting; but, in the minds of most visitors, the story of Monte Carlo begins and ends with the Casino. Sax had no taste for gambling—he played no card games, and I never knew him to stir himself to the extent of a five-shilling bet on the Derby—yet the Casino exercised a strong fascination over him too. For this there were several reasons, none of them connected with the hope of obtaining sudden wealth.

This colorful stage on which human passions ran high was surely one to which he could not well have remained cold. Most men are gamblers, even if he was not, and the mere idea of "The Man who Broke the Bank at Monte Carlo" was sufficient to bring fortune to the comedian who sang the song. Here real-life comedy and tragedy were mixed up in the garish world of entertainment, offering as much to the keen-eyed observer as to the player.

It was early one afternoon, when play was not high, that Sax (en route for the bar) chanced to notice a young man whose expression was so curiously agitated that he lingered nearby for a while, covertly watching. Clearly an Englishman, he wore clothes well-cut but shabby. Presently Sax noted, to his astonishment, that he was nervously toying with a number of those impressive thousand-franc chips which are occasionally won but rarely staked.

What was he going to do? During the next four or five spins, he did nothing. Then, stepping forward, he placed a maximum on the third dozen (odds 25 to 12 against), turned, and walked away. But there was nothing nonchalant in the movement. The very pose of his shoulders spoke of agonized uncertainty. The ball fell . . . the number was thirty-six.

He had won! The man spun around, his face transfigured. Watching him gather up the proceeds, Sax wondered. If he were a mad gambler, he would endeavor to repeat his success. But he did not. Turning, he walked from the room and, following discreetly, Sax saw him go straight to the cashier, cash in all his plaques, and leave the Casino. Obviously, the maximum he risked represented all he had. What desperate need drove him to the mad plunge? No one will ever know.

This time, in the best traditions of the fairy story, fortune had smiled on the unfortunate. But, in the many weeks which he spent in Monte Carlo, Sax saw also the reverse side of the picture. Seated, one afternoon, in the American bar of the Hotel de Paris, he witnessed the entry of another young Englishman, well-groomed but with a weakness in his face accentuated by such an expression of abject despair as to chill the heart of the beholder. Three times in a row he ordered "Double scotch and soda," drained the glass, and repulsing all attempts to draw him into conversation, strode off across the Square. Again Sax wondered . . . but not for long. The haggard young man shot himself at nine o'clock that evening.

There are many books which, making much of such extremes, insist that the professional gambler is doomed sooner or later to heavy loss. Sax noted, however, that this might fairly apply only to the sensational gambler seeking to break the bank. Simple observation left no gainsaying that the hill at Monaco accommodated quite a small colony of professional players—a large proportion of them women—to whom the tables were the sole means of livelihood. But these were players modest in their demands and prepared, if necessary, to spend many hours in the rooms. This, as a career, had no lure for Sax. It smacked too strongly of his youthful sufferings in Threadneedle Street.

Intriguing though it might be, it was not the human drama alone which, time and again, drew Sax back to Monte Carlo. From the date of his first visit, he found himself fascinated to quite an equal degree by what he termed the problem of Roulette. The wheel (attributed to Pascal) was no sooner invented than players had begun to devise "systems" to master its hazards. And, surprising though it may seem in view of his distaste for gambling, Sax himself became one of their number.

Most "systems"—and there are many—are, in fact, systems of arranging stakes in such a way as to compensate for losses or to take advantage of gains. This did not interest Sax. With some amusement, he noted in the history of Monte Carlo a particularly down-to-earth kind of "system" practiced, in the early days of the Casino, by a terrible Englishman named Jaggers. This adventurer employed a large staff to make elaborate records from morning to night, in order to discover which wheels were biased. He won £120,000. Thereafter it was decided that the wheels should be tested regularly by a team of skilled engineers, and no bias can now be detected.

But there is yet another system of a totally different nature. The French writer, Roger Vailland, has declared that with every fresh spin of the wheel, the world begins anew. In other words, logically, no sequence of winning numbers can either be affected by what has gone before, or affect what follows. Here, then, was a problem directly related to Sax's special interest: the unexplored laws of the Unseen. Did some unsuspected principle of Nature govern a relationship between numbers, or did it not? Though anything but a brilliant mathematician, as an enthusiastic occultist, he made up his mind to investigate.

Over the years, the question had become a hobby, in the sense that he expected to derive no financial benefit from it. In the sense that everything he did was a part of his studies, Sax had no hobbies. Having amassed some formidable lists of figures, he came to the conclusion that an ordered pattern might exist, but it was far too complex to be handled by a single player. Gathering around him a group of friends interested in Roulette, he began to make annual pilgrimages to the Casino, acting as chief to a team of players trained to make the lightning calculations and disposition of stakes which the system demanded. For many seasons, they became a notable feature of the Monte Carlo scene. But the fact that Sax was no mad gambler is clearly indicated in that, for once, he was a great deal more careful in his finances than he usually was in his daily life. At the commencement of an assault, they would set aside a fixed capital and, if they lost it, the session would be over.

But they never did lose it. As with all his occult researches, the results which Sax obtained were interesting but inconclusive. During what he called sequences of "anti-predominances," it was sometimes necessary to stay at a table for eight or nine hours in order to come out all square. On the other hand, during one season, they were able to show a steady profit of about three hundred pounds a week.

Their most spectacular endeavor, however, probably took place one day when, after half an hour's absence in the bar, Sax returned to find his secretary sweating liberally over an enormous pile of winnings and nearly cross-eyed with worry as he tried to cope with the calculations to follow. Sax sat down and they played out the run. But it did not work out according to plan, and they finished by losing all that had been gained. Afterwards, going over the score in the quiet of his room, Sax made the shocking discovery that the original win had been made on a stake placed in error. This should have established the base for an entirely new set of figures, and had those figures been followed, they would infallibly have broken the bank. But as he said philosophically, in the fevered excitement of the Casino, he doubted if even Einstein would have been equal to it.

Although in a minority with his system of mysteriously related numbers, Sax was not alone. Others held to the same belief, sometimes employing weird and wonderful methods to substantiate it. I am not sure that anyone actually tried prayer and incantation, but Sax once saw two Portuguese enthusiasts lug in a kind of miniature computer. This thing apparently required so much operation that it enabled them to decide upon a number only at intervals of about ten minutes. Up to the moment that he left the table, they had staked six times—and lost six times.

Some time later, he received a personal visit from an inventor armed with a somewhat similar machine, small but incredibly weighty. Sax was interested to the extent of agreeing to a test in his apartment. (Records of play at Monte Carlo are, of course, available in print, so that any session can be re-played theoretically.) But at the end of two hours, the inventor was roughly minus four thousand points.

Due to his interest in this rather public kind of activity, Sax received a good deal of correspondence from hopefuls anxious to sell him infallible systems, or to induce him to finance them. To these his reply was refreshingly sober. If one had an infallible system capable of being dealt with by a single player, the only amount necessary would be one's fare to Monte Carlo and, say, ten pounds in hand.

There was yet another aspect of the Casino which appealed strongly to Sax and this, I think was the atmosphere of a tiny, self-contained kingdom, smoothly run according to its own laws and customs. The Casino is much more than a gambling house. It contains the theatre once renowned for the first nights of Diaghilev, a school for croupiers, and an up-to-date hospital. A miniature state within the miniature state of Monaco, it is Monte Carlo's one and only "View." Seen at night, from the road above, it is (to quote Sax in *The Bride of Fu Manchu*) "a unique spectacle—the blazing color of the flower-beds, flood-lighted and set amid palms; the emerald green of terraced lawns falling away to that ornate frontage—theatrical but unforgettable."

One vignette of the inner life in that Temple of Mammon—like a scene from a stage thriller—Sax once witnessed when an elderly man either fainted or died (he did not learn which) at a table in the big public room. A signal was given. A panel in the wall opened and attendants appeared. Simply and without fuss, they lifted the insensible victim bodily, chair and all, and carried him out. The panel closed. Another chair was quietly put in position and, though the room was crowded, less than a dozen people were aware of the incident.

27

LITTLE GATTON

FU MANCHU HAD BECOME A FRANKENSTEIN'S MONSTER, SEDUCING HIS creator with the lure of wealth. Yet it was Egypt and its age-old mysteries which continued chiefly to fire the imagination of Sax. Already, he felt, he had been away too long and a further visit was imperative.

Intending this to be only a short episode, he went out to Cairo alone. As always, the vast collection of antiquities at the Museum, much enhanced by the addition of the priceless Tutankhamen items, commanded his attention; principally, however, he felt himself stirred by the incredibly preserved features of Seti I which, whenever he set eyes upon them, invariably put him in mind of Fu Manchu. This, perhaps, was the inspiration which led him, in later stories, to develop the Chinese doctor's personality away from that of the mere arch-villain of Limehouse which he had originally been, until he became a god-like being, indifferent to human standards of good and evil.

Briefly, on the terrace at Shepheard's, he rubbed shoulders with Sir Arthur Conan Doyle. They had become acquainted some time earlier, drawn together by a common interest in the occult. It was some months since they had met, and during that time their formerly cordial relations had been strained by a somewhat uncalled-for attack which the creator of Sherlock Holmes had seen fit to make on the integrity of the late Harry Houdini, charging him with persecuting spiritualists while at the same time making

224

use of occult forces himself. To this, on behalf of his departed friend, Sax replied promptly and hotly. However, at this encounter, he felt a twinge of remorse for his angry words. A glance told him that Doyle was a man near to death and aware of it.

No small part of the success of Sax's stories lay in the fact that they were not merely tales of mystery and suspense but liberally spiced with action. Though the mystic element might appeal to him the more strongly, he knew that he could not afford to spend all his time dreaming in museums and drifting gradually out of touch with the rapidly changing world. This was no doubt the reason why, on this occasion, he seems to have sought younger and livelier company than he usually kept.

For some days, Sax left the Egyptologists and the wise men of Islam to their own scholarly devices, and consorted with the personnel of the Royal Air Force. Having the trick of making himself popular when he wanted to, he got along with them very well —too well, perhaps; in the end, he was invited to take a strictly unofficial flight over the Gizeh Plateau. Probably he was induced to accept by the fact that he had already viewed the Pyramids from every angle but above. He did not enjoy the experience.

If Sax had ever travelled in a jet airliner, he would certainly have considered the flight no more than boring. But a joy-ride in a two-seater fighter plane of the early 1930's, in the company of an exuberant young man who light-heartedly put the machine through every known maneuver of aerial combat en route, was quite another matter. Sax came down leaving his stomach some thousands of feet aloft, and stuck to ships for the rest of his life.

With that his latest adventures in Egypt might have ended but, at this stage in the proceedings, he became literally and painfully immobilized by an excruciating malady of the left foot. This was an affliction which he had suffered before and one which continued to plague him, on odd occasions, for many years afterwards. It had first occurred, he said, when he was homeward bound on a Royal Mail steamer (presumably returning from one of his visits to Madeira). The doctors told him it was gout, but this he indignantly refuted. To those who have never had it, gout is a slightly absurd illness associated with choleric ex-colonels who drink too much port. Sax, who was neither choleric, nor an ex-colonel, nor a port drinker, had a marked aversion to suffering from such a thing. He insisted that the trouble dated from the intrusion of a diabolical and unidentified insect under the big toenail. But, to his great annoyance, no one ever believed him, not even Elizabeth.

As a rule, the trouble cleared up in a few days, but this time it did not. Sax remained confined to his room at Shepheard's, resting the afflicted foot (which was the standard cure) and drinking large quantities of Jamaica rum (which was not). Elizabeth, alarmed by his long absence and gathering from his letter that all was not well with him, thereupon packed in haste and took passage for Egypt in the next ship.

Happily, by the time she arrived, Sax was on both feet again. But, in sharp contrast to his behavior in earlier days, he was now so eager for his wife's companionship that he could not wait for her to reach Cairo nor even for the ship to dock. On the day that the *S. S. Assyria* was scheduled to put in, he caught the train to Port Said, only to learn that she was many hours overdue and might not make port before the next morning. Sax went to earth at the Eastern Exchange Hotel and, having waited up till midnight, finally retired to bed leaving strict instructions that he was to be called as soon as the *Assyria* was sighted.

Three hours later she was sighted, and he was called. Transport at that hour was a problem but, having come to the conclusion that the evil reputation of Port Said was more legendary than real, Sax decided to walk. Making his way through perfectly empty streets, he reached the Canal side just as the lights of the *Assyria* became visible as she crept in slowly to her moorings. An Arab boatman—the only human being he had encountered since leaving the hotel—took him out promptly and he boarded the vessel with such despatch that he found himself the first visitor from shore.

Now that Elizabeth had arrived, the business trip very rightly became a holiday. After a leisured few days in Cairo, they journeyed up the Nile to Luxor, where, at last, they were able to finish the program of sightseeing uncompleted during their financially-embarrassed honeymoon. They revisited the Valley of the Kings and saw the tomb of Tutankhamen which had not yet been discovered at the time of their first visit.

On these excursions, they were now accompanied by a particularly charming and efficient dragoman, by name Mahommed.

Dragomans are often pestiferous, but when you chance to come across an expert of the old school, you find a simple but cultured man with the soul of a gentleman. Such was Mahommed. He treated Elizabeth like Dresden china, and Elizabeth, unused to such attention, was captivated to the extent that, she said, she felt like falling in love with him. Towards the end of their stay, Mahommed invited them to his home. It was a four-storied building where he lived in the midst of an enormous family ranging from grandparents to grandsons. As each new generation came along, a new floor was added and the house grew taller.

But the trip to Luxor was not to end before Elizabeth had displayed her peculiar genius for getting into trouble through no fault of her own. Warning portents appeared in the shape of an immaculately-clad, arrogant-looking Turk who, on numerous occasions, seemed to be passing by the hotel in his ornate but old-fashioned carriage at precisely the moment they emerged. When this happened, the carriage would halt, and studiously avoiding Sax, the supercilious owner would smile down deliberately and meaningly at Elizabeth. While Sax found this irritating Mahommed found it alarming. "Sir!" he gasped. "My lady must never go out alone! That man very rich with many ladies!"

As it happened, there was not much likelihood at the time that Elizabeth would go out alone. Neither of them, however, took the warning very seriously.

Several days later, a new face appeared in the hotel—not a particularly prepossessing face. It belonged to a strange-looking Greek, slightly cross-eyed, who persistently wormed his way into conversation. Neither Sax nor Elizabeth liked him, but their efforts to avoid him appeared curiously unsuccessful. Wherever they went, the Greek was either there before them or arrived shortly after.

In due event they decided to accompany two other hotel guests to a local race meeting. This necessitated a short journey by donkey, which Elizabeth regarded with some misgiving. Her donkeys had a habit of either halting at their discretion, or turning around and proceeding placidly in reverse of the intended direction. But the donkey she got that day did neither of these things. It was apparently inspired by Iblis, king of all the Arab demons. No sooner was she on its back than the creature gave one mighty bound and, with an energy quite unusual in its breed, was off like a thoroughbred. Elizabeth, riding side-saddle, clung on desperately, cursing and praying by turns.

Now, to be mounted on a runaway donkey may be less dignified than to be mounted on a runaway horse, but it is equally perilous. If she lost her hold, there was every possibility of her being seriously injured or killed. The mad donkey careened around corners, scraping her against walls, galloped up precipitous slopes, and pelted through narrow ravines overhung by towering cliffs. Elizabeth, sure of being thrown off at every next moment, suddenly became conscious of flying hoofbeats to the rear and a voice crying, "Hang on! Hang on! I'll save you!"

For a moment, she thought that it was Sax, but—alas for romance—Sax was no donkey-man. It was the abominable Greek. Urging his mount alongside, he leaned over and then—the crowning absurdity—shouted:

"Promise to be in the garden tonight, alone, at 8:30, and I'll save you!"

Elizabeth, not particularly conscious of the absurdity and with no slightest feeling of conscience, promised without any hesitation. As the man grabbed the bridle and, displaying considerably more strength that he looked capable of, checked the runaway to a standstill, she met the triumphant gleam of his eyes and read in them the truth. It was not on behalf of himself that he made this ridiculous assignation, but in the interests of a master, the Turk with many ladies.

Needless to say, she lost no time in communicating the facts to Sax, reasoning that a promise given under duress was no promise. Sax, in turn, promptly made contact with an official. I am not aware of his name or rank but, in tribute to the Fu Manchu series, let us say that it was Superintendent Weymouth of the Cairo police force.

That night there was a suitable reception party waiting in the hotel garden at 8:30, but Elizabeth was not a member of it.

"I know who the blighter is," Weymouth said darkly, "and I know what he is—though so far, we haven't been able to pin it on him. He's turned up in connection with the disappearance of several young women."

For a reputedly skillful operator, the cross-eyed Greek's

methods strike one as curiously naive. Possibly they were suitably matched to the naiveté of Oriental women; possibly he took the proverbial bond of the British word too literally. At all events, he was adroit enough to smell the ambush. He never turned up, and a subsequent call at his last known habitat found him gone without trace. Coincidentally, the rich Turk decided to take a holiday in Europe.

Freed from the limitations which a restricted budget had imposed upon their earlier explorations, the Sax Rohmers were able to continue their journey upstream to Aswan. Not that Aswan has a lot to offer in the way of sightseeing, if one excepts such modern marvels as the Great Dam. From Sax's point of view, a site of greater interest was the granite quarry which contains the Unfinished Obelisk. Still attached to the parent rock on the underside, it measures nearly a hundred feet in length and would have been the highest in the land, but it is cracked.

"One hesitates to speculate," Sax said, "on what may have happened to the man who cracked it!"

A gracefully indolent sailing-boat took them across the Nile. On the opposite bank, the old Coptic monastery appealed again to his imagination; transferred to the Oasis of Siwa, it made an appropriate setting for some chapters of the book which he now had in mind. Thence, some few days later, an overnight train journey brought them back to Cairo, where Sax still had unfinished business to transact which, for the time being, he preferred not to mention to Elizabeth.

Sax had long held to the belief that "thoughts are things," which, if true, would go a long way towards accounting for the "atmosphere" felt by sensitive persons directly upon entering some previously unvisited place. In the series of short stories titled *The Dream Detective* he had suggested that this theory might be put on a working basis and, even though this was fiction, such was actually his belief. He had tried it and, to some extent, succeeded.

On one occasion, having failed in his youthful attempts to penetrate the secrets of Holm Peel, he had contrived to spend a night in the castle compound (though I am not sure when he did this) in order to try the method of "astral exploration" as he termed it. The first step in such an experiment is the most difficult; it consists of inducing a particular kind of auto-hypnosis.

Having achieved this "receptive" condition, Sax's first impressions were, not unnaturally, of picnics and laughter—the "aura" of Peel Castle is, today, contributed chiefly by holidaymakers. But once he had managed to free himself from these extraneous phenomena, he was astonished to find that his next impressions were not, as he had anticipated, medieval but pagan. From this he concluded that the events which had taken place there in the dim ages of pre-Christian history had, in emotional importance, overshadowed any drama enacted there later.

Now that he had developed this curious form of research at least to the point where he could place some faith in it as a practical possibility, he was anxious to try it out in Egypt. He was determined, if possible, to spend a night inside the Great Pyramid. At that date, such a project was by no means impossible for anyone who had a mind to it. No tiresome formalities were necessary. After dark, the place was deserted and the passage left wide open to anyone who cared to enter it—on the reasonable assumption that no one ever would. Back in Cairo, Sax transferred their quarters to Mena House Hotel, within easy walking distance, and prepared for the attempt, the results of which were not quite what he expected.

Elizabeth, who strongly disapproved of metaphysical experiments, was left blissfully ignorant of the whole thing. She had no idea why they had come to Mena House. The upshot of this was that, once again, she found herself alone in their room at some time not far short of dawn and, when a sufficient interval had passed for her to become thoroughly alarmed, got up to search the hotel.

But Sax had slipped out so unobtrusively that nobody had seen him leave. This was just such a situation as Elizabeth had already faced on countless occasions during the past twenty-five years or so, but one to which she could never become reconciled. On the contrary, each new disappearance merely served to strengthen her fear that one day he would disappear once too often.

Inquiry within the hotel failing to produce either Sax or any news of him, the entire staff, up to and including the manager, was eventually dragged out of bed. Congregated in the foyer, they stood in an uneasy, slightly frightened group around Elizabeth, who was now urgently demanding that they send for the police.

Such was the state of things when, a moment later, Sax came bursting in, unkempt and wild-eyed, his light tropical suit curiously streaked and spattered all over with weird grey patches. He resembled a fugitive from a Dickensian lunatic asylum. Shouldering aside all opposition, and with no word of explanation, he thundered up the stairs. Elizabeth, following, reached their room in time to hear the bathroom door bang behind him. A sound of running water followed, and it was a long time before Sax emerged.

Over a late breakfast, he finally condescended to give an account of himself. "The Great Pyramid guards its secrets," he finished, sadly. "For some kind of spiritual assault, I had counted myself prepared. I had, however, forgotten that the place is the headquarters of a considerable legion of bats. And what I was not prepared for was a bombardment of bat dung!"

"You should have taken an umbrella!" his wife said, unsympathetically.

It was after this third (and last) trip to Egypt that the name of Eve came once more, briefly, to Sax's notice. He came across it by chance in a terse newspaper item. Eve had been found shot dead in a Chicago apartment, whether by her own hand or by the hand of another remains obscure. Such, then, was the not wholly unexpected end of the woman who represented the only serious indiscretion of Sax's life. Too little is known about Eve to make anything like an obituary possible, even if she deserved one. She died as she had lived, a figure of mystery.

Undeniably, during the time of her association with Sax, she had been physically attractive—seductively beautiful. Elizabeth (who met her only on the two occasions already noted) freely admits as much. For some reason which neither of them could quite define, she reminded them both of Poppaea, the consort of Nero. Readers curious to learn Sax's impression of her can probably obtain them from *Grey Face*. I suspect that he had Eve in mind when he created the character of Poppaea Sabinov.

What is more interesting is the fact that Eve had apparently been married, though whether she was widowed, divorced, or merely separated from her husband is not clear. This had a peculiar effect upon Sax. Somewhat contrary to the notions of today, he seems from the earliest times to have visualised the *femme fatale*

231

as a married woman. He created his "Madame de Medici" years before he met Eve, and continued in this vein, down to the much-married "Sumuru" of the 1950's. His youthful reading had a lot to do with this. As a boy, Sax was much attracted to the work of Dumas, and to that historical period in general. This was the heyday of the great courtesans of Europe, all of whom, in accordance with contemporary fashions, became married women first and courtesans afterwards. Eve's conquest was therefore rendered the easier by Sax's conviction, amounting almost to superstition, that she belonged to a class impossible to resist. But his later encounter with Nanette no doubt convinced him that, for all that, the twentieth century teenager is the new temptress.

The Great Fog of 1934, which paralyzed London traffic for nearly a week, gave Sax the kick-off for his next Fu Manchu story. Likewise, his skillful and dramatic write-up of that phenomenal episode probably added a good deal to the somewhat erroneous idea of foreigners that London is a city interminably blacked-out by impenetrable fog. Saving his newly-acquired Egyptian settings for stories more to his taste, Sax restored *The Trail of Fu Manchu* to the former and already rapidly vanishing locale of London's Chinatown.

But during this year, Sax gave most of his available time to a new and vastly ambitious experiment in house-building. Henceforward, he decided, his general headquarters would be in the country, keeping merely an adequate base in London for his necessary work in town. For this latter, he fixed upon a small, modern apartment in Sloane Street.

Meanwhile, they looked for a suitable site in the neighborhood of Lovelands Way. They found it adjacent to the wide stretch of common land lying between the twin towns of Reigate and Redhill. Here, situated amid other sizeable holdings, stood a rambling Victorian mansion on the crest of a slope running down to a valley, the opposite side rising to the densely wooded heights of Reigate Hill.

At her first sight of the gardens, Elizabeth knew them for the most beautiful she had ever seen. Yet, in the same moment, her sixth sense operated again and she felt a sense of tragedy. There was nothing sinister or malevolent in the atmosphere of the place, but rather a prevailing undercurrent of sadness. This she put down to her sorrow at leaving her country cottage. She abandoned it with regret, for she had been happy there and she had no ambition to become the queen of a Fu Manchu palace. But, as always, she allowed her own wishes to count for nothing against the all-important ideal of helping Sax to achieve what he wanted.

An army of workmen moved in. The old Victorian mansion was torn down and the new house erected upon the foundations. As before, both exterior and interior were the joint effort of Elizabeth and Sax.

Just at this time, Sax's favorite ship, the old *Mauretania*, completed her term of faithful service and went to the scrap yards. Sax made a journey to Southampton and rescued the beautiful bleached oak panelling of the Smoking Room, to install it in his dining room where, later, it behaved most strangely in times of bad weather, creaking and groaning as it had done when the ship plowed through heavy seas. No doubt there is some natural explanation of this phenomenon, but it was, nonetheless, even to the frequent visitor, slightly unsettling.

The extensive grounds of the place covered fourteen acres. Mere figures mean little, but in terms of real space this would just have accommodated the Great Pyramid. A walk around the perimeter occupied the same time, roughly twenty-five minutes. Within this considerable domain were other dwellings: a gate lodge, a chauffeur's cottage, and a gardener's cottage, in addition to outbuildings and three greenhouses. Thus the Sax Rohmer territory now comprised a tiny, self-contained empire. Bordered by trees, and suitably distant from the town, it was a world in which a man of imagination could surround himself with all that was dear to his heart and forget that any other world existed beyond.

Gatton Park was nearby, and "Gatton" found its way into most of the names of the properties in that district. Sax modestly complied with the tradition, calling his home "Little Gatton." But neither in scale nor in conception was there anything little about it.

28

THE MAN I KNEW

THE BUILDING OF LITTLE GATTON OCCUPIED FIFTEEN MONTHS. DURING that time, Sax wrote the story inspired by his recent visit to Egypt, *The Bat Flies Low*. I am prepared to admit that I may be prejudiced about this story, since it was the first which ever came to me from his own hands and remains today among my most treasured possessions. Nevertheless, I honestly consider it an exceptionally fine work.

Briefly, *The Bat Flies Low* is concerned with a hypothesis that the ancient Egyptians may have possessed a system of lighting —a kind of "stored sunlight"—unknown to us today. The story further mentions a museum piece of unidentified purpose, which may have been a "solar lamp," and the plot is woven around the attempts of an American electric company to rediscover the principle.

I mention these various details for the interesting fact that, assuming them to be merely a product of Sax's fertile imagination, I later asked him if such was indeed the case. To my great surprise, he told me that it was not. Just such a theory *did* exist, an actual relic had existed, and an American company had employed a research team on the project. The factual outcome—bleakly different from Sax's story—was that, after a year's work, the researchers (headed, I think he said, by a Swedish scientist) reported that they believed a further few months of study would enable them to reproduce this long-forgotten system. Thereupon, belat-

234

edly, the sponsors woke up to the fact that, if they did, they would create a thing which would outdate all their profitable stock lines of electrical equipment. The research team was hastily disbanded. I do not know where Sax got hold of this information but, as a story behind a story, it is certainly worth the telling. Such out-of-the-way anecdotes popularly supposed to be no more than flights of fancy, were a notable feature of his storehouse of strange knowledge.

The story took its appointed place in *Collier's*, but the editors of the magazine were still eager for more exploits of Fu Manchu. Having, for the time being, satisfied his artistic leanings with the Egyptian tale, Sax gracefully complied. He did more than comply. This time he decided to go the whole way—to reward his American supporters by transferring the activities of Fu Manchu to the United States.

In May 1935, while the workmen put the finishing touches to Little Gatton, Sax and Elizabeth arrived in New York. It was their first visit in almost three years, and reports of their arrival fill a whole scrapbook of press cuttings. Sax was now so much an established figure in current American literature that he was felt to be an American property, and the newspapers admonished him gently for the "long time" he had been absent from their shores.

True to his usual technique of working on information gathered at first hand, Sax intended to make a quick but comprehensive study of crime and police methods in New York. In the vast network of gangsterdom thrown out of work by the repeal of prohibition, he saw a ready-made source of conscripts to the army of Fu Manchu. Moreover, in the confused political scene, he was quick to see a suitable theme for the story. The colorful, ruggedly uncouth figure of Huey Long, one-time Governor of Louisiana, whose aims hinted frankly at dictatorship, whose slogan "Every man a king" captured the imagination of millions, and whose headlong career ended, dramatically, in assassination, was the very prototype of a Fu Manchu victim.

The New York Police Department co-operated nobly and with boisterous enthusiasm. Detectives from Center Street turned up at the Waldorf-Astoria and hurried Sax off, intent on showing him the secret life of their Chinatown. When, at 4 A.M., they had still not returned, Elizabeth began to wonder if they really were

235

detectives—the visitors had all been in plain clothes. It occurred to her that he might have been kidnapped. But she need not have worried. Following their investigations of the underworld, the party had simply gravitated quite naturally to a convenient bar.

Sax came back tired and a little shaken by the expedition. The strongarm tactics of his hosts left him rather shocked. Purely for his own edification, they had forced their way into private houses, interrupted family dinner parties, and bulldozed their way to the very doors of a *Tong* temple. All this the Chinese population endured with Oriental philosophy. But the culminating point came when his hosts attempted to take a picture of him with a band of attractively evil-looking Asiatics. No sooner was the camera produced than the whole group of unwilling "extras" dispersed hot-foot through doors and windows, for they were all of them illegal immigrants!

In further pursuit of his inquiries, Sax paid a visit to Chicago, where he was persuaded to make one of his rare appearances before the microphone at a broadcasting studio.

While in New York, he had given a press interview and, asked how he would deal with the crime problem made himself temporarily notorious by replying that he would round up all confirmed offenders, banish them to an uninhabited island, and leave them to destroy one another. Sax was no believer in the theory of re-education and reformation. Punishment of the criminal he regarded, quite frankly, as a judicial revenge and a deterrent by example. Kindness to dumb animals he carried to the limit of absurdity, but human animals he considered capable of responsibility for their actions and fairly liable to the reward of their transgressions. Once, I remember, he briefly crossed swords with George Bernard Shaw who, in his well-known guise of social reformer, had burst into print, advocating the abolition of corporal punishment. Sax wrote to the same editors, sardonically inquiring whether G. B. S. proposed to substitute a term of imprisonment devoted to the compulsory reading of his own works. Sax believed in government by the whip and the axe, though I doubt whether he would have stood by this in practice. Elizabeth, however, who should know better than I, disagrees. She says he would have.

Relations with *Collier's* had become cordial in the extreme. Because of her shrewd judgment concerning *The Emperor of Amer-*
236

ica stories, Elizabeth was now regarded there with something like reverence. Tom Beck, the editor-in-chief, whose respect extended to a close personal friendship, urged them to stay on with Sax to become a permanent member of the editorial staff.

But, for all the honors which he received in that country, Sax found the materialism of everyday life in America unsatisfying to his tastes. If he had accepted, this story might have had a different end; it is difficult to guess. Whether he would have gained by it or not, he would have been denied the brief enjoyment of his little kingdom in Surrey that he was to have before the war-clouds gathered anew. And, for the fact that he did not accept, I, at least, may feel selfishly grateful, for had he done so, I should never have met him.

The Sax Rohmers had moved into Little Gatton so shortly before I came upon the scene that I had some difficulty in finding the place. The nameplate had yet to be fixed by the gate. Nevertheless, no sooner had I set eyes upon the house than I knew that none other than Sax Rohmer could have built it. Seen from the road, not much was visible but a hint of white stone walls and the dormer windows of an upper story covered by the long sweep of the most fantastic roof that ever graced the Surry countryside. It was tiled in a multicolored patchwork of blue, red, purple, with a sparse touch of gold. Had the checkwork been regular, the effect must have been garish and vulgar, but, patternless, it had the aspect of that floral carpet which Sax and Elizabeth had seen in the Lebanon hills.

Of my feelings at that time, and of my first meeting with Elizabeth, it would be easy for me to write at length. But here it is more appropriate that I should pass on rapidly to the night when, several weeks later, I found myself waiting, breathless with anticipation, in Sax's book-lined study.

The motif of the furnishings was exotic: Middle Eastern with, here and there, touches of ancient Egypt and China. Framed illustrations to "Fires of Baal" hung upon the walls. There were no half-measures with Sax. It was typical of him that, having consented to see me, he should do so not on neutral ground but in the intimacy of the sanctum to which none but his closest friends penetrated. Two or three minutes passed; then footsteps sounded briskly and the door opened.

If I have so far neglected to give any personal description of Sax Rohmer, it is because I have preferred to remember him as I saw him at that moment. In every respect, he was then at the prime of life. Surely there could be no better moment at which to describe him.

I saw a man nonchalantly clad in ancient flannel trousers and a polo-necked sweater. My first impression was that of a light-weight boxer. I sensed an intense vitality which, for a while, I mistook for physical toughness, not realizing that it was—or could be—wholly mental.

Knowing that *Fu Manchu* had first been published in 1913, I estimated his age at forty, lacking which knowledge I should have been tempted to think him younger. He was, in fact, fifty-two. As yet, his hair showed few traces of grey but, commencing to recede, it disclosed a brow of Shakespearean proportions. But no one who ever saw Sax failed to be immediately and, usually, the most of all impressed by his eyes. They were strange eyes. Somewhat deep-set, veiled by those uncomfortably long lashes and shadowed by luxuriant eyebrows, they formed appropriate pools of darkness alive with submerged mystery. In strong sunlight, they were seen to be blue; at other times, they appeared violet. On a less worldly plane, Sax's eyes had other qualities harder to name and more difficult still to describe. In *Grey Face*, he has mentioned "the eyes of a man who has practiced hypnotism" and, if that practice really does leave some tangible feature, it had certainly done so where he himself was concerned. When he looked at you directly, you sometimes felt that he did not see you at all; sometimes, on the contrary, that he looked directly into your soul.

I can hardly feel surprised that women were often terrified of him. Women, despite their protests, have no objection to men whose eyes seem to undress them, but they have the strongest aversion to being dissected. Nevertheless, meeting the regard of those penetrating eyes, I knew that there was nothing to fear. Though, in that softly-lighted room, his eyes at first seemed to me jet black, they had not the hard, cruel glitter of onyx but rather the velvety warmth of the Egyptian night which he loved so well.

His handshake was firm; the mystic was, I noted, subordinate to the healthy virility of "a man's man." During those first few minutes, while I tried to link up something in his writings with the

238

outward personality of the man I saw, I thought of the popular (and inaccurate) saying that an author always writes his first book about himself. Sax had not done that, but the necessary hint was there. Rightly or wrongly, I thought then (and still do) that Nayland Smith represented his youthful ideal of the type of man that he might have wished to be, and Dr. Petrie the type of man that he thought he could be. In varying degrees, he possessed the attributes of both.

Nayland Smith's staccato, machine-gun type of speech (which, for some reason he seemed to admire) he had failed to cultivate. He spoke quietly, with the musical inheritance of his Irish ancestors, having perhaps the most genuinely cultured voice I have ever listened to: the voice of a man who loves English, unmarred either by dialect or public school affectations. He chose his words carefully, and spoke to an astonishing degree as he wrote. (Sax's fondness for parentheses is a marked characteristic of his style—and not uncommon among other writers. But I have never encountered anyone else who used them in everyday speaking.)

One further singularity intruded upon our conversation. Sax suffered occasionally from a peculiar affliction of the eye muscles. Irritated, perhaps, by the overlong lashes, they would suddenly turn upwards till only the whites showed, and he appeared blind. This was most alarming. It happened only rarely, but it chanced to happen while we were talking, and I was about to ask him if he were all right when the spasm passed.

Not surprisingly, perhaps, I do not very clearly remember what we discussed. Certainly, I had no slightest intention of obtruding my own affairs into the conversation, least of all to let it be known that I too aspired to be a writer. But, with that keen perception which would have made him a formidable addition to the staff of Scotland Yard, Sax guessed it and challenged me with it. And no sooner had I admitted it than he said, "Let me see what you have written. I may be able to help."

I took him at his word, as he had meant me to do, and from that time onwards he read and criticized everything that I wrote. God knows how he could have detected any merit in it, but, firmly and patiently, he took my education in hand and, within a year, I had sold my first story, whereat Sax was unselfishly delighted, saying that I had done it at nearly the same age as himself.

This, above all, was the striking thing about the amazing man—his quick sympathy, his absolute freedom from meanness, his readiness to encourage any whom he felt to be on the same path. Of his friend Houdini, Sax wrote: "His generosity, not only of mind but of spirit, set him apart in a selfish world." I would write the same of Sax.

Early the following year, *President Fu Manchu* was published in *Collier's*, making the eighth of the series. Written for the particular gratification of the American public, it was an adequate tale, but somewhat lacked the bizarre elements notable in the others. I was not particularly attracted to it. Neither was Sax. Currently, he was engaged on another story with an Egyptian setting, having this in mind not for a book but as a film scenario designed for Marlene Dietrich. The idea was well received, and the upshot was that he received an invitation to go to Hollywood and work there on the final script. This, however, did not at all appeal to him. Thinking of the experience of his friend, P. G. Wodehouse, who, not so long previously, had been called to Hollywood and paid to stay there for many weeks, doing precisely nothing, and fearing that he might well be involved in a similar adventure, he flatly refused to go. Consequently, the deal fell through.

Sax converted the film script into a novel, under the title of *White Velvet*, in which form it actually became one of his better books. At the same time, he adapted it for radio presentation and—the story being concerned with a theatrical touring group in Egypt—wrote incidental music and lyrics. In this latter activity of his youthful days, his pen had lost nothing of its skill, and I have nostalgic memories of the wistful "Cold as Snow," which I thought particularly appealing.

The *White Velvet* radio series was duly featured by the B.B.C. Though broadcasting in England had been firmly established since the mid-1920's, Sax had not done much with this medium. The reason, simply enough, is that no national broadcasting service offered fees worthwhile to top-ranking writers. In America in the early 1930's, *Collier's* had engineered a Fu Manchu radio series (and, I believe, as series based on *The Emperor of America*) but this they had done in the name of "publicity" so that Sax received no money from that source. Some years later, the London-based I.B.C., operating "pirate" transmitters from Radio Luxembourg and Radio Normandie, set about a long series of sponsored programs based on the first three Fu Manchu books. More than fifty episodes were broadcast. The adaptations were done by Sax himself, with some assistance from Elizabeth—even I helped a little—and were no doubt the most faithful versions of the original stories that have so far appeared "on the air."

A few years later Sax was commissioned to contribute an original episode to a B.B.C. radio series entitled *What Happened at 8:20*. He did so, and the script was accepted. Thereafter, a highly peculiar thing happened. Listening to the episode broadcast during the week preceding that in which his own was to be played, Sax was amazed and enraged to observe that the entire final scene had been "lifted" from his script and fitted into this other contributor's effort. A furious communication with the drama department of the B.B.C. followed. No explanation was forthcoming, but he was tactfully invited to submit an alternative script, and was paid for both.[18]

Though the charge was irrefutable and justice wholly upon his side, this somewhat shady business no doubt left relations a trifle strained. Nor, as it happened, did Sax's subsequent behavior do much to endear him to the B.B.C. At the opening of the scheduled broadcast, he was to appear in person. He had agreed to this reluctantly and, in due course, off he went to the Eccentric Club, to meet D. A. Clarke-Smith who, somehow or other, always seemed to take part in his stage pieces and was taking part in this one, the intention being that they should have a few drinks and then go to the studio together.

Less than half an hour remained to go when Elizabeth, remembering her husband's hazy concept of time, presently thought of telephoning the club to make sure that they really were on their way. And, as she had half-suspected, they were not. Consternation, and a precipitous taxi ride to Broadcasting House; Sax erupted into the studio, hot and ruffled, so much so that he failed to heed the warning light. It flicked on, catching him in mid-speech, and some millions of delighted listeners heard him salute them with the words, ". . . no bloody fear!"

This was unique, not only for the B.B.C., but also for Sax since, odd though it may seem, he very rarely swore. Despite all the violence which one might be tempted to expect from the nature of his stories, he was so curiously gentle in his own life that I never even heard him raise his voice in anger. At that particular moment, he was certainly excited, but I doubt whether he was angry. Sax had suffered too much in the way of plagiarism to be much disturbed by it. His attitude was generally one of resigned indifference.

Plagiarism is difficult to discover, more difficult to prove, and rarely worth following up. In the case of so exceptionally well-known a writer it can, furthermore, take several forms: blatant, covert, and even unconscious. Generations will pass, for example, before even the most conscientious of authors can write of a Chinese villain without evoking echoes of Fu Manchu.[19]

But equally extreme cases were not lacking. In my high school days, I had come across a writer of boys' detective stories who had incontrovertibly abstracted the complete plot of *Bat Wing*, episode by episode. I drew Sax's attention to this piece of brigandage, but he was not disturbed. "They wouldn't have the money, even if we sued them," he said, philosophically. "So what's the use?"

A secondary but no less troublesome kind of affront, impossible to track down, is what I might term "plagiarism by analogy." Older readers who saw the original Boris Karloff film *The Mummy* —not the several imitations which followed—may have noted, as I did, that it bore all the hallmarks of a Sax Rohmer story. That is to say, neither characters nor episodes corresponded with anything that he had actually written, yet it was a story that one might expect him to have written. I was not surprised to learn that, in fact, the same studio had received, but rejected, a proposed film treatment of his *Brood of the Witch Queen*.

29

THE TRAGIC VALLEY

WITH ADMIRABLE PLANNING AND INSTINCTIVE GOOD TASTE, SAX HAD achieved his kingdom of fantasy, but the number of subjects required to accomplish the smooth running of it was not small, and the administration of the whole thing a sore charge upon Elizabeth. To the daily business of household management on a vastly increased scale had now to be added an amount of office work consisting of accounts, insurance contributions, and wages not inferior to that of an average-sized business. She was anything but idle.

The resident population of Little Gatton included a butler and his wife (the cook) who lived in the gate lodge. The other two cottages were respectively occupied by the chauffeur and his wife, and the head gardener and his wife. Four under-gardeners lived out, likewise a "daily help." Two suitably attractive parlormaids shared quarters in the main building. One would like to imagine that they wore exotic, revealing outfits, but what they actually wore were smart green uniforms designed by Elizabeth. The butler exchanged the traditional vestments of his profession for a white jacket, and looked more like a ship's steward.

Danny the Scotch terrier, who had been with the family so long that his coat was liberally streaked with grey hairs, was the only household animal. Sax regretted that there was no cat, but, "It wouldn't be fair to the birds," he said.

Adjacent to the long windows of the lounge—a vast room which occupied two-thirds of the ground floor—a sizeable aviary fronted on the terrace. The number of feathered inhabitants varied from time to time; usually there were about fourteen. One of Elizabeth's numerous brothers made a hobby of breeding canaries, and had managed to create a pure white one without impairing its voice. This singular specimen occupied a cage all to itself in the dining room.

A family of grey squirrels enjoyed squatters' rights in the big tulip tree, halfway down the lawn.

Alongside the kitchen, a narrow, passage-like space was fitted up as a bar—it contained nearly everything drinkably alcoholic known to man's imagination—with three sliding hatches in the *Mauretania* panelling communicating with the dining room. At a glance, the house had seemingly been designed for giving large-scale parties, though comparatively few took place. In fact, it had simply been designed to provide facilities for the owner to do anything he might want to do.

Discussing the question of an appropriate party after they moved in, and finding that even these lavish provisions would be inadequate for all the people who *had* to be invited, Sax and Elizabeth hit upon what they thought to be a good idea. They would throw open the house for a week and leave their friends to come in any time they chose. It was not a good idea. The guests arrived in reasonably-sized batches, drank themselves into king-sized hangovers and lay around semi-conscious till, finally, they could drag themselves away just as the next batch arrived. Instead of being sporadic, it became a continuous relay. "We saw the last of them off," Elizabeth said sadly, "propping each other up in the doorway." The staff handed in their notices in a body.

So far as parties went, the place was altogether too convenient. With the great size of it—the multiplicity of secluded corners and bedrooms—couples tended to drift off. One never knew whither they might have withdrawn, or even if they had gone home.

On a warm summer night, my own favorite spot was the tiny island, approached from the lower shore of the lotus pool by a Japanese half-moon bridge. Here there was a rustic bench, over-hung with some kind of flowering creeper. In the dark water below, golden orfe flashed with a glitter of scales between the lily pads. Ahead, the whole four-acre expanse of lawn mounted

244

smoothly to the white-walled house glowing with softly lit windows, moonlight transforming the checkered roof to a patchwork of blue and silver.

Sax, who had shown no previous ambition to be a car owner, now possessed two, a small Daimler and an imposing Rolls Royce coupe-de-ville. The isolated situation of his new headquarters made these necessary. Little Gatton was more than a mile from the shops and Elizabeth, for whose use the Daimler was intended, had to learn to drive. She accomplished this efficiently enough, but hated it. The bigger car was required for Sax's frequent trips to town, and had to be chauffeur-driven. He, of course, had no intentions of learning to drive. He had other things to think about than road signs and gear levers.

Jointly, they used the Rolls also for their annual trips around England, which had now become part of an established routine. Once, too, they shipped it across to France to follow the familiar route of the Monte Carlo rally down to the south. Whenever he could find the time, Sax was still occupied with his roulette schemes and his search to solve the mystery of numbers.

Passing through Paris, on that occasion, they found themselves once again rubbing shoulders with history. As they usually did, they put up for the night at the Meurice. To their annoyance, however, the occupiers of the adjoining suite of rooms were creating so colossal a din, late into the night, that they were at length compelled to complain to the management. The din ceased.

Next morning, Sax felt a little sorry when he learned that their noisy neighbors had been the entourage of the Duke and Duchess of Windsor, on their way into voluntary exile. For the former Prince of Wales, having lived in close proximity to him, he felt something like a personal affection. Moreover, Sax was a staunch Royalist. Though he could easily transfer his loyalty to the unfortunate monarch's successor, he was bitterly opposed to the interference of the State and, more particularly, of the Church with what he held to be the private life of the Royal Family.

Even with the more modest of cars, most people can accomplish a journey through France without much adventure. But, characteristically, Sax and Elizabeth could not so manage it in a Rolls. Somehow or other, they got it stuck on a snow-covered

245

road, high up in the mountains, and appeared quite likely to be frozen to death when another car arrived to tow them out.

So, eventually, they came to the coast. Here there occurred yet one more curious instance worthy of record on that trip. Coming out, one morning, to the car, Elizabeth found the chauffeur in casual conversation with a maid from the hotel. As she looked at them, another flash of that strange inspiration for which no process of reason could account crossed her thoughts. "Barham," she said presently, "you're going to marry that girl!"

Barham was puzzled. Not only was the girl a chance acquaintance, but he was already married. Nevertheless, Elizabeth, as usual, was right. Several years later his wife died, and he did marry the girl.

Elizabeth had tried to forget that premonition of tragedy which she had felt on first entering the grounds of Little Gatton. They had built the house and moved in without mishap. But she was shortly afterwards startled to hear her thoughts echoed by a girl who came there seeking employment. "It's the most beautiful garden I've ever seen," the girl confessed, naively, "but it does put me in mind of a graveyard!" All the same, she joined the household staff. Tragically, it was not for very long. Some few weeks later, she was knocked off her bicycle and killed outside the house.

The events of the years which followed in that tragic valley were more than a little strange. Within the house and the grounds in which it stood, there was never a hint of any malign influence. Yet, all around, death struck persistently. A further traffic accident in the lane outside killed two boys, not that it was a busy or dangerous thoroughfare, but merely a cul-de-sac giving access to the houses which it served. In a house nearby, a small girl was burned to death. Depressed by an unhappy love affair, a youth from the house next door shot himself in his car. In a shed at the bottom of the lane, a gardener committed suicide by hanging.

On the opposite slope from the windows of Little Gatton, one could see the roof of another sizeable property. The mother of the family living in that house arranged to escort her daughter abroad—to Egypt, I believe—where she was to be married. But the girl never reached her fiance's side. She died on the boat. Afterwards, the war years came and the same house was destroyed in the air raids. And shortly before the war Sax's nominal "secretary" succumbed to a sudden heart attack.

Altogether more in the way of coincidence than I would care to include in a work if fiction and expect to be believed. Thankfully, for some strange reason, Little Gatton remained a haven of safety. Perhaps it was the powerful influence of Sax.

Although he was so much concerned, now, with the turning out of best-selling novels, Sax had by no means abandoned his beliefs in occult forces and occasional experiments therewith. Some of his readers, aware of this, plagued him upon the subject, pressing for details, and finally he was persuaded to bring some notoriety upon himself by the publication of a magazine article in which he discussed the possibilities of "astral travel," releasing the spirit from the material body, and sending it upon voyages of exploration, and actually giving particulars as to the means by which the feat should be attempted. He confessed that he had tried it, but was rather non-committal about the results.[20]

Elizabeth, however, is quite forthright about saying that he succeeded. She swears that there was a night when she saw a shadowy "second Sax" detach itself from the recumbent form of her husband, glide to the door of their bedroom, and turn to look back in her direction. But, she insists, that "other form" was his evil counterpart. The face was that of a devil.

In quite another sense of the term, Sax's unworldliness became a marked feature of those early days at Little Gatton. With everything that he could conceivably need handy to his fingertips, and knowing himself to be totally irresponsible with money, he gave up carrying any at all. Elizabeth, left with the business of paying for everything, found this embarrassing. She had no objection to being the business manager of the team—in fact, she knew that she had to be—but when it came down to the details of cab fares and cinema tickets, she rebelled. In the hope of solving the problem, she drew £100 in one pound notes from the bank, put the money in a drawer of Sax's desk, and told him to place some of the notes in his pocket when they were going out anywhere. But it was no use. He never remembered.

Some weeks having elapsed, Elizabeth tried the experiment of going secretly to his desk, and extracting fifty pounds from the bundle. The same night, she asked him to count the remainder.

Sax did so and, on finding it to total fifty pounds, showed no trace of surprise. He merely supposed that he had somehow spent the other fifty. She gave up.

Sax wrote no book-length story during 1937. He was then engaged on a series of short stories concerning a master illusionist named Bazarada, which he wrote as a tribute to the memory of Harry Houdini. The stories were published in *Collier's* during 1937 and 1938 and, in the year following, were put together as a short novel under the title "Salute to Bazarada," in the collection *Salute to Bazarada and Other Stories.*

Despite the fact that I was now personally in the picture, Sax's comings and goings were extremely difficult to follow. Once, having some appointment to make, I telephoned the house, asking for Elizabeth, for a fortnight previously I had seen a newspaper article which mentioned that Sax had that day sailed for New York. To my astonishment he answered me in person.

"I stayed there two days!" he explained, nonchalantly.

Another, lengthier trip was, however, in the offing. Further Fu Manchu stories had to be written, and Sax was anxious to link up the Doctor's activities with the Voodoo island of Haiti. In Jamaica, he had failed to secure the material he wanted concerning that weird form of sorcery, and some closer inquiry was, he felt, long overdue.

Plans were made, and the journey undertaken, with Elizabeth once again in tow. They proceeded via Cristobal. Here Sax had to be, with some difficulty, dissuaded from purchasing a shrunken head. In Egypt, he had shown an equal disposition to buy a sarcophagus. But Elizabeth was adamant about both.

The Isthmus of Darien, which joins the North American continent to the South, is mantled with dense jungles infested by dangerous members of the cat family, poisonous reptiles, and noxious insects of every size and variety. Sax, who had sometimes feared that he might have strained the bounds of credulity with some of the live instruments of villainy employed in his stories, found to his surprise that his estimates had been no more than conservative.

In Panama, Sax was privileged to see the private collection maintained by a noted authority on the fauna of the Canal Zone, a singular personage who handled his venomous specimens with the casual indifference of a circus performer. He had, he said, been bitten so often that he was virtually immune. Sax, leaning over the low wall of a snake pit, watched in amazement not unmixed with alarm while his host strolled about the floor of the place among that nightmare population of wriggling horrors, grabbed and lifted up snakes, squeezing their throats to display their poison fangs for his inspection.

But the highlight of the proceedings came when a bird-eating spider with hairy legs the thickness of a man's fingers was captured and, grossly perched on the back of the doctor's left hand, held up to a proximity of less than two feet from his visitor's face whereat Sax, who had seen the thing jump farther than that, visibly recoiled.

On the same visit, but more reasonably confined behind glass, he was shown a six-inch millipede, blood red in color and said to carry enough venom to kill ten men. Later, in the room of an American acquaintance staying at the same hotel, he was, as he put it, "present at the execution" of an earwig-like creature fully seven inches in length, which had made an unwelcome appearance between the bedsheets. These things Elizabeth had, not long afterwards, some urgent cause to remember.

From the moment that they set foot in Haiti, they entered an other-world atmosphere to which the oddities of Cristobal had been a fitting introduction. A touch of the macabre intruded even into the customs sheds, where a yawning, gorgeously-uniformed official showed no interest in the contents of their baggage but became volubly excited when he found Elizabeth to be in possession of an apple. This, he insisted, could not be allowed into the country at any price, and he must confiscate it.

"Oh no you don't!" Elizabeth said indignantly, and ate it.

They moved into the one habitable hotel in Port-au-Prince, where they found themselves to be the only European guests.

I may as well say here and now that Sax's attempts to penetrate the secrets of Voodoo were not very successful. His purpose was known, and the local inhabitants uncooperative. Everywhere he was met with suspicious looks, thinly veiled hostility and open obstruction.

But he received all that he needed in the way of dramatic

atmosphere. The very air of the place reeked of mystery. Day and night, drums throbbed distantly in the hills—no one could be found to say why. But, strangest of all, perhaps, was the behavior of the cocks—of which there seemed to be an inordinately large number—for these traditional heralds of the morning made the night raucous with their crowing from dusk till dawn.

Seated, one evening, alone on the dimly lit terrace of the hotel, Sax and Elizabeth were mildly intrigued by the sudden appearance of a native girl who carried a feather fan. Making her way to a long cane chair in the shadows, the newcomer reclined languorously upon it and, quietly fanning herself, watched them both with a grave, unwinking stare which she made no attempt to disguise.

After some minutes, this continued scrutiny became rather unnerving and Elizabeth was about to try the experiment of speaking to the girl when she stood up silently and vanished into the building.

Curious to know the reason for this somewhat odd behavior, Sax followed quickly on her heels but, nevertheless failing to find her in the lobby, asked the man at the desk to tell him the identity of the person who had just entered. The man shook his head blankly.

Sax persisted and described the girl.

Looking rather uneasy, and with seemingly unnecessary vehemence, the clerk assured him that there was no such person at the hotel and that no one had come into the lobby before him.

Haiti was like that, all the way through—stimulating to the imagination, but unrewarding as to information.

Tourism was, as yet, an undeveloped feature of the island's economy. The food proved quite unacceptable to Sax's simple but fastidious palate and, once again, he was forced to exist on a diet of cheese. At the end of a week's stay, he was told that he had eaten all the cheese on the island.

Meantime, Elizabeth suffered her second encounter with an abominable insect. It happened one night in their hotel bedroom. Sax was seated at a small table, writing up his notes by the light of a shaded lamp. The heat and the humidity were oppressive. Elizabeth lay at full length on her bed, under a tent-like awning of mosquito netting, and sensibly devoid of any stitch of clothing.

So, peacefully somnolent, like a cover artist's portrayal of the Sleeping Princess, she remained till, all at once, the awful fact dawned on her that she shared her couch with a brown, four-inch monstrosity that was *inside* the netting. She sat up with a shriek. Simultaneously, the thing folded itself in half, leapt a yard high, and came down on top of her. Elizabeth shrieked again, and tried to claw her way out of the netting only to become hopelessly entangled in it. The unknown creature (probably as alarmed as she was) went dancing around in prodigious bounds, each accompanied by a dry, snapping sound.

Sax sent his chair flying and rushed to her assistance—or, rather, to her confusion. His feverish attempts to disentangle her from the netting only entangled her the more inextricably. The three-sided battle went on madly and noisily for a few minutes till, at length, the whole outfit was torn from the frame and Elizabeth rolled on the floor, like a netted mermaid. From this undignified position, Sax managed finally to extricate her, but they never found out what happened to the abominable insect. It was probably squashed in the melée.

From Elizabeth's description, it seemed likely to me that the thing was actually nothing more lethal than one of the larger kinds of singing insect, but she did not take kindly to the suggestion.

"It didn't sing!" she said indignantly. "It just flew and jumped all over me!"

Whatever it was, Sax never lost an opportunity to make capital of the experience, and it duly went into the next-but-one Fu Manchu story as the horror of the Snapping Fingers.

Sax reserved his Haitian adventure for a later book, and the ninth of the series, *The Drums of Fu Manchu*, was set partly in London and partly in Venice.

By this time I had become a fairly frequent visitor to Little Gatton. I had opportunities to get to know the best of the man, to know his faults, and to love him no less for them, since they made him human.

Sax's work was now famous not only in England and America, and in all English-speaking countries, but literally throughout the world. Though the Nazis had suppressed his formerly popular German editions, his books were elsewhere available in French,

Italian, Spanish, Portuguese, Dutch, Greek, Swedish, Hungarian, Danish, Polish, Czech, and Arabic. Japanese publishers (who, at that time, were highly unreliable) also issued translations in their language, but did not pay for them. Likewise unpaid, but readily contributed by Sax, were printings in Braille for the use of the blind.

In his own lifetime, he had become something of a legend. Everyone knew his work, everyone knew his name, but few had seen even so much as a photograph of him or heard his voice. An unconscious tribute to these circumstances was, I remember, paid around this time by a confidence trickster who gained the interest of his victims by telling them that he was Sax Rohmer.

Yet my impressions of Sax and Elizabeth in those days were the simple family relations of a devoted couple who lived in a mansion and treated each other like students sharing a bed-sitting-room.

Elizabeth was neither then nor at any time commonly called Elizabeth. I doubt whether anyone has ever been called upon to answer to so many different names as she has. Her relatives usually called her "Rose" or "Rosie." I called her "Lisbeth"—most of her own short stories being published under the name of Lisbeth Knox. But most troublesome of all was the tireless inventiveness of Sax. In the days of his youth, Sax had been one of a group in which it was fashionable to give nicknames to everybody. Among the outlaws of Oakmead Road, he himself for some totally obscure reason had been known as "Digger."[21] The habit stuck and, throughout the fifty years of their married life, he went through a string of pet-names for Elizabeth. By turns, she was Curly, Pobble, Boodle, Kindly, Hicky, Smith, Darn, Little Horse, Goofie, Dinky, and Hookum. When I first knew them, the series had got as far as "Darn."

At the same time, without our being aware of it, the carefree days of life at the top were rapidly drawing to a close. Between them, Sax and Elizabeth devised the script of a stage play, titled *The Body's Upstairs*. Negotiations for production were begun and seemed to be going well. But the threat of war already hung heavy on the air.

I remember a night when, for some reason that I forget, I called upon Sax at 11:30. As usual, the great house was a fantasy of lighted windows shining through the trees. A yellow lantern glowed invitingly above the entrance. From the road, one had only to push open the wrought-iron gate to step into a fairyland in which the troubled world outside seemed empty and without significance. That night we forgot the luxurious armchairs and settees of the lounge, and stood together in the bar, resting our elbows on the counter. Something in the conversation turned upon the Great War "which," Sax said gravely, "if we're to have another, was nothing but a skirmish."

A few weeks later, the blow fell. On the last night of 1939, I stood again in the huge lounge, one of the thirty-six guests at the last of the grand scale New Year parties held in that house. Heavy drapes of Mexican folkweave discreetly concealed the blacked-out windows; wall lamps and standards, gleaming on the rock-like, amber plasterwork of walls and ceiling, turned the room into an Aladdin's cavern. As the chimes of Big Ben sounded midnight from the big radiogram, Sax shook hands with me. "Please God we may all be here next year!" he said fervently.

30

ARMAGEDDON

IT WAS CLEAR AT THE OUTSET THAT THE SECOND WORLD WAR WAS GOING to be a vastly different proposition from the First, so far as authors were concerned. In this new outbreak of international madness, there were no great reputations to be made, but only to be lost. Many of England's top-line writers transferred themselves promptly to the United States. They did not fear for their skins, but they feared for their work.

But Sax, who had the most reason to go, stayed obstinately where he was. That patriotic fervor which he had displayed in the earlier debacle again came to the fore and, so long as his country was in trouble, nothing would shift him.

The result to him personally was, of course, disastrous. Immediately on the outbreak of hostilities, Sax resumed those highly secret activities which had occupied him during the latter part of the so-called Great War. As before, Elizabeth did not know what they were and did not try to find out. Purely at a guess, they may have been concerned with the "cracking" of enemy codes and possibly also with radio propaganda. At all events, it was desk work which did not require him to leave Little Gatton, where, from time to time, he received mysterious visitors.

Other mysterious visitors seem to have come from quite another source. There were sundry incidents. All activity, personal and national, having been withdrawn to the Surrey headquarters, the flat in Sloane Street was sublet. Significantly, it was first ac-

254

quired by a titled German, supposedly of Jewish extraction and in flight from the Nazi terror. This gentleman subsequently made several seemingly innocuous and purposeless appearances at Little Gatton, which Sax did not quite like. In due course, his tenant was quietly removed by officers of the Special Branch.

Hopefully, Sax got out his file of nefarious plans for the assassination of Ludendorff and Hindenburg, updated them to cover the assassination of Hitler, Goering, and Himmler, and again submitted them to the War Office. Needless to say, they were once again received with the unvoiced comment of being "not quite cricket" and rejected out of hand. Or were they? So much has happened since those days that one tends to forget the earlier stages—as, for example, the bomb attempt on Hitler's life, on the night of November 8, 1939, accompanied by a pitched battle between Wehrmacht and SS officers in Berlin.

Elizabeth, as usual, did her share and more. No sooner had the evacuation of children from London commenced than the hospitality of the house was extended to fifteen Jewish boys from the East End. Here they no doubt had the time of their lives, for Elizabeth knew no way of treating anybody under her roof other than as an honored guest. In due course, they were replaced by officers of the Canadian Army.

Meanwhile, Sax wrote *The Island of Fu Manchu*, based on his trip to Haiti. In sharp contrast to the Fu Manchu stories which he had written during the First World War, this latest adventure took place against the actual wartime background of that date. Tenth in the Fu Manchu series, it was the last in that group of great novels which the sophisticated tastes of the 1930's had made possible. Henceforward there would be no comparable opportunity.

As yet, in the early days of 1940, the shooting war had not extended to Britain, far less to the quiet hills of Surrey. But the Battle of Britain, which shortly followed, was staged in the skies above southeast England, and the inhabitants of Little Gatton had a grandstand view. Day after day, they saw the Luftwaffe planes fly over in perfect formation, shining silver in the summer sunlight, till the fighters came up from nearby Gatwick. Then the whole thing would break up into a crazy pattern of spinning shapes and crossed vapor trails, accompanied by the howl of power-diving

Spitfires and the harsh clatter of machine guns.

It was on one of those noisy days that a large piece of shrapnel penetrated the bathroom window while Sax was in occupation. Not knowing exactly what kind of missile had entered, and not waiting to find out, it was thereupon his turn to make a hasty exit from his bath.

The Battle of Britain ended, and the night raids on London began. Sax and Elizabeth converted the extensive cellars, which had formed part of the older property, into a super air-raid shelter, equipped with bunks, a radio, and even a miniature bar. This they offered to the use of any in the district who felt like sleeping there. Fortunately, however, the environs of Reigate were not on the Luftwaffe target and little damage was suffered locally. (Up in London, the old house in Bruton Street, with its Extra Inhabitant possibly still in residence, received a direct hit and was totally destroyed.)

Throughout the dark days of 1941, nothing seemed to go right for the Allies. By mid-summer, though Hitler's unexpected attack on Russia seemed to remove, or at least to postpone, any threat of a German invasion across the Channel, the Nazis effectively occupied the whole of Europe.

I saw little of Sax during that year. We in England were all somewhat preoccupied with matters other than personal. I do not know but suspect that most of Sax's work for Military Intelligence was done at that time. It is significant that he wrote nothing, despite the fact that this was the last period during which it might have been reasonably possible for him to keep up a close contact with the United States. Then, in December, Japan entered the war and America had troubles of her own.

Meanwhile, in Britain, with the establishment of army camps on a wartime footing, the billeting of military personnel in civilian homes had come to an end. The Canadian detachment was withdrawn from Little Gatton and Sax's pocket-sized kingdom left with a degree of autonomy quite beyond his intentions. To my gratified amazement, it was then that he invited me to come and join the siege.

I despair of making his motives understood—for they were such as were common only in a vanished society. In spirit, Sax was essentially one with the ancient Great Masters of the arts and

256

sciences, each of whom took to himself his Disciple. It seemed to him perfectly logical and straightforward to do the same. There was no need to seek further for an explanation. From the very beginning, we had taken each other at face value; polite subterfuges were not required.

Elizabeth, I remember, just smiled and said quietly, "We must all stick together."

And we did. The resident staff of Little Gatton now consisted uniquely of Thorndale, the head gardener, and his son; they did their noble best to cope with the work formerly done by five. The gate lodge and the chauffeur's cottage had been rented out. The cooking and the labor of keeping that enormous house clean and tidy rested solely upon Elizabeth, aided by a woman who came in twice a week.

For a part of the time, some of the place was closed, the furniture under dust sheets. Heating was often a problem, for we could never get enough fuel to feed the iron Moloch which supplied the radiators. In winter, the great lounge remained unusable. But, during the summer months, we somehow got the whole thing going again, and the kingdom of dreams came back into its own.

It was a strange feeling then to sit out on the terrace with the fleecy clouds above and the wide green lawns below, utterly remote from the holocaust of which no visible hint penetrated, knowing oneself a part with that highest expression of a supreme artist's imagination which yet miraculously survived, yet at the same time knowing that ultimately it must perish. Isolated we were, in fact as much as fancy. Both the cars were laid up, and shopping meant a half hour's walk down to the town. So far as rationed foodstuffs were concerned, we were no better off than the rest of the populace—the Sax Rohmers had no dealings with the Black Market—but the extensive kitchen gardens kept us well supplied with fresh vegetables.

The working population of the household included forty-six hens, which lived in a wired-in enclosure and had to be duly registered with the Ministry of Food. At times, they were an embarrassment, for hens are the most unlovable, most unpredictable creatures that man has attempted to harness to his service. On sundry occasions, all forty-six would go on strike and produce nothing for days on end; alternatively, they would go off on a laying spree and inundate us with eggs. Long before hostilities were over, Elizabeth would cheerfully have strangled and boiled the lot of them, but they were too tough even for that.

In the somewhat odd atmosphere of this uneasy paradise, with hell let loose outside, I came to know the Sax Rohmers as members of my own family. This, I found out, was not to make any new discoveries about them, but simply to confirm beyond all possible doubt that they were precisely the people I had always thought them to be.

Some who knew Sax called him secretive. Yes—secretive he was; but I dislike the use of the term because it suggests deceit. And no more transparently honest man ever drew breath. Other than in the company of his intimate friends, he kept his opinions to himself, knowing that, unusual as they generally were, they would be ridiculed by men of lesser understanding. He was human enough not to enjoy this. Again, he had that secretiveness about his writing which characterizes the artist. It was not precisely showmanship, but rather a fear of revealing his work in an unfinished state which might cause him to lose confidence in it. At other times—and this was the closest he came to deceit—he would try to conceal matters which, if known, might be hurtful to those whom he loved. To this extent, then, he was secretive and no more. Certainly, he had none of that short-sighted professional jealousy which urges some otherwise great men to keep their techniques locked away from their would-be followers. Sax had called me to his side for the express purpose of allowing me to learn them and, throughout the next fifteen months, he spared no effort to make sure that I did.

Over the years, Sax had developed a highly efficient method of working which now differed somewhat from his earlier procedures. The first and most urgent necessity, he said, was "to get something on paper." His notes for the episode which he proposed to write, totalling, perhaps, some two or three thousand words, consisted usually of a single sheet of paper scrawled across with tersely cryptic words and phrases which only he could decipher. (Occasionally, *he* couldn't!) Any more detailed notes would, he considered, restrict the free flow of self-expression and render the finished work lifeless.

Operating at an alarming speed from these simple mnemonics,

258

he would next record the first draft on a dictaphone. The wax cylinders—magnetic tape had not yet appeared on the market—were then sent up to London, where they were transcribed into double-spaced typescript.

Mrs. Esmond, who performed this work, was an elderly lady who had been his regular typist for many years. Highly efficient at her job and devoted to Sax, like the rest of us, she was not lacking that touch of the unusual which seemed to go along with all his acquaintances. She was bilingual in English and French, having been brought up in France, and once solemnly assured me that she always said her prayers in French, because she wouldn't dream of addressing "le bon Dieu" other than in that language.

Sax next went to work on the typed copy, spending many hours on it, carefully considering every word and making numerous alterations. It was in this way that his stories acquired their high literary polish. Sometimes I have known him to go pacing his room for five or ten minutes at a time, scowling horribly and drawing furiously at his pipe while he considered the choice of a single word.

On some few occasions, he would afterwards, rather shame-facedly, ask me to retype the script because he had made so many corrections that he feared even Mrs. Esmond might not be able to read it. Having used a machine since I was nine years old, I was already a proficient typist. Nevertheless, it was typical of Sax that he would not allow me to repay his hospitality by doing his work regularly. This, he felt, would be a breach of his unwritten agreement with his old acquaintance and an imposition on me. When Sax chose to give, he gave freely from the greatness of his heart; he would make no bargains.

I learned the secret of the great inlaid coffer from Damascus, which stood in his study. It was half-filled with a mass of papers—totally without order—fragments of uncompleted manuscripts, ideas for stories, suggestions for films scripts and plays, synopses. Whenever it happened that Sax could think of no suitable theme for a required story, the box would be opened and the papers set flying in all directions while he searched among them for inspiration.

"Good material," he said grimly, "is never wasted!"

Most of that good material, I fear, will never see the light.

Some of it I remember well. Completing the collection of short stories titled *Tales of Secret Egypt* was one curious effort, "Pomegranate Flower"—a gem of humor, in which Sax had expertly forged Burton's style, so that it had all the aspects of a translation from the *Thousand Nights and a Night*. And, in the box, there was another. Among the fragmentary material was a ferocious yarn about a bare-breasted female pirate in the South Seas. There were several scenes from a mystic play something in the nature of *Wulfheim* concerning a mad violinist, one line from which sticks in my memory: "*You* dare to criticise *me*! You who do not know B-flat from a bull's backside. . . ."

Once, I recall, I mentioned to Sax that I had thought of writing something about an odd character who wore fur-lined overcoats in midsummer and shivered incessantly, being, in fact, none other than the Devil. Sax laughed good-humoredly, opened the box and showed me a manuscript. It was called "The Cold Man." Artist though he was, he had learned the necessity of restricting artistry to the execution of his work, and the futility of writing something for no better reason than that it amused him.

"Never put pen to paper," he said grimly, "until you've made up your mind where you're going to sell it!"

But, just then, that was precisely the snag. If, under Sax's expert guidance, I did not soar to the ranks of best-selling authors, that was not his fault. Neither was it wholly mine. In 1939, there were more than two dozen monthly magazines in England devoted to the publication of fiction. Now every one of them had folded. The Sunday newspapers which formerly had featured serials, consisted of a meager few sheets with no space for anything but the news. Books were still being published occasionally; in fact, little though it advantaged me, I actually wrote and sold one. But paper rationing restricted everything to a single edition, apart from the fact that (contrary to popular misconceptions) publication in book form constitutes the last and least of an author's sources of revenue.

This was a vastly different situation from that of the First World War. So far as England was concerned, fiction had been rationed out of existence. This was part of the high cost of our war effort. Many who saw in this second great clash of nations the total destruction of our material civilization lived to learn

260

their fears groundless. The world did not perish. But at the time, for the world of popular literature, this was indeed Armageddon.

31

TWILIGHT OF THE GODS

DURING 1942, THE CAT-AND-DOG STRUGGLE IN NORTH AFRICA AND THE lively display of intrigue going on simultaneously in Iraq, Syria, and Iran, inspired Sax to a number of short stories dealing with the adventures of a Camel Corps officer whom he named Bimbâshi Barûk. These were published, somewhat spasmodically, in *Collier's.*

Maintaining the vital link with the United States at this time was a nerve-wracking business. Airmail was expensive, subject to loss and unpredictable delays, and sea-mail out of the question. Hardly a story went out unaccompanied by a frantic exchange of cables inquiring what had happened to it.

There is, among the general public, a tendency to imagine that a world-famous writer has only to put his name to anything in order to sell it. This is quite untrue. If the editor does not like some particular story, he will not buy it, regardless of who may have written it.

Current events, among other things, have a powerful influence on the saleability of a manuscript. I recall that Sax wrote one story, "The Rubber-faced Man," which I thought excellent, although nobody would buy it. More than twenty years later— considerably after his death—the time became right for it, and it was published.[22]

All these vicissitudes Sax accepted as the natural hazards of his profession. But, in the meantime, he was being subjected to quite unnatural hazards. The ordinary running expenses of Little Gatton—plus heavy wartime insurance—were frankly impossible. With the first year of the war, the level of his annual income had dropped by something like ninety per cent. Nevertheless, taxation was ferocious. *Collier's* continued to pay him £400 for each short story; taxes paid, he actually kept £120. The struggle to survive was carried on only by the capital expenditure of Elizabeth's savings, and we all knew that if they ran out before the war ended, as they were almost certain to do, we had to give up.

It is difficult for me to write of those days without bitterness, for it is bitter indeed to see the vision of a great artist, and one's friend, shattered systematically and converted into the wherewithal of destruction. But Sax felt no bitterness. Among us, he was the patriot. I do not think that the rest of us were patriots. To us, Sax and his ideals represented the best that England had to offer and, if they were to be lost, it was very difficult to see what we were fighting for.

Not that we were ourselves doing very much that could be termed fighting. My personal contribution to the war effort consisted of a few hours' service in the local telephone exchange, a persistent tendency to asthma every morning of my life—a legacy from my father—having precluded the possibility of my doing anything more useful. We did what we were told, more being neither required nor desired.

The British War Office felt that it knew its own business best —which, perhaps, it did—and was inclined to resent rather than encourage helpful suggestions. They were not interested in Sax's ingenious ideas for winning the war, and still less in my own simple (but perfectly accurate) predictions of Japanese strategy in the Pacific.

I feel no shame, then, in saying that all which really concerned me was what I could do to help Sax. And, God knows, it was all too little.

Lacking other markets in England, Sax wrote six radio plays for the B.B.C., under the title *Myself and Gaston Max*. These he adapted, with some help from Elizabeth, from a series of short stories published just before the war, but not yet available in book form.23

Despite difficulties, there were still occasions when life was wonderful at Little Gatton. On sunny days—and that summer was a good one—the gardens were exquisite, but the interior of the house was at its most impressive after dark. Then, with the curtains drawn, a profusion of standards and strategically placed table lamps would light up the place, alternating patches of bright illumination with shadowy depths, like a stage-set lit by spotlights.

In this appropriate setting, some of the happiest hours of my life were spent, as I sat in an armchair opposite Sax, listening to many of the tales that have gone into this present history. Whether in writing or in speaking, he was a born raconteur. And no little of his skill lay in his extra-dry sense of humor, often expressed in his talent for turning the well-worn cliché into an unexpected jewel of wit. A fairly typical example occurred one night when we found ourselves eating some locally purchased pastries which, we though fell sadly below the desirable standard. I remarked as much.

"Oh, I've had worse," Sax said conventionally. He considered for a moment, then added thoughtfully, "I forget where!" He was a man who laughed little but smiled often.

As the reader will no doubt have gathered by now, the Sax Rohmers were childless. But this did not bother them. Sax disliked small children, though chiefly in the sense that he disliked their company, just as he disliked the company of any person with whom he could not talk intelligently. In the presence of such beings, he became awkward and embarrassed, finding their trivial topics of conversation unattractive to him and no less irritated by the realization that all he himself said fell upon deaf ears.

More than that, he is on record as having declared that few people of his acquaintance were fit to produce children. "Quality in mankind," he said, "and not quantity is what our chaotic world needs!"

This is rather mysterious in view of the fact that Sax considered heredity to play little or no part in the determination of character. His firm belief in reincarnation led him to the opinion that spiritual attributes are passed on otherwise than through ties of blood.

In this seemingly contrary view of eugenics, I think he referred principally to physical qualifications for parentage, including his own tendencies to somnambulism and mine towards asthma. At the same time, he was well alive to it that basic spiritual qualities can be modified, submerged, and even in some cases, destroyed by environment, that much of the common similarity between parents and children, once mistakenly ascribed to heredity, is simply due to education in the home. Thus, in speaking of unfitness to produce children, what he more precisely intended was unfitness to bring them up.

Strangely enough, however, the fact that Sax and Elizabeth had no children was not due to any deliberate attempt at avoiding them. Somehow, to the relief of both, it just did not happen.

Englishmen are notoriously contemptuous of strict legality when they feel themselves fortified by moral justification. Consequently, when we found ourselves short of liqueurs to go along with our coffee, Sax's old urges to chemical experiment came out again, and we decided to manufacture them for ourselves. I think that I may now safely confess to the crime. Anyway, needless to say, we did not succeed. Sax's attempts at chemistry never did.

We obtained the necessary apparatus and set up an illicit still in a bathroom, because Elizabeth would not have it in her kitchen. Here, however, we had no gas supply, so we had to energize the thing with a spirit lamp. This duly produced a violent stench of alcohol over half the house, apart from which we produced nothing. Why, I don't know. Illiterate lay-abouts in the corn country have done it, but we could not. In the end, I think, we might have done better to put the alcohol into the product rather than the burner.

With the long, dark nights of winter, the Blitz on London recommenced. Nightly, the Luftwaffe bombers droned over at high altitude, invisible. Sometimes the outer fringe of the London barrage appeared like sparks over the horizon and, when the wind was in the right quarter, with an accompaniment of sullen rumbling like distant thunder. But at Reigate we remained well out of it.

The German Intelligence Service evidently did not know that an important center of army command occupied a network of tunnels under the hill. Working on the switchboards, I knew this, and trembled for our safety, Little Gatton being situated on the opposite slope of the valley. But nothing ever happened. The searchlights fingered the clouds and, occasionally, the guns at the top of Reigate Hill would blaze into action, but they never hit anything.

Ironically, it was, finally, these same guns which gave us our worst scare. By some appalling mischance, the anti-aircraft shells were incorrectly fused. They fell back unexploded upon the town and burst in the streets. They blew the face out of the town clock and killed four people standing in a bus queue. Three shells made holes in our kitchen garden, and another took the chimney off the gardener's cottage.

This was one of the nights when I happened to be in the telephone exchange. When I came back to the house, Sax and Elizabeth said they had spent the most alarming evening of the war to date—under the dining room table.

Although, as I have said, Hitler's spies failed to detect the existence of significant military installations at Reigate, their information in general was altogether too accurate around this time to please the British Government. There were bound to be leaks which could not easily be stopped; a more urgent problem lay in discovering the means by which information was got out of the country.

Sax, with a good deal of experience in cryptography and a good deal more in the entertainment business, presently noted the extraordinary amount of not very relevant material used by some of the artists who appeared semi-regularly "on the air." It occurred to him as feasible that information might be coded into wisecracks and even into music, and our own broadcast transmitters made the means of conveying it to the enemy. The more he thought about it, the more likely it seemed, and finally he put up the suggestion to high quarters in which, I believe, it caused some considerable alarm.

However, so far as we know, nothing was done about it and, after an interval, Sax decided to use the idea for a story about espionage in wartime London. In this he had no very strong support from *Collier's*, where reaction to the proposed novel was somewhat cautious. They liked the opening chapters, but were wary about entering into hard and fast contracts with British

266

authors who might not live to fulfill them.

Nevertheless, Sax went ahead. It was altogether a worrying experience. Even when he had completed the work, the magazine editors remained in two minds about publishing it. At this time, many Americans were not unnaturally irritated by British tendencies to regard the Pacific war as a side issue. On their part, there was a corresponding tendency to feel that the side issue lay in the West and that Britain was a "gone goose." Sax's old friend Tom Beck cabled him sadly: "You can have no idea of the change of heart in this country."

Concentrating all his mental energies on the production of a long story, Sax was never able to stand up well to an additional strain of doubts and fears as to the result. Again, Elizabeth found herself anxious about his health and suggested a short rest at a hotel in Cornwall. Sax answered, in an agony of frustration, that they could not afford it. His feelings may well be imagined. That, from the pinnacle of success, he should have sunk so low as to be troubled by the expense of a simple holiday in the country was little short of intolerable.

But Elizabeth insisted. Suddenly she felt herself inspired by that strange sixth sense which, as she said, never operated except for the benefit of some other person, and she was convinced that, afford it or not, all would be well. "Everything will be all right," she assured him. "You know that I'm never wrong."

Sax gave way, and they went off for a fortnight to St. Ives. I need hardly say that she was not wrong. They had not been there two days before a second cable arrived from Tom Beck, saying that *Collier's* had decided to buy the story, after all. This was the book which duly appeared as *Seven Sins*. But, at present it is something of a collector's item—at least, in England—the wartime edition being much restricted and soon out of print.

In the interim, I had the fantastic experience of finding myself left in charge of Little Gatton. Luckily, I had really nothing to do but stave off the horde of acquaintances who, learning of the Sax Rohmers' absence, would have liked to move in and drink the bar dry. All the same, making a nightly round of the house, on the look-out for unlocked doors or blackouts left undrawn, I was conscious of a weighty responsibility.

Foolhardy as the Sax Rohmers' decision to hold on may seem

267

to have been, they had to live somewhere, and there was still the outside possibility that the war might end in time to save the situation. Viewed from yet another angle, it was just such an example of that brave defiance of impossible odds which, just then, was making stirring pages of history in many parts of the world. Little Gatton was the last stronghold of imaginative culture in a society which had thrown all culture aside for the grim prosecution of hostilities. But the sands of time were running low.

I have said that, even before the war, Sax had become something of a legend in his own lifetime. Now that he was so completely withdrawn from the outside world, that was even more true —a fact of which I had striking and somewhat amusing evidence. It happened, one day, that I had gone up to town on business, and chanced to open my conversation with a tradesman by asking him if he knew the name of Sax Rohmer.

"Oh, yes!" he said confidently. "He died three or four years ago!"

"Really?" I said curiously. "I do hope not! I'm living with him!"

My informant was a trifle embarrassed.

A few more months passed, at the end of which it became obvious to us all that our personal struggle could not much longer be continued. Little Gatton was finally put up for sale, and I moved on to London.

Here, although I was never required to face the terrors of a battlefield, I experienced, along with several million Londoners, the uncomfortable distinction of sitting on the target. During the remainder of the war, I went around from one switchboard to another—thirty-six of them, if I remember rightly—and they were not, as many people thought, situated in well-equipped air raid shelters. They were all on the top floors of buildings, and covered by glass roofs which no one had attempted to reinforce other than by the addition of a coat of black paint and chicken wire. I had a chance of observing just how effective this was when one of my companions was blinded by flying splinters.

I am not aware of the precise date, but it must have been around this time that the irrepressible Frank Wyatt, the next door neighbor and close friend of the Sax Rohmers' days at Herne Hill, captained a ship in the first convoy sent to the relief of Malta. They were heavily strafed. Frank saw a bomb vanish down the funnel of his own ship and, instinctively, burst into a hoot of laughter at the absurdity of it. It was very nearly his last laugh, for, in the next instant, the deck burst up under his feet and he was catapulted into the Mediterranean. He never went to sea again, but I am happy to say that he survived, to settle in comfortable retirement in Australia.

Sax and Elizabeth remained at Little Gatton for another year, and were still there when the flying bomb attacks began in the summer of 1944. The Reigate area then came very much into the picture. Droves of these airborne horrors spluttered over, en route for London, and the anti-aircraft defenses—hastily spread out to cope with this new menace—made good shooting practice.

On one notable occasion, the younger Thorndale, who assisted his father in looking after the gardens and who, poor devil, could not get into the army because he had flat feet, found himself pursued up the lawn by a low-flying specimen planing down to strike. He lost his head completely and instead of lying down or running in the opposite direction, pelted hell-for-leather up the slope, trying to outdistance it. Happily, it outdistanced him and sailed narrowly over the roof of the house, to explode a safe way beyond.

Soon afterwards, the place was bought—at rather less than half its value—by Sir Malcolm Campbell, of speed-record fame. But the mysteriously protective influence which Sax had seemed able to exert over the Tragic Valley evidently did not extend to his successor. He had scarcely moved in before another flying bomb scored a near-miss and smashed all the windows.

For the next few weeks, Sax and Elizabeth lived at a hotel in the town. Here they had similar adventures of their own. Awakened, one night, by a considerable crash, Elizabeth looked up sleepily to see the night sky in front of her eyes and was about to admonish Sax for having yet once again forgotten to close the blackout curtains when she realized that it was not the curtains which were missing, but the window itself.

The ancient lady who ran the hotel appeared in curl-papers and a Victorian nightdress, and quaveringly inquired what had happened. Elizabeth told her.

"Oh, is that all?" said the old lady, and went back to bed.

Despite these alarms and excursions, the Sax Rohmers decided to return to London. They reclaimed their property in Sloane Street, and came back there in time to witness the final act of the drama: the coming of the V-2 rockets. This was Hitler's last cast against Britain, and his last mistake. Though the V-2 admitted of no defense and annihilated all that it hit, it created neither the psychological terror nor the widespread superficial damage of the flying bomb.

Soon, the war drew to its inglorious conclusion—for no one viewing the world as it then was, or as it is now, could honestly refer to it as glorious. The Sax Rohmers were left to pick up what they could from the pieces.

32

BRAVE NEW WILDERNESS

THE BRITAIN WHICH EMERGED FROM WORLD WAR II WAS NO BRIGHT LAND glowing with opportunity. Not one of the old-established fiction magazines had survived; none recommenced publication, and no new enterprises opened in their place. The taste for reading had disappeared, along with hats and waistcoats, and before it could be recultivated, the overwhelming competition of television was shortly to create a nation of onlookers. These were hardly conditions likely to offer much encouragement to a writer.

In the absence of any other reasonable outlet for his talents, it was natural that Sax's thoughts should again turn towards the theatre. He began where he had left off, with a carefully revised version of *The Body's Upstairs*. In fact, he revised it twice. Failing to make any headway with the first, he prepared a second edition, even trying the experiment of converting the original three acts into a fashionable two. (The two-act drama was a short-lived attempt to present some "new" kind of theatre in post-war England. It was not appreciated by theatre managers, for profit on the sale of ice-cream runs up to six hundred per cent and they wanted two intervals in which to sell it.)

Sax's tentative excursion into this "up-to-date" form had no better success. The play was marred by a basic weakness, namely, that none of the female characters was required to strip. And, lacking such clear-cut indications of popular appeal, scripts seemed curiously baffling to the new generation of producers called upon to read them.

"I can't tell whether it's a good play or not," confessed one who, at that time occupied a notable position in show business. "Of course," he added hastily, "I would know if I saw it staged. . . ."

In the hiatus of the war years, the brilliant and long-experienced directors of entertainment had vanished. Both in the theatre and the cinema, decisions were now made by newcomers who had bought their way in with money acquired in some completely different line, men inspired only by a blind confidence in "knowing what the public wanted" and which subsequent developments proved they did not know.

A fairly typical event occurred not long afterwards. It happened that a young man named Michael Martin-Harvey had somehow managed to secure a contract for the books and lyrics of a musical based on Hans Christian Andersen's fairytale, "The Chinese Nightingale." He was a pleasant personality and I would hesitate to imply that he lacked artistic talent, but he was without stage experience. In view of this, and noting the "Chinese" theme, the management thought immediately of inviting Sax to collaborate. Here they chose more wisely than they realized, for though Sax was anything but an expert on China, he had a very thorough background in musicals and lyric-writing.

Music for the proposed show was to be provided by Kennedy Russell, another wise choice, since he also was an experienced and popular composer. Prospects appeared bright. Sax went to work on the script and, frankly speaking, by the time he had finished with it there was not much left of Michael Martin-Harvey's original. Up until this episode, I had not directly known Sax as a songwriter, and I was honestly astonished. I had never felt much attracted to this kind of thing, yet even I could see that his work was brilliant.

So far as the plot went, not a great deal was required. As with all musicals, the songs were the main concern, and these were excellent. For the rest, Sax devised a historical story of ancient China, very tenuously linked with the theme of the fairytale, in which—obviously enough, just then—Japan was to be the villain.

Here I was privileged to act as the authority. Having been engaged on a close study of Japanese affairs ever since leaving high school, I liked to feel that if I was in any way useful to Sax, it was as his "Far East consultant." We ascribed some thoroughly libellous behavior to Fujiwara Kamatari, Japan's last envoy to the Chinese court in the seventh century, and finished up with what was, I think, a story sound enough to support the notably fine lyrics and music.

The show went into production, and then came the disaster. During rehearsals, the self-styled theatrical experts tore the whole thing to pieces. (Michael Martin-Harvey tore the script to pieces —literally—and threw it in their faces.) They rewrote everything, and by the opening, there was precious little that was either Sax Rohmer or Michael Martin-Harvey.

Sax went to see the first night and afterwards advised me to give it a miss. I took his advice, and did. Six weeks later, the inept effort very properly "folded." And so, by the gross mishandling of inexperienced men who preferred their own judgment to that of the authors they had commissioned, ended an endeavor which, by all appearances, should have been a striking success.

During the brief postwar phase of Sax's final activities in England, I was again closely in touch. Due to the eventual retirement of Mrs. Esmond, then in her seventies, I was compelled to take over the typing of his manuscripts, because, he said, I was now the only person in London who could read his handwriting. Sax wrote a clear but baffling script which, at first glance, more closely resembled Arabic than English. I commend the reader to try deciphering the specimen reproduced in this volume.

In this sadly restricted field of opportunity, the slightly despised B.B.C. came once more into the picture. At their usual disparagingly low rates of remuneration, they entered into a contract for a series of eight radio plays. Fu Manchu was still too dangerous a proposition for the B.B.C., which liked to avoid criticism from any quarter, so Sax created for them a character named Sumuru who, in effect, was a female Fu Manchu, a glamorous witch of totally untraceable nationality, heading an international organization which fought with strange devices. He did not think very highly of the character, or of the stories, but just as it had happened with *The Emperor of America*, both were later to enjoy an unexpected degree of popularity.

Ending their long spell of confinement in England, the Sax

273

Rohmers paid a short visit to Monte Carlo—their last. Although money was going out faster than it was coming in, they were not destitute. Happily, they had managed to save enough from the wreck of Little Gatton to provide them with a fairly substantial capital. But it could not last forever.

As the months wore on, with no sign of recovery in any part of the entertainment business, Sax had finally to admit that his only hope lay in the United States. The War had not driven him out of England, but the Peace would. No sufficient market for his work existed and such market as there was could be approached only through the detestable and dubiously honest channels of personal influence. Simultaneously, the newly triumphant Socialist government seemed to be going all out to bleed the last drop of wealth from those who had once possessed any.

This was the commencement of the social phenomenon later to be called the Brain Drain, which robbed the country of its most gifted intellects, beginning with the world of the arts. If he were to live at all, it was imperative that Sax should go to America and stay there until he had done what he might to pick up the threads of his formerly prosperous career.

In preparation for the exodus, he wrote a Fu Manchu stage play with an American setting. It was in his mind that, even in New York, the theatre was likely to provide him with a better chance than the sadly disrupted publishing business. There, at least, Fu Manchu was again a possibility. The tidal wave of Chinese Communism which had swept their late allies into exile had alerted Americans to the very real existence of a Yellow Peril. In addition to this play, he wrote a novel based on the B.B.C. series, entitled *The Sins of Sumuru*. But he was not very hopeful about selling it.

The flat in Sloane Street was closed down, and the furniture put into store with the bulk of other items from Little Gatton. Funds for the journey were low, for the rigid control of finance did not permit them to take with them even the sums remaining to their credit. With two new manuscripts in his luggage and a weighty load of sadness in his heart, Sax set sail once more for the New World.

Sax and Elizabeth set up their new base camp in a small apartment on the West Side which, contrary to the expectations of

274

Londoners, is *not* the fashionable quarter of New York. Very much of a base camp it was. Here they were back again virtually to the days of Wyke Gardens—worse, perhaps, without even an Ada to help. The place consisted of two rooms, plus a kitchen and a bathroom. These they rented empty, and furnished sparsely with a few essentials obtained on the installment plan. Sax's books and papers went into racks contrived from orange boxes. Elizabeth's sister, long since resident in New York, appeared on the scene again and helped to sew curtains.

Ironically, it was that same winter which, throughout the Western Hemisphere, was to be the worst in living memory—when ice floes appeared off the east coast of England and the sea froze. In New York, conditions were no better. Blizzards howled through Manhattan, so that the man-made ravines of lofty buildings were converted into the semblance of Alpine passes. Cars stood abandoned in the streets, with a yard-thick canopy of snow piled up on their roofs. Neither the English nor the American fuel resources were equal to the demand. Everywhere there were power cuts. The oil-fired central heating system of the Sax Rohmers' modest apartment ceased to function.

In the meantime, Sax's struggle to re-establish his market in the United States was proving every bit as difficult as he had feared. This time, the Americans were not waiting for him with open arms. Few of his old friends remained active in the business. In the bleak years of the War, his great reputation had been largely forgotten, and the prejudice against British authors which had sprung up during those same years remained strong.

Adding to his tribulations, he found himself once more rooming alongside a piano-playing neighbor. This one was female, but no Eileen Joyce. She was a learner who stumbled doggedly, day after day, through the same exercise and, day after day, made the same mistakes. After hearing the ninth or tenth fruitless repetition, Sax would cast down his pen savagely and abandon his attempts at writing. "Damn it!" he exploded. "Won't the blasted woman *ever* get it right?"

The unrewarding efforts of his neighbor were not merely disturbing to the ear but tauntingly symbolic, for during those first few months, Sax himself could get nowhere. The Fu Manchu play was politely received and, for a time, prospects of production appeared good. Yet, in the end, it was rejected. Seeing nothing else to do with it, he converted the script into a novel, and with this he was more successful. *Collier's* accepted it and *The Shadow of Fu Manchu* duly became the eleventh of the series.

Elizabeth, as it happened, was not in the apartment when the good news arrived. Sax, rushing off to the office to discuss terms, left a hastily scribbled note for her: "Mink coat in the offing!" It was still typical of him that the first thing he should think about was a present for Elizabeth.

In order to continue living in the United States, it was necessary for Sax and Elizabeth to gain admission on the quota of foreign residents, and this could only be done from outside. Subletting the apartment with its hire-purchased furniture, they transferred themselves temporarily to Jamaica. Here, at least, being within the sterling area, they could draw upon their "frozen" banking account in England. With fine weather and charming surroundings, it was not an arduous experience, and during the several months which they spent there, Sax was able to obtain an intimate knowledge of the island which he turned to good account later. Fortunately, too, they had made firm friends in Jamaica, including the Governor and the Cordova family, who ran the *Gleaner* and who were in a position to exert a useful influence towards speeding up the official procedures for re-entry to the United States.

Returning, they moved into a furnished apartment off Madison Avenue. Sax had now come to the conclusion that theatrical prospects in New York were no better than they had been in London. Therefore, he decided to adopt the same measures with *The Body's Upstairs* that he had done with *The Shadow of Fu Manchu*. Under the title of *Hangover House* it became a novel of the detective-story genre, the first of this type which he had actually written since *Bat Wing*. This novel was also purchased by *Collier's*; it was the last Sax Rohmer story that would see print in that magazine.

The outlook for the future continued to be precarious, but hopeful enough for Sax and Elizabeth to feel that they might establish themselves more solidly by shipping over their remaining furniture from England. Neither of them liked living in large cities —Sax had completely lost the taste—and they looked forward to setting up a new headquarters (though necessarily on a much-reduced scale) at a convenient distance outside New York.

Back in London, I went down to Harrod's storerooms, catalogued Sax's extensive library, and checked inventory lists. All the better pieces of furniture that were reasonably portable were crated up and dispatched. Other items were sold; some went to relatives and friends. I personally inherited the unique, mosaic-shaded lamp which had stood on Sax's writing desk during our first meeting, and lugged it proudly around the world ever afterwards.

When the furniture arrived, Sax and Elizabeth found suitable premises in Greenwich, Connecticut. Here they remained for some time, Sax devoting most of his energies to short stories.

At this juncture a new, if not very elegant, market opened up with a quite unexpected bid for *The Sins of Sumuru*, which Sax had not seriously thought would sell to anyone. The Fawcett Publishing Company, which turned out first editions in paperback format, saw glamorous possibilities in this female stand-in for Fu Manchu. Sax, who had never written anything for the paperback market, felt that the whole thing was vaguely undignified. But such had become the prevailing fashion of the day, and he consoled himself with the idea that in England at least the story would subsequently obtain the status of a hard cover, which, in fact, it did. He accepted the offer, and Fawcett's launched Sumuru under the more promising title of *Nude in Mink*.

This rather amusing contradiction in terms was inspired by the fact that, just as Eve had once staged a dramatic entry at Bruton Street, based on a scene from *The Yellow Claw*, Sax had sardonically turned the tables by causing his new heroine to make her appearance in the same fashion clad only in a mink coat.

Once again, a story which he had written simply as a make-shift achieved results beyond his expectations. During the next few months, so far as book sales went, Sumuru came close to rivalling the fame of Fu Manchu.

33

THE GATES OF KARMA

SAX AND ELIZABETH WERE NOW IN A POSITION TO TAKE A HOLIDAY IN England, where adequate funds still remained to their credit. This, however, could be only a temporary respite; they knew that if their struggle to regain their position in the United States was to be carried on, they had to go back. Again the furniture went into storage while they recrossed the Atlantic.

Since they had now no premises in Britain, they moved into a furnished apartment in Marsham Court, Westminster. Here, over dinner, I had a further meeting with Sax, a blessed ignorance of the future hiding from me the fact that it was also to be the last. I heard the story of their adventures in New York. With more than a little ironic amusement, he told me of his unlooked-for success with Sumuru and said that if that was what the American public wanted he would write some more.

One thing which troubled him at the time was the condition of his beloved Egypt which, torn by hostilities with Israel, political dissent, and the collapse of British authority, was in uproar. He said that even if order were restored, he would never go there again, for the gracious life of Cairo had vanished forever.

Rather to my surprise, Sax mentioned *Wulfheim*, showing that the artist in him was far from dead. He had long since given up any hopes of staging this mystic play which he had written some twenty-five years previously, but he was determined now to publish it as a novel. This, perhaps, was a reaction against the ever-decreasing standards to which he was being forced. In such an attempt, he said, the reputation of Sax Rohmer would be a hindrance rather than an asset—publishers looking for exotic violence would have nothing to do with it—so he would submit the work under another name.

Knowing the situation to be what it was, I was politely incredulous. Nevertheless, he did it. Several months later, using his mother's maiden name, he published *Wulfheim* as by "Michael Furey." Naturally, the book had no wider sales than *The Orchard of Tears*, but the remarkable thing is that he could do it. In these unlikely conditions, with a dreamy, theosophical novel and a completely unknown name, he broke into the closed shop of authorship for the second time in one lifetime. The intrinsic literary ability of a man who could do that is nothing short of phenomenal.

Back in New York, Sax and Elizabeth went first into furnished accommodation on Madison Avenue, then, when they had obtained unfurnished quarters in nearby Park Avenue, withdrew their furniture from storage and moved in there.

Throughout the next four years or so, Sumuru continued to be the mainstay of their existence. Sax wrote *The Slaves of Sumuru* (which Fawcett titled simply *Sumuru*) and then *Virgin in Flames* (in America, *The Fire Goddess*). This latter was probably the best of the series, being set in Jamaica and containing a marked amount of colorful atmosphere which Sax had absorbed during his long stay there.

But Sumuru and her band of twentieth-century Amazons, though they captivated the public well enough, failed to live up to the hopes of the publishers. In this daring society of lawless females, Fawcett's had envisaged possibilities of detailed anatomical descriptions, awful atrocities perpetrated on shrinking feminine flesh, and bold delineation of sexual activity. Persistent in their demands, they rang up the apartment, sent around their representatives, and, in just so many words, said so.

This kind of attempted interference in the work of a writer who had been an international success since World War I rendered Elizabeth furious (but not speechless—for Elizabeth, though sometimes furious, was never speechless). Sax, however, endured this

279

well-meant advice with patient good humor, and did nothing about it. Beyond the fact that Sumuru and her associates spent most of their time either transparently robed or decorously nude, sex appeal remained at a strictly pre-war level.

If those last years in America must be regarded as a period of decline, I would nevertheless hotly deny that they represented any decline in Sax's skill. In order to live, he was compelled now to deal with a public which wanted not his best work but his worst. That which was in decline was the literary standard of popular fiction, and this was a phenomenon common throughout the English-speaking nations. Young men whose late teens and early twenties had been squandered in the sandy wastes of Libya and the poisonous humidity of the Malayan jungle—men who had lived with death and survived—had had neither the opportunity nor the inclination to appreciate the niceties of language. Exciting reading, to them, meant episodes of violence and, above all, sex, described no matter how, so long as they were plentiful enough.

In the face of this general assault, high class fiction was increasingly restricted to a coterie of intellectuals—commercially insignificant—among whom it would presently degenerate into *avant-garde* abstractions and such absurdities as the anti-novel.

Collier's Weekly, which, with *Saturday Evening Post*, had formerly shared the distinction of top rank in American periodicals, had itself fallen upon evil days. Tom Beck categorically asserted that, on two previous occasions, when sales had fallen dangerously low, it was the immense popularity of the stories contributed by Sax which had lifted them out of the depression. Perhaps he could have done it again, but he did not have the chance. The ownership of *Collier's* changed hands; Tom Beck was out, and so was Sax—and, quite shortly afterwards, so was the magazine.

Most of the stories which Sax wrote hereafter were published in *This Week*. He wrote a fair number, but, even in this field, artistic opportunity was sadly restricted. The short story of post-war days had, as he said, become "a mere synopsis." Within this framework, he had no elbow room either for the colorful descriptive matter or the ingenious development of plots which, together, had made his work famous.

280

As an outlet for lengthier works, only Fawcett's remained. Sax wrote a fourth Sumuru adventure for them, which they titled *The Return of Sumuru*. In England, it was called *Sand and Satin*. At approximately the same date, he also wrote his third detective novel, *The Moon is Red*, which, however, was published only in England. This latter tale was inspired by a visit to Florida, and by the career of Elizabeth's brother Bill, who, after making a notable name for himself on the variety stages of Europe and America, had for many years been settled in Miami.

Journeys outside the United States, at this time, were necessarily confined to the West Indies. They made several, though Elizabeth is now unable to recall exact details. They revisited Haiti and found it still steeped in that same atmosphere of mystery, the drums still beating, the cocks still crowing at the moon, but from the point of view of tourist development, now very efficient and completely Americanized.

On another occasion, they visited the Bahamas, where Sax was once again able to try out his roulette system on the tables at Nassau. This was precisely the time when he might have felt some real interest in breaking the bank; unfortunately, he found that it worked not so well here as at Monte Carlo.

A third time, they went to Jamaica, exchanging the social life of Kingston for a quiet hotel in the hills above Ocho Rios. Here they met with one minor adventure, going out for a walk and losing themselves on the return journey. Darkness fell while they were still seeking some sign of habitation—a tropical darkness spangled with the green pinpoint lights of a myriad fireflies and filled with a whispering chorus of cicadas. Stumbling on by starlight, they eventually came to a group of unlit buildings and, searching among them in the hope of finding someone to furnish directions, were surprised to discover that they were in the back premises of the hotel in which they were staying. Elizabeth concluded that they had probably made a circuit of the island, but as Jamaica is about one hundred and forty-six miles long, I rather doubt it.

Just as in England, the rising generation of those who had been born too late to suffer directly from the war years failed to cultivate a taste for reading because their attention was captivated by the new alternative of television. It became obvious to Sax

281

that, if his efforts were to be as widely appreciated as they had been hitherto, he must now attempt to give them expression in this medium.

Here he thought again, firstly, of Fu Manchu. With the active collaboration of Elizabeth, he wrote a script which, after some considerable negotiation, appeared on television screens in the form of a "pilot film." In line with all Sax's theatrical endeavors, there was no lack of famous names in the cast. Cedric Hardwicke was in it, John Newman, and Rita Gam. Nevertheless, no backers came forward to sponsor a series. The position of the United States *vis-a-vis* Chinese villainy remained somewhat equivocal. On the one hand, they disapproved of Red China; on the other, they supported Chiang Kai-shek in Formosa.

Sax's attempts to make headway, not only with Fu Manchu but with other projects, seemed during this period to be met with an undefined yet unmistakable opposition. Time and again, plans would be carried through every preliminary stage with glowing prospects of success, only to be vetoed at the last moment.

This occurred so persistently that, in the end, he came to believe that he was actively opposed by Communist influence. As I do not know what grounds he may have had for such a belief, I can offer no opinion, but I know that Sax was the last man in the world to suffer from any kind of persecution complex.

For Fawcett's, Sax wrote *Sinister Madonna*, the fifth and last of the Sumuru series. These stories were certainly not the best of his work, yet when Sax Rohmer's writings come to be more seriously studied (as they certainly will be), the inquirer will find more in them than may appear at first sight. Reading them, and contrasting them with Fu Manchu, one realizes that Sax had now definitely discarded the ideal of a world of efficiency for a world of aesthetic beauty. There is a hint, too, of a suspicion that ends may sometimes justify means; it is notable that, whereas Fu Manchu is invariably thwarted, Sumuru usually wins on points.

Evidences are there, likewise, of the fascination and, at the same time, distrust which he felt towards Christian ritual and monasticism. Good Catholics would probably consider Sumuru's organization little short of sacrilegious. Still others might be led to believe that Sax advocated the idea of a matriarchy. This last I doubt. I cannot see Sax as having any serious leanings towards a world governed by women, but contemplating the shocking mess which male supremacy has thus far made of it, I can see that his sardonic sense of humor would prompt him to propose it as a theory.

One further excursion into strange places remains to be recorded. Pursuing their Caribbean explorations, Sax and Elizabeth visited Cuba. Here, as often happened, it was Elizabeth who had most of the adventures. During their stay, they went to see the odd game of *pelota*, said to be the fastest game in the world, and Elizabeth, who had never previously felt enthusiasm for any kind of sport, became so excited that she snatched the hat off the head of the man standing in front of her and hurled it into the air. However, she said, he was very understanding about it.

Later, she also had adventures of a less amusing nature. For no discernible reason, she was assailed by one of those rare attacks of hiccoughs which begin by being ludicrous and finish by becoming deadly. It lasted for three days and nearly killed her.

And then, as if this were not enough, she had yet another encounter with a spider. This time, it really bit her, producing an alarming swelling under the armpit that required medical attention.

The inexorable cycle of Destiny, as Sax might have put it, had now returned to the point at which he was fated once more to become the victim of treachery. Or, if you prefer strictly rational terms, Sax's career had again reached a stage offering possibilities of dishonest advantage to the unscrupulous.

The unscrupulous, in this case, was personified by a man whom I will call Streeter, forbearing to give his real name only because Sax would not have wished me to. Sax's principles, in such matters, were refreshingly humanistic. He had no objections to speaking ill of the dead, but no provocation would goad him to speak ill of the living.

As in the episode of his first agent, to whom he had been introduced through the well-meant offices of his old friend, T. P. O'Connor, it likewise happened that the connection with Streeter was brought about by persons whose intentions were wholly of the best. In New York, Sax and Elizabeth moved, naturally enough, within a circle of friends whose background recalled the old school of established literature. The fateful meeting occurred at a cocktail party given by the Beecher-Stowe family and attended by an impressive list of celebrities, among whom many were old acquaintances. Sarah Churchill was there; so was Lady Huggins, wife of the Governor of Jamaica.

Presently, in the course of discussion, the topic of television came up and, with it, the difficulties which Sax had so far experienced in that line of show business. Hereupon, several of his friends warmly recommended him to open negotiations with another guest at the same party, the aforesaid Streeter. Streeter and his partner (a qualified lawyer) were neither producers nor agents but described themselves as promoters, a further vague link in the chain of middlemen which had now come to exist in the world of commercial literature, and which had so little to do with authorship.

Sax had already met the man, briefly, during the making of the Fu Manchu "pilot film," so knew that he had some connections with television. The precise nature of them remained obscure, but if Streeter could and would assist him in this field, there appeared to be nothing to be lost by allowing him to try. Talks followed, leading to an odd arrangement whereby the film, radio, and television rights of Sax's stories were to become the negotiable property of a limited company with a board of directors consisting of Streeter and his partner, Sax and Elizabeth.

I can well believe that Sax had only the haziest idea of what it was all about; presumably, he was to receive his fees in the form of dividends; presumably, too, this would be the equivalent to paying a fifty per cent commission to an agent (instead of the usual ten or fifteen per cent), assuming that it was to be a level four-way split. But even this would be better than nothing.

When the agreement was drawn up, Sax could make neither head nor tail of it and wisely said that he would sign it after taking legal advice. At this, Streeter said boldly:

"Why should you do that when you have a lawyer in your own company?"

As a stroke of diplomacy, this was masterful. If he wished to do business with the pair, Sax could hardly begin by saying that he doubted their integrity, nor in fact at that time had he any good reason to do so. He conceded that an outside opinion would be superfluous, and signed.

284

For a while thereafter, all seemed to go well. Streeter was as good as his word and it was not long before a commercially sponsored company had been induced to make a contract for twenty-six television plays featuring Fu Manchu. At the same time, considerably to Sax's annoyance, they released some sensational publicity, saying that they had bought the Fu Manchu rights for a million pounds. They had, of course, done nothing of the sort. They had merely agreed to take a series at a very much lower figure—of which Sax had as yet received nothing.

Nevertheless, business appeared to be looking up and, on the strength of this, Sax and Elizabeth felt justified in taking another short trip to England. They had not been there for three years. Sax was feeling distinctly homesick and becoming daily more tired of struggling to make his way in a literary world which seemed to have more the aspect of the Stock Exchange than the Authors Club.

They spent a week in Bournemouth, then came up to town for a few more weeks at Park West, in North London. By this time, I was now caught up in stage management, somewhere in the north of England, and unfortunately I did not see them. Coming across a newspaper announcement of the "million pound deal," I mentally rejoiced at my old friend's success, knowing nothing of the facts. And, thus far, the full facts of the matter were not known even to him.

Despite the fascination which the mysterious East had exercised over him since boyhood, Sax felt a strong kinship with England, and his earliest writings suggest that he had even, for a time, hoped to make his name as an author of historical romances. Acutely sensitive to atmosphere, he felt the pageant of European history strong upon him and disliked life in America because there he was remote from it, a stranger.

Now that even the fantasy world of fiction had become so much subordinate to the dull world of business transactions, he dreaded the thought of going back there. But there was no help for it. On their return, they tried once again to establish themselves outside New York, going to White Plains, in Westchester County. Here, as Elizabeth said, they began by occupying pleasant premises on the top floor of an apartment building, and as conditions later deteriorated, moved progressively downward till they finally occupied the basement.

Thirteen of the proposed Fu Manchu plays were screened and, for a time, future prospects looked bright. Following up this new era of Fu Manchu, Sax was able to turn his back on Sumuru, and persuade Fawcett's to accept *Re-enter Fu Manchu* as his next book.

And it was then that the storm broke. To his astonishment, Streeter and his partner immediately claimed the publication rights as the property of the company. Bewildered and indignant, Sax discovered that, far from having entered into an agreement restricted to films, radio, and television, he had been tricked into signing a contract which gave his partners control of the complete rights of everything, past, present and future. Worse, since he and Elizabeth together held less than fifty per cent of the nominal shares in the company, they could actually be voted out of it and left with no claim to anything.

The balloon went up and burst. Threatened with legal proceedings, Streeter cynically invited the Sax Rohmers to try, saying that they would not easily find any lawyer prepared to take action against a member of the same profession—his partner—and that, even if they did, they would not have enough money to secure his services.

But he had not counted on the fighting spirit of Elizabeth. This was the kind of crisis in which Sax was never very useful. His whole lifetime had been spent in cultivating the ability to create works of art—sordid squabbles to obtain the just reward of his labors were completely outside his scope. It was Elizabeth, as always, who combed the legal quarters of New York, searching for an advocate. As Streeter had confidently predicted, it was not easy. Eventually, however, she found her man and learned from him that their erstwhile partners had already been four times brought to court on similar charges.

They had now someone to act for them, but—business is business!—at a retaining fee of five thousand dollars. To raise the money, Elizabeth sold her jewelry and most of the furniture. Then there was nothing to do but wait, and that was difficult enough, for it was nearly two years before the case could be heard.

Meanwhile, the situation was parlous. Sax's source of revenue was restricted simply to a few short stories. With the lawsuit pending, only Stewart Beach of *This Week* was willing to pay him for his work, other publishers saying that it was not yet clear to whom the money belonged.

In the desperate attempts to make both ends meet, Elizabeth herself turned back to authorship and presently produced a novel of the detective-story category, titled *Bianca in Black*. It was an efficiently-written tale and did quite well. Unavoidably, working in this field, Elizabeth was indirectly subject to a good deal of influence from Sax and benefitted directly from the same kind of help and advice that he had once given me. Nevertheless, *Bianca in Black* is not a story written by Sax and published under his wife's name. It is essentially Elizabeth's own work—and well worth reading. (For some still unknown reason, the publishers billed the book as by the *daughter* of Sax Rohmer.)

When, eventually, the suit against Streeter came up for hearing, the Sax Rohmers had sunk—literally—to the basement and could not even afford taxi fares into New York. During the several days that the court proceedings lasted, they were compelled to make early morning journeys via the public transport system. After nearly sixty years of active working life, this was a terrible strain on Sax, who now began to look tired, ill, and all at once old. Sometimes he seemed scarcely able to climb the steps to the courthouse, and Elizabeth felt anxious for his life.

Justice triumphed. Streeter and his partner were found guilty of misrepresentation, the fraudulent contract was declared void, and the lawful ownership of Sax's own work came back into his hands. The same lawyer who had secured this verdict thereupon offered to secure payment of the fees for the twenty-six television plays—which Sax had not received—on the understanding, of course, that he would retain a substantial percentage. In this, however, he was only half successful. He obtained payment for the thirteen scripts actually produced, but not for the remainder agreed upon in the contract. Nevertheless—such is the way of the legal profession—he boldly demanded his own percentage on the whole twenty-six! Sax's share of the spurious "million pound deal" worked out at about eight thousand pounds.

With the hateful episode of the lawsuit safely behind him, Sax set to work on his thirteenth Fu Manchu novel. Here, to the gratification of readers, he at last set the story in China. This was a departure from his firmly established rule of writing only of places he had visited, and he had to make up for it with a mass of detailed research work. Once again, it was Fawcett's who published the result, under the title *Emperor Fu Manchu.*

Though the business of the last few months had aged him in appearance to a shocking degree, Sax was beginning to recover his physical strength and his self-confidence in making a living—his self-confidence as a writer, he had never lost. Times without number, the switchback of life had plunged him into the depths, leaving him to fight his way up again.

But this time it was not to be. In the early days of 1959 came that strange outbreak of Asiatic 'flu, as the newspapers called it, an illness which began as nothing more alarming than a feverish cold and passed quickly, leaving the victim in an odd state of weakness during which the slightest overstrain produced complete and fatal collapse. Nothing quite like it had appeared before; no one seemed to know anything about it.

Sax was stricken by it, and failed to be careful. That driving energy of will drove him on against the dictates of his body, and the bothersome "cold in the head" was followed by an appalling hemorrhage. In the days which ensued, lengthening into weeks, his strength ebbed perceptibly. Elizabeth, frightened by his condition, brought two specialists out from New York. But their counsel was productive of no useful result.

Sax was now possessed by one single thought: he must get back to England. For the first time, something like the idea of retirement seemed to occupy his mind. He had fought too earnestly and too long. Now he felt too tired and dispirited to struggle on for the empty victory of finding himself a celebrity in a postwar world of literature which he despised. Now his sole ambition was to go home, to sell out, lock, stock and barrel, the rights of everything he had written and live quietly on the capital.

But the mere business of regaining his health sufficiently to travel was almost more than he could manage. Three times the sailing date was postponed. Finally, when he could gather the strength to achieve it, he walked slowly along the corridor from their basement flat, Elizabeth holding on to him and now supporting him as much physically as she had always done morally.

288

"Don't worry about anything!" she insisted, fiercely. "You are never coming back here—never! I'll come back alone and clear up everything."

She did return—but not as she had thought, for, by that time, she was a widow.

They reached the docks and boarded the ship. The same night, in their cabin, Sax had his second hemorrhage. It left him shaken and so weak that when they reached Southampton he was really a stretcher case. All the same, he insisted on walking ashore and made it.

For the next three weeks, they occupied a service flat in London. They were days of anxiety for Elizabeth during which Sax's condition gradually worsened. He became unable to eat anything and scarcely able to walk more than a few steps. At night, his sleep was broken by fits of coughing.

Elizabeth, nursing him day and night, found her own strength failing and was terrified. She detested the thought of leaving his care to other hands, yet she herself was now over seventy years of age and she knew that, if she collapsed, he would have nobody. She discussed the possibility of obtaining resident nurses, and was informed by the doctors that none were available. (Much later, she learned, with some bitterness, that this was untrue.)

As there seemed to be no alternative, he was moved to University College Hospital, and here the last three weeks of his life were spent. Happily, he suffered no pain, but it was a cruelly protracted parting, for though nothing was said between them, both knew that he was dying. No single illness afflicted him, but a combination of pneumonia, arteriosclerosis, and the persistent hemorrhages. Little by little, he was slipping away under her eyes, a profound lassitude drifting inevitably to coma. Up to the last moment of consciousness, his mind remained unclouded, and his thoughts were still only of Elizabeth.

"Am I frightening you?" he whispered.

Now, at the end, the memory that women were often made afraid by the strangeness of his eyes was strong upon him, and he feared that the strangeness of approaching death might frighten Elizabeth.

I have said at the beginning that he died "a young man." His mental powers were those of a young man to the end. Physically, he appeared likewise young till that final collapse; then, in the course of a few weeks, age came upon him. Not mere illness but disillusion had a lot to do with it. He had fought to achieve mastery over a world that had crumbled about him, and in the tawdry, makeshift world which came after he had no place. With a singular lack of scientific precision but a wealth of understanding, the doctor who signed his death certificate said, "He was just burned out."

When at length it became clear that no hope of recovery existed, the attending physicians urged Elizabeth to obtain her husband's power of attorney while he was still able to give it, and the last time that Sax held a pen between his fingers was to make the simple cross that was all he could manage for a signature. The next day, for he was still conscious, though unable to speak, Elizabeth told him, "I have sold the rights of Fu Manchu!"

It was the only lie she ever told him, for she knew that his only worry was for her. Between them, they had just seven hundred pounds left. For the next three years, life was hard for her; but, in the end, the lie became truth. Film rights and new editions of Sax's books provided for her comfortably.

On June 1st, 1959, the saga of fifty years' marriage came to an end. The lovers parted, as Sax would say, to meet again and share new adventures in ages yet unborn. The twentieth-century incarnation of that powerful yet strangely gentle spirit had reached its fulfilment, and the Gates of Karma opened to its return.

AFTERWORD: THE LEGACY

SAX ROHMER'S LITERARY LEGACY, IN TERMS OF HIS PUBLISHED WORKS, consists of forty-one novels, eleven collections of short stories, two non-fiction books, and several dozen short stories and articles reposing in the back files of magazines and newspapers. In terms of the adaptations in films, radio, television, and comic strips, and in terms of his influence on other writers and on popular fiction in general, the extent of the legacy may never be accurately known. I think it is appropriate to conclude this account of the life of the "Master of Villainy" with some comments on the body of his work.

One feature which emerges prominently, but unexpectedly, from any close study of Sax Rohmer's work is its authenticity. In view of the fact that he wrote deliberately to mystify—this being what his readers wanted—this is rather surprising. A good portion of the "thrills" obtained in reading Sax Rohmer comes from being brought face to face with the unknown, perhaps the unknowable. Yet he did not stoop to create this effect by sheer invention. Many writers do, and regard it as entirely legitimate. But when Sax Rohmer wrote familiarly of exotic curiosities such as "the Well of Zem-zem" or "*tsan ihang*, sweet perfume of Tibet," readers could take for gospel that these things existed.

Although he drew the line at spreading misinformation, he

did not object to a little misdirection. While restricting himself to the facts, he made much use of the mysterious-sounding. He would usually prefer the Assyrian "Bel" to the better-known "Baal" of the Old Testament. Again, when he refers to something being "black as the rocks of Shellal," one is tempted to think of a location in Hell. Shellal, in fact, lies on the Nile, not far from Aswan.

Once his sardonic sense of humor prompted him to play a trick on the reader. With suitable gravity and impressiveness, he mentioned "a character resembling the Arab letter *'alif*." There were no comments. No one, apparently, realized that *'alif* is a vertical straight line.

But apart from these half whimsical excursions into mystery making, Sax Rohmer relied honestly upon references to exotic oddities dug up in a never-ending program of research. His storehouse of these, and his exact knowledge of them, were alike staggering.

"What on earth," I asked him, on one occasion, "is the Deadly Honey of Trebizond?"

"Honey gathered from a species of poisonous azalea native to that region," he said promptly, looking at me rather as if everybody ought to know.

In his fictional employment of poisons, and, particularly, of poisonous insects, he was more scrupulously accurate than many authors of his day. During his youthful days in London, many of his friends had been medical students. He lost no chance of acquiring useful information from them, sometimes even accompanying them on their hospital rounds.

When, for dramatic purposes, he occasionally allowed Fu Manchu to make use of some notably outlandish horror, he was always careful to observe that it was an *unknown* species. But where matters of everyday life were concerned, he stuck doggedly to the facts, to the extent that he would not have one of his characters board a train till he had checked its existence in the railway timetable. Here, moreover, he did his utmost to avoid that most subtle of all pitfalls, the temptation to take things for granted. How many writers, I wonder, have assumed, without checking, that the origin of a call made on a dial telephone may later be traced by the police? Sax Rohmer knew it to be impossible, because he took the trouble to find out.

292

Loath to take anything for granted, he hated to write of any place he had not visited and, short of murder, to describe anything he had not done. He did once go to the length of trying opium, but got nothing out of it. It simply made him sick.

On the odd occasions when mistakes crept into Sax Rohmer's work, they were usually the result of his working methods, going hell-for-leather to get something on paper, to keep up with the rapid pace of his imagination. The subsequent polishing, to which he devoted so much time and energy, was chiefly concerned with stylistics, so that, once in half a million words or so some mis-statement might slip through unnoticed.

I once took him up on the fact that a certain police constable mentioned in one of his stories had become a police sergeant three chapters later.

"H'm!" he said, darkly. "Somewhat rapid promotion!"

When Sax Rohmer first began to write the Fu Manchu series, he had not the faintest idea that he would still be writing it forty years later. Even when it was well under way he did not—as many authors have done—set up dossiers and card-index systems to keep track of what he had said. He continued to keep everything in his head.

One minor detail worth noting is that the names which Sax Rohmer chose for his characters are not examples of careless mistakes. He was perfectly well aware, from the outset, that "Fu Manchu" was impossible. (It is a combination of two Chinese surnames.)

His policy with regard to names shows a marked influence of the writing world in which he had been brought up. At the turn of the century, authors felt an exaggerated fear of libel. This led, on the one hand, to that oft-seen declaration that "all characters are fictitious" and, on the other, to the unlikely and frequently absurd names favored by many writers of that period.

As a matter of fact, neither of these hopeful devices represents any defense in law. Sax Rohmer and his contemporaries had sense enough to know that, but by then the practice had become a convention. Within his own limits, he adhered to it. His personal method of dealing with foreign names was to create names which were non-existent but true to type.

Sax Rohmer's earliest stories are as eminently readable today as they were fifty years ago, and as they will be fifty years hence. They are founded on the elements of wonder, charm, and suspenseful storytelling that have appealed naturally to readers throughout the ages. But in this very fact there lies a certain risk. The casual reader, carried along by the pace of the story, is sometimes apt to think of it as taking place at the present day. Then, coming across something which fails to check with his experience, he criticizes it, unjustly and to his own loss. Lacking an appreciation of the social background, no reader can hope to obtain the maximum pleasure from his reading. Sax Rohmer's stories were not written long enough ago for them to have become period pieces, which makes the tendency to this kind of anachronistic approach all the more common. We tend to forget that customs and beliefs have changed rapidly during the past half century, and precipitously during the past two decades. What Sax Rohmer wrote accurately represented the ideas current among his readers at that time.

Anyone who has followed this account so far knows by now that his attitude towards sex was anything but puritanical. Nor had he any objections to sex in fiction. In the latter part of his life, his unwillingness to match up with the standards of a more permissive age was due to something quite different. He objected to sex as a *substitute* for good writing.

Today's readers may be staggered to learn that, in the 1920's and even later, his stories were often regarded as rather shocking. The codes which they expressed were not simply in line with those of his day, but usually a jump ahead of them. In 1936, with *White Velvet*, he gave his approval to premarital relations between engaged couples, to the marked disapproval of the Bishop of London.

Sax Rohmer moved with the times, both in outlook and expression. But, in the sense that his work never lost the color and charm of an Arabian Nights fantasy, he remained conservative. He deplored the brash, rough-hewn creations of postwar "art" whether in music, painting or literature, and no prospect of financial reward could induce him to join what he termed "the cult of ugliness."

In 1935, with the enthusiastic extravagance of youth, I described Sax Rohmer as "the last great master of the English language." Certainly he exhibited, from his earliest work onward, a profound knowledge of the language. He came into the fiction market along with a group of other authors who were seeking to break away from the over-elaborated styles of Victorian literature, while still maintaining a deep respect for English prose. This respect he retained all his life. As fashions changed, he adapted himself to them so that throughout the 1920's and 1930's his work continued to present a mirror of prevailing trends in the first rank of popular fiction.

At what date twentieth century tendencies toward simplification passed over into the debit column is a point to be hotly disputed according to one's personal tastes. But for Sax Rohmer the point came shortly after the Second World War, when popular "style" ceased to have any visible relationship with language.

Popular fiction today has fallen upon hard times. But when twentieth century popular literature receives the attention which it merits, prominent on the bookshelves of the future will be the collected works of Sax Rohmer.

[1]This was probably in the spring or summer of 1911, but precise publication data are lacking. According to Nigel Morland, Rohmer wrote frequently for such weekly papers as *Tit-Bits* and *Answers*; the "Limehouse" article may have appeared in one of these publications.

[2]The two schools most often mentioned in this connection are King's College, in the Strand, London, and King's College School in Wimbledon. Both schools have been queried, and their records for the period 1892-1902 show no trace of a pupil named Arthur Henry (or Sarsfield) Ward.

[3]An interesting circumstance is reported by Nigel Morland. Around the turn of the century, there was an elderly gentleman named Billy Sarsfield who worked as proof-reader and general handy man on the *Balham and Tooting News*, and whom Rohmer knew and greatly admired. Coincidence? It is said that James Hilton based the character of "Mr. Chips" partly on Billy Sarsfield.

[4]The *Commercial Intelligence* was a publication devoted to market news "for the Home Trader and Exporter." The paper was founded by Henry Sell in 1898, and was edited by Sir Leo (George) Chiozza. It ran until November 1913, when it was incorporated into *Export World*.

In an interview in the "Talk of the Town" column in *The New Yorker*, 29 November 1947, Rohmer was quoted as saying, "My mother's family [. . .] were friends of T. P. O'Connor, the famous Irish editor, who opened the way for me in journalism."

[5]The brief essay on Rohmer in Anice Page Cooper's *Authors and Others* (Doubleday, 1927) mentions that one drawing was accepted for publication by the humor magazine *Judy*.

[6]"The Leopard-Couch" was published in the 30 January 1904 issue of *Chambers's Journal*. No trace has yet been found of "The Mysterious Mummy" in *Pearson's Magazine*.

[7]In his autobiography *Over Seventy* (London: Herbert Jenkins, 1957), Wodehouse describes Turnovers as "thousand-word articles of unparalleled dullness. You dug these out of reference books and got a guinea for them."

[8]There is a chronological anomaly in the account of the eel-boat trip which it has not been possible to resolve. Supposedly the trip occurred prior to Rohmer's first meeting with Elizabeth, which took place in the summer of 1905. Yet the story "The McVillin," which is said to have brought about the trip, was not published until the December 1906 issue of *Pearson's Magazine*. Could the editor have delayed its publication for more than a year (perhaps in hope of obtaining further stories in the series)?

At any rate, Rohmer did write at least one additional story of The McVillin, entitled "The Ebony Casket." It is not known when this was written, or where it was published.

[9]Parts of this account are paraphrased from Rohmer's article "The Phantom Hound of Holm Peel" in the Manchester *Empire News*, 20 February 1938. The legend of the phantom hound provided the background for the title story in the collection *The Secret of Holm Peel*; this story was first published in 1912. A fuller version of the legend may be found in the article "Famous Hauntings: The Phantom Dog of Peel Castle" by Elliot O'Donnell, in *The Premier*, 4 June 1920.

[10]Arthur Greening was the publisher who first brought Baroness Orczy's *The Scarlet Pimpernel* to the public, after it had been turned down by most of the publishing houses in London. Unfortunately, he was not able to profit by the enormous popularity of the book (it sold nearly half a million copies): the firm went into bankruptcy late in 1912.

[11]It is likely that Inspector Yeo was the model on which Rohmer based the character of Chief Inspector (later Superintendent) Daniel "Red" Kerry— see the Prefatory Notice in the British editions of the novel *Dope*.

[12]Subsequently, Methuen reprinted the book twenty times. It has had a combined total of more than forty different hardcover and paperbound editions in the U. S. and Britain, and is still in print in both countries today.

The Fu Manchu stories had been sold also to the American magazine *Collier's Weekly*, which was destined to publish the bulk of Rohmer's work during the next thirty-five years. The stories appeared in the magazine during the spring of 1913, and were published in book form by McBride, Nast & Co. in September of the same year under the title *The Insidious Dr. Fu-Manchu*. The stories were just as successful in the U. S. as they had been in Britain.

Another series of stories, titled *Hassan of Aleppo* or *The Quest of the Sacred Slipper*, also found a ready reception in the U. S. These appeared in *Short Stories* magazine from November 1913 to June 1914. Publication in book form was delayed until 1919.

The year 1913 was a highly productive one for Rohmer. His characters Captain O'Hagan and Moris Klaw made their debuts in April of that year, the former in *The London Magazine* and the latter in *The New Magazine*. The three O'Hagan stories were reprinted in the U. S. later in the year, but the Moris Klaw series was less well treated; four of the stories appeared in the U. S. in 1915, but it was not until the publication of the book *The Dream Detective* in 1925 that the complete series was made available to American readers.

[13]The first installment of *Brood of the Witch Queen* appeared in the first issue of *The Premier*, and throughout the following six years Rohmer's fiction was a mainstay of the magazine, contributing much to the latter's popularity. It was here that the serializations of *The Yellow Claw* and *The Green Eyes of Bast* appeared, as well as the "Abû Tabâh" stories (collected in *Tales of Secret Egypt*) and such well-known tales as "The Curse of a Thousand Kisses" and "In the Valley of the Sorceress."

[14]Both series appeared first in the U. S., in *Collier's Weekly*, stretching from November 1914 to June 1917. The British magazine versions lagged

behind by a few months. Both the U. S. and British book editions were in print before the magazine serializations were complete.

15A limited edition was finally published in New York in 1970 (see Appendix A). (Although the book is dated 1969, it was not released until late the following year.)

16*The Golden Scorpion* and *Dope* first saw print almost simultaneously: the magazine serialization of the former began in January 1919 and that of the latter in February. The book editions were published later in the year in the opposite order.

17Although *The Eye of Siva,* as such, never appeared in print, Rohmer utilized the setting, the plot, and most of the characters (some with altered names) in a story which he wrote while the play was running in London. This was "The Voice of Kali," which was published in the U. S. in Doubleday's *Short Stories* magazine, 10 December 1923.

18The second script was entitled "The Peculiar Case of the Poppy Club." It was broadcast by the B.B.C. in late December 1938 or early January 1939, and was later broadcast in Australia as well. Two years later, Rohmer turned this radio play into a short story called "Supper at the Poppy Club," but the latter apparently was never published.

19Among the most explicit examples of Fu Manchu imitations are two short-lived pulp magazines published in 1935-1936: *The Mysterious Wu Fang* and *Dr. Yen Sin*. The featured novels in the latter magazine were the work of Donald E. Keyhoe, who almost twenty years later would achieve moderate fame as the author of *The Flying Saucers Are Real* and related books.

20The article, written in 1934, was published in the September 1935 issue of *Nash's Magazine* as "Astral Voyages," and in the November 1935 issue of *The Forum* as "A Journey in Space." Rohmer's experiment in astral projection also figures prominently in the article "Houdini Saved the Day for Sax Rohmer" by Carl Warton, in the Boston *Sunday Herald,* 8 March 1931. (I am indebted to John Harwood for calling this to my attention.)

21This nick-name was perpetuated in a series of Cockney-dialect humorous sketches, which included "Digger's Aunt," " 'Rupert'," and the much-reprinted "Narky." The narrator of the Crime Magnet stories (see note 23 below) was also called "Digger."

22The story was published in the November 1966 issue of the *Edgar Wallace Mystery Magazine* under the title "The Night of the Jackal."

23The original series featured Bernard De Treville, known as "The Crime Magnet," a character very similar to one of Rohmer's early creations, Captain Bernard O'Hagan. A total of sixteen De Treville stories were published in the newspaper supplement *This Week* between September 1937 and May 1945. In the radio adaptations the character of Gaston Max (see Appendix B) was substituted for that of De Treville.

APPENDIX A: Chronological Bibliography of the Books of Sax Rohmer

All of Sax Rohmer's publications in book form are here listed in chronological order according to the date of the first edition. Omnibus volumes and abridgements are listed in the appropriate places, but otherwise no attempt has been made to record the innumerable reprint editions. It should be noted that the date of first book publication may vary by as much as several years from the date of original publication in serial form, so that the following list does not always reflect the order in which the books were actually written.

R. E. B.

PAUSE! London: Greening & Co., Ltd. 1910
[Published anonymously; a collection of essays and prose sketches based on ideas by George Robey.]

LITTLE TICH. A Book of Travels and Wanderings, by Little Tich
London: Greening & Co., Ltd. 1911
["Autobiography" of Little Tich (Harry Relph), ghost-written by Rohmer.]

THE MYSTERY OF DR.
FU-MANCHU London: Methuen 1913
as THE INSIDIOUS DR.
FU-MANCHU N.Y.: McBride, Nast 1913

THE SINS OF SÉVERAC BABLON London: Cassell 1914
N.Y.: Bookfinger 1967

THE ROMANCE OF SORCERY London: Methuen 1914
N.Y.: E. P. Dutton 1915

abridged editions London: Methuen 1923
N.Y.: E. P. Dutton 1924

THE YELLOW CLAW N.Y.: McBride, Nast 1915
London: Methuen 1915

THE DEVIL DOCTOR London: Methuen 1916
as THE RETURN OF DR.
FU-MANCHU N.Y.: McBride 1916

THE EXPLOITS OF CAPTAIN London: Jarrolds 1916
O'HAGAN N.Y.: Bookfinger 1968
[He Patronises Pamela, He Clears the Course for True Love,
He Meets the Leopard Lady, He Buries an Old Love, He Deals

with Don Juan, He Honours the Grand Duke]

THE SI-FAN MYSTERIES	London: Methuen	1917
as THE HAND OF FU-MANCHU	N.Y.: McBride	1917
BROOD OF THE WITCH QUEEN	London: C. Arthur Pearson	1918
	N.Y.: Doubleday, Page	1924
TALES OF SECRET EGYPT	London: Methuen	1918
	N.Y.: McBride	1919

[Tales of Abû Tabâh: The Yashmak of Pearls, The Death-Ring of Sneferu, The Lady of the Lattice, Omar of Ispahân, Breath of Allah, The Whispering Mummy; Other Tales: Lord of the Jackals, Lure of Souls, The Secret of Ismail, Harûn Pasha, In the Valley of the Sorceress, Pomegranate Flower]

THE ORCHARD OF TEARS	London: Methuen	1918
	N.Y.: Bookfinger	1970
THE QUEST OF THE SACRED SLIPPER	London: C. Arthur Pearson	1919
	N.Y.: Doubleday, Page	1919
DOPE	London: Cassell	1919
	N.Y.: McBride	1919
THE GOLDEN SCORPION	London: Methuen	1919
	N.Y.: McBride	1920
THE DREAM DETECTIVE	London: Jarrolds	1920
	N.Y.: Doubleday, Page	1925

[The Tragedies in the Greek Room, The Potsherd of Anubis, The Crusader's Ax, The Ivory Statue, The Blue Rajah, The Whispering Poplars, The Headless Mummies, The Haunting of Grange, The Veil of Isis; U.S. edition contains an additional episode: The Chord in G]

THE GREEN EYES OF BÂST	London: Cassell	1920
	N.Y.: McBride	1920
THE HAUNTING OF LOW FENNEL	London: C. Arthur Pearson	1920

[The Haunting of Low Fennel, The Valley of the Just, The Blue Monkey, The Riddle of Ragstaff, The Master of Hollow Grange, The Curse of a Thousand Kisses, The Turquoise Necklace]

BAT-WING	London: Cassell	1921
	N.Y.: Doubleday, Page	1921
FIRE-TONGUE	London: Cassell	1921
	N.Y.: Doubleday, Page	1922
TALES OF CHINATOWN	London: Cassell	1922
	N.Y.: Doubleday, Page	1922

[The Daughter of Huang Chow, Kerry's Kid, The Pigtail of Hi

Wing Ho, The House of the Golden Joss, The Man with the
Shaven Skull, The White Hat, Tchériapin, The Dance of the
Veils, The Hand of the Mandarin Quong, The Key of the
Temple of Heaven]

GREY FACE	London: Cassell	1924
	N.Y.: Doubleday, Page	1924
YELLOW SHADOWS	London: Cassell	1925
	N.Y.: Doubleday, Page	1926
MOON OF MADNESS	N.Y.: Doubleday, Page	1927
	London: Cassell	1927
SHE WHO SLEEPS	N.Y.: Doubleday, Doran	1928
	London: Cassell	1928
THE EMPEROR OF AMERICA	N.Y.: The Crime Club	1929
	London: Cassell	1929

THE BOOK OF FU-MANCHU   London: Hurst & Blackett   1929
   [The Mystery of Dr. Fu-Manchu, The Devil Doctor, The Si-Fan
   Mysteries]

THE BOOK OF FU-MANCHU   N.Y.: McBride   1929
   [The Insidious Dr. Fu-Manchu, The Return of Dr. Fu-Manchu,
   The Hand of Fu-Manchu, The Golden Scorpion]

THE DAY THE WORLD ENDED	N.Y.: The Crime Club	1930
	London: Cassell	1930
DAUGHTER OF FU MANCHU	N.Y.: The Crime Club	1931
	London: Cassell	1931
YU'AN HEE SEE LAUGHS	N.Y.: The Crime Club	1932
	London: Cassell	1932
TALES OF EAST AND WEST	London: Cassell	1932

   [Tales of the East: The Black Mandarin, Father of Thieves,
   The Turkish Yataghan, Spirit of the Black Hawk, Fires of
   Baal; Tales of the West: Mark of the Monkey, The Squirrel
   Man, The Cardinal's Stair, Torture, The M'Villin]

THE MASK OF FU MANCHU	N.Y.: The Crime Club	1932
	London: Cassell	1933
TALES OF EAST AND WEST	N.Y.: The Crime Club	1933

   [Tales of the East: The Black Mandarin, The Valley of the
   Just, The Turquoise Necklace, The Curse of a Thousand Kisses,
   Spirit of the Black Hawk, The Turkish Yataghan, Light of
   Atlantis; Tales of the West: The Haunting of Low Fennel, At
   the Palace da Nostra, The Master of Hollow Grange, The
   Cardinal's Stair, The Riddle of Ragstaff, Torture]

FU MANCHU'S BRIDE	N.Y.: The Crime Club	1933
as THE BRIDE OF FU MANCHU	London: Cassell	1933
THE TRAIL OF FU MANCHU	N.Y.: The Crime Club	1934
	London: Cassell	1934
THE BAT FLIES LOW	N.Y.: The Crime Club	1935
	London: Cassell	1935
PRESIDENT FU MANCHU	N.Y.: The Crime Club	1936
	London: Cassell	1936
WHITE VELVET	N.Y.: Doubleday, Doran	1936
	London: Cassell	1936

THE GOLDEN SCORPION
   OMNIBUS   N.Y.: Grosset & Dunlap   1938
     [The Golden Scorpion, Dope]

THE SAX ROHMER OMNIBUS   N.Y.: Grosset & Dunlap   1938
   [The Yellow Claw, Tales of Secret Egypt]

SALUTE TO BAZARADA AND
   OTHER STORIES   London: Cassell   1939
     [Salute to Bazarada, The Treasure Chest Murders, Death of
     Boris Korsakov, Skull Face, Sheba's Love-Pearls, Limehouse
     Rhapsody]

THE DRUMS OF FU MANCHU	N.Y.: The Crime Club	1939
	London: Cassell	1939
THE ISLAND OF FU MANCHU	N.Y.: The Crime Club	1941
	London: Cassell	1941
SEVEN SINS	N.Y.: McBride	1943
	London: Cassell	1944
EGYPTIAN NIGHTS	London: Robert Hale	1944
BIMBÂSHI BARÛK OF EGYPT	N.Y.: McBride	1944

   [Mystery Strikes at Ragstaff Hill, The Bimbâshi Meets Up with
   A 14, Murder Strikes at Lychgate, The Laughing Buddha Finds
   a Purchaser, Warning from Rose of the Desert, Lotus Yuan
   Loses Her Vanity Case, The Scarab of Lapis Lazuli, Vengeance
   at the Lily Pool, Adventure in the Libyan Desert, Pool-o'-the-
   Moon Sees Bimbâshi Barûk]

NOTE: EGYPTIAN NIGHTS and BIMBÂSHI BARÛK OF
   EGYPT are the same, except that the former is presented as
   a novel while the latter is presented as a collection of ten
   separate stories.

SHADOW OF FU MANCHU	N.Y.: The Crime Club	1948
	London: Herbert Jenkins	1949

HANGOVER HOUSE	N.Y.: Random House	1949
	London: Herbert Jenkins	1950
NUDE IN MINK	N.Y.: Fawcett	(pb) 1950
as SINS OF SUMURU	London: Herbert Jenkins	1950
WULFHEIM, as by Michael Furey	London: Jarrolds	1950
SUMURU	N.Y.: Fawcett	(pb) 1951
as SLAVES OF SUMURU	London: Herbert Jenkins	1952
THE FIRE GODDESS	N.Y.: Fawcett	(pb) 1952
as VIRGIN IN FLAMES	London: Herbert Jenkins	1953
THE MOON IS RED	London: Herbert Jenkins	1954
RETURN OF SUMURU	N.Y.: Fawcett	(pb) 1954
as SAND AND SATIN	London: Herbert Jenkins	1955
SINISTER MADONNA	London: Herbert Jenkins	1956
	N.Y.: Fawcett	(pb) 1956
RE-ENTER FU MANCHU	Greenwich, Conn.: Fawcett	(pb) 1957
as RE-ENTER DR. FU MANCHU	London: Herbert Jenkins	1957
EMPEROR FU MANCHU	London: Herbert Jenkins	1959
	Greenwich, Conn.: Fawcett	(pb) 1959
THE SECRET OF HOLM PEEL AND OTHER STRANGE STORIES	N.Y.: Ace Books	(pb) 1970

[The Secret of Holm Peel, The Owl Hoots Twice, A House Possessed, The Eyes of Fu Manchu, The Mystery of the Marsh Hole, Bazarada, For Love of Mistress Mary, Brother Wing Commanders]

NOTES

[1]The Crime Club volumes were published by Doubleday, Doran & Co. (later Doubleday & Co.). Although the home base of Doubleday is in Garden City, N.Y., the preceding checklist uses simply "N.Y." for the sake of brevity.

[2]The Fawcett paperbacks were published under the trade imprint of Gold Medal Books.

[3]A slightly different version of the preceding checklist appeared as an appendix to "Sax Rohmer: An Informal Survey" by R. E. Briney, in THE MYSTERY WRITER'S ART, edited by Francis M. Nevins, Jr., and published by this Press in 1971.

APPENDIX B: Checklist of Characters and Series

1. The Fu Manchu series

The Mystery of Dr. Fu-Manchu (*The Insidious Dr. Fu-Manchu*)
The Devil Doctor (*The Return of Dr. Fu-Manchu*)
The Si-Fan Mysteries (*The Hand of Fu-Manchu*)
[*The Golden Scorpion*]
[*The Book of Fu-Manchu*]
Daughter of Fu Manchu
The Mask of Fu Manchu
The Bride of Fu Manchu (*Fu Manchu's Bride*)
The Trail of Fu Manchu
President Fu Manchu
The Drums of Fu Manchu
The Island of Fu Manchu
Shadow of Fu Manchu
Re-Enter Dr. Fu Manchu
Emperor Fu Manchu

The Golden Scorpion is only peripherally related to the Fu Manchu series. *The Book of Fu Manchu* is an omnibus volume.

There are three Fu Manchu short stories, of which only one has appeared in book form ("The Eyes of Fu Manchu" in *The Secret of Holm Peel and Other Strange Stories*).

In the first three Fu Manchu books, the villain is opposed by Nayland Smith and Dr. Petrie; Smith continues throughout the series, but in later books Petrie is replaced by a succession of subsidiary protagonists. There are three short stories in which Nayland Smith appears without Fu Manchu: "The Blue Monkey" (in *The Haunting of Low Fennel*), in which Smith and Petrie appear anonymously; "Mark of the Monkey" (in the British edition of *Tales of East and West*); and "The Turkish Yataghan" (in *Tales of East and West*).

2. The Sumuru series

Sins of Sumuru (*Nude in Mink*)
Slaves of Sumuru (*Sumuru*)
Virgin in Flames (*The Fire Goddess*)
Sand and Satin (*Return of Sumuru*)
Sinister Madonna

3. The Gaston Max series

The Yellow Claw
The Golden Scorpion
The Day the World Ended

3. The Gaston Max series (continued)
    Seven Sins

4. The Paul Harley series
    Bat-Wing
    Fire-Tongue

Harley is mentioned, but does not appear, in *The Sins of Severac Bablon.* He is the featured detective in the play *The Eye of Siva,* and. in eleven short stories; three of the latter are in *Tales of Chinatown,* two in *Tales of East and West* (U. S. edition), and three in *Salute to Bazarada and Other Stories.*

5. The "Red" Kerry series
    Dope
    Yellow Shadows

Kerry also appears in the first two stories in *Tales of Chinatown.*

Three other series characters have had their adventures collected in individual volumes: Captain O'Hagan and Bimbâshi Barûk in the books which bear their names, and Moris Klaw in *The Dream Detective.* The numerous adventures (at least sixteen) of another character, Bernard De Treville, have so far appeared only in periodicals.

INDEX

605